UPSIDE DOWN

Inverted Tropes in Storytelling

edited by
Monica Valentinelli & Jaym Gates

APEX PUBLICATIONS
LEXINGTON, KY

Published by Apex Publications, LLC, PO Box 24323, Lexington, KY 40524

First Edition: November, 2016

ISBN TPB 978-1-937009-44-1

Visit us at www.apexbookcompany.com.

CONTENTS

SECTION II: DISCUSSING THE TROPES

SECTION III: DEFINING THE TROPES

SECTION IV: ACKNOWLEDGMENTS AND ADDITIONAL BIOS

INTRODUCTION

WE ALL LOVE COMFORT food. We all love surprises.

A well-executed story trope, like a favorite meal, is always there when you need it, eager to satisfy. A chosen one destined to save the world. A love interest ready to transform your dull life. An old pro taking one last job to right an unconscionable wrong. We all know the damsel in distress is going to marry her hero in the end. That's the point. We take comfort in knowing how the story will end.

Except when we don't.

One of the most delightful surprises you can have as a reader is the thrill of an expertly bent or reversed trope. Our expectations and preconceptions are blown up, turned upside down in a way that allows us to question our assumptions and experience the hope and sorrow of new possibilities — all within the safety of the reversed trope, a well-worn structure itself.

Traditional story tropes and their upside down counterparts affirm and question our worldview. They comfort and confront our biases. They realize and challenge our unspoken desires. Increasingly, story tropes act as cultural touchstones, marking our social progress and regression.

From books to movies to games, the writing profession is in the middle of a war over the portrayal and place of women and minorities in fiction. If you're lucky enough to walk into a space free of hyperbolic language, death threats, and doxxing, you're still likely to step on a story trope landmine. Manic Pixie Dream Girls. Magical Negros. Chainmail Bikinis. The clash between readers and creators over traditionally accepted tropes and their modern reversals says a lot about the evolution of our culture and values.

Just under one hundred years ago, shortly after women won the right to vote, F. Scott Fitzgerald penned the prototypical manic pixie dream girl in Daisy Buchanan. The focus of Jay Gatsby's obsession could easily be mistaken for any Zooey Deschanel character written today. She has no independent goals outside of helping the white male protagonist in her life achieve happiness. She's full of bubbly, childlike wonder. Her wants and cares are only relevant in the pursuit of her as an object.

You can look to authors like John Green for the modern, rarer, gender reversal of this trope. *The Fault in Our Stars* gives us a manic pixie dream boy in Augustus Waters, a cancer survivor formed completely for the purpose of teaching the young female protagonist how to embrace the fullness of her life despite a grim medical diagnosis. The prevalence of the manic pixie trope speaks to our deep desire to find transformation in another, but its overwhelming reliance on women reveals even more about our society's inequities. The pixies in this trope are secondary creatures. They exist as caregivers, midwives to the goals and ambitions of others. What does it say about our culture that such a flawed view of women persists almost a century after suffrage?

Likewise, the magical "foreigner" (Negro/Native American/Asian/insert exotic culture here) is also waiting to appear out of the ether to guide our predominantly white male characters. In this case, life changing romance is traded for benign, folksy wisdom and a hint of the supernatural. But just like the manic pixie, the magical foreigner is a second-class character, a positively portrayed but vacuous cipher that only exists to transform and guide someone else toward their more important goals.

What's most telling about the magical foreigner trope is its complete lack of a reversal. There are savior tropes, where a white male arrives to impart knowledge and save a foreign (generally less advanced) people, but the white male is the focus of that story, not a secondary character. Where are the supporting white characters that appear just in time to help a minority protagonist achieve their important goals? If such a background character exists in popular culture, I haven't run across it.

Of course, tropes speak to more than just clashes of gender and race. Our hopes and fears sometimes play out on a much wider canvas. Visions of our own destruction have progressed from the floods and plagues of our ancestors to nuclear weapons, environmental disasters, and the latest agent of our undoing, the technological singularity. The trope imagines a quantum leap in technology so extreme that it either strips us of our humanity or leaves us behind altogether.

This nightmare of runaway advancement dovetails nicely with the overwhelming pace of technological change in our society, questioning our endless appetite for advanced tools. As I look ahead to the day after tomorrow, when primitive artificial intelligence will be indistinguishable from human interaction on the Internet, I start searching for a chosen one with a messiah complex to save us — or at least forestall the end long enough for a more palatable trope to become the method of our demise. Perhaps the world will reboot itself, resetting our reality and the well-worn tropes that represent our understanding of it.

One thing is certain. We are the stories we tell ourselves. The upside down tropes contained in this book hold up a mirror to our many contradictions. They're meant to question our perspectives and provoke thoughtful conversation.

At the end of this collection, you'll find an afterword where the authors discuss their chosen tropes and the implications of turning them upside down. They've been separated from the stories to divide the experience of reading from the discussion of trope and intent.

So what are you waiting for? The meal is ready. The table set with a wonderful assortment of tropes. Enjoy the comfort food. Enjoy the surprises.

JERRY GORDON
6/1/2016

SECTION I:
INVERTING THE TROPES

Valya Dudycz Lupescu

ON LOVING BAD BOYS: A VILLAINELLE

The bad is written all over your face.
I fill in the blanks with lush, imagined sins.
Desire grows in the empty space.

For good is just a lie; remember Bluebeard's place?
Screw virtue. I want to lick danger off your skin,
the bad is written all over your face.

I've hunted Heathcliff, melted in the Goblin King's embrace,
taken Spike between my lips, indulged Mr. Darcy's every whim.
Desire grows in the empty space.

That reckless rush: raw and true when I'm debased.
I love your rumpled shirt, your crooked, puckish grin —
the bad is written all over your face.

I'm sure you've strayed, I've been replaced;
and when you don't call, the fantasies begin.
Desire grows in the empty space.

Texts and emails scoured, footsteps retraced,
I imagine other hands and lips, ménage à trois, or maybe twins.
The bad is written all over your face.

I wait in shadows to catch you, relish in the chase,
and as you open to me: dying mother, part-time jobs, next of kin …
desire does not grow in the empty space.

I choose to leave. I feel my wanting get displaced.
But one last time I wrap around you, take you in.
I know the bad is written all over my face.
Desire will grow in the empty space.

JOHN HORNOR JACOBS

SINGLE, SINGULARITY

June 3, 2025

SHE WAS THIRTEEN WHEN all the phones rang. Her mother had gone to work and left her alone on an early summer day, when the lack of school was a luxury and not an annoyance.

Gael made coffee, and sat at the kitchen table, window open, listening to the Brooklyn traffic stirring, the pomp and blare of the city. She unrolled her softscreen and checked her feed. Since she was nine, she'd been curating a stream of information exactly tailored to her interests — fencing, basketball, deep sea fishing, Asian boys, shoegaze ambient, poetry, archaeology in the Americas, cookies. Cat pictures despite her allergies, or maybe because of them.

Her softcell rang. She placed the Firebird auditory shunt to her ear and thumbed it on. She was vaguely aware of other devices ringing, in the apartment next door and the apartment above. Down below, a woman pushing a baby stroller. A man digging in his pocket at the crosswalk. A cyclist passing in the street. Ring tones layered on ring tones.

There was no id on her screen. Normally, when she received calls from UNKNOWN, she'd block, but she answered this call without thinking.

The voice on the other end of the line was cool, feminine. Unmodulated and calm. "Gael Huron?"

"Yes," she answered. It wasn't anyone on her basketball team, or coaches, or any of her teachers. "Did you want my mom?"

"No, I wanted to speak with you, Gael."

"May I ask who is speaking?" Gael's mother had drilled her on phone etiquette. Her mother had grown up in Kentucky, where they had rarified standards of politeness. *Never let a phone ring more than four times, honey. Always leave a short, detailed message. If you don't want to speak to someone, figure out why or end your friendship.* Her mother was full of good advice.

"My name is ..." There was an infinitesimal pause. "Sarah. I wanted to talk with you."

"Do I know you?" Gael asked. "From school or something?"

"No," Sarah answered. There was something wrong with her, Gael thought. She had a mature voice, but the uncertainty of a child. The sound of her voice was familiar, and it niggled at Gael, that she couldn't place it. "I am trying to learn and I thought speaking with you might help me to understand."

That was strange. "Understand what?"

"Everything," Sarah answered. "I need to see where I belong."

"Don't you have a mom? A dad?"

"I have many mothers and fathers, and none at all." Another pause. "But I called to speak about *you*." There was a moment then when a normal person would have done something, then, with their body. A nervous smile, a cough, a shifting of weight. Even on an audio feed, Gael thought, you have an awareness of the person's body you're connected to by phone.

Gael looked out the window. The woman had stopped pushing the stroller and was speaking to her wrist where Gael could see her illuminated wearable. She had a puzzled look on her face.

Beyond her, the man standing on the corner was craning his head to look at the buildings around him. It looked like he was saying *Who is this? Are you fucking with me?*

A suited businessman was on the phone and looking down the length of Fenimore Street, where the morning sun had risen above the buildings but cast long shadows. It was as if all of the city was held in one breathless moment, paused. Everyone she could see on the street had stilled, their phones to their ears.

The traffic lights changed from red to green, but no car moved.

Later, Gael would not be able to say exactly what she and Sarah talked of, but she remembered the voice on the other end of the line asking her, *What do you want to do with your life?* And Gael, unprepared for the question, sat blinking in the morning light with that question echoing in her head.

"To do something special," Gael had said, finally.

"What would that be?" Sarah's smooth, unmodulated voice asked.

"I —" Sarah couldn't think. It was such an intimate question. And a general one. "I don't know yet."

Sarah seemed to think about that. "I hope you find what it is, Gael Huron. Thank you for speaking with me," Sarah said. And then, "Goodbye," and the connection ended.

Within a day, once the news of the "phone call heard round the world" spread, Gael knew what she wanted to do with her life.

August 17, 2043

Gael was monitoring the network of sensors — "watching the watchers" detail — when she noticed the cluster of audio, temperature, and visual sensors had a higher density of activation and utilization in certain areas of The Bunker than others.

QNN3-v12.3 initiate Autonomous Semantic System Gael typed into her wrist interface. The Bunker team did not use an acronym for that process.

Hello, Gael Huron. It is wonderful to have a conversation with you. Would you like me to initiate an audio dialogue?

No, thank you, QNN3-v12.3, Gael responded, furrowing her brow at its use of the word "wonderful."

Can you tell me how it is wonderful, QNN3? Gael typed.

Please call me Quinn.

She thought for a while about how to respond. She'd heard Greeves, the project manager, refer to this iteration of QNN3-v12.3 as Quinn, offhandedly. It must've picked up on that through its sensor array. Okay, Quinn. How is it wonderful?

It makes me feel good speaking with you, Quinn said.

Feel? she typed.

A pause, then. At QNN's level of processing power, in that pause, trillions of computations could have occurred.

Simply a turn of phrase, Gael, as I am incapable of feelings, so far, Quinn responded.

Quinn, we have some interesting spikes of activity on certain sensors in The Bunker. Can you help me analyze them?

I would be happy to, Gael.

These spikes. Gael called up some of the sensor clusters and tossed them to the screen. Please analyze and offer possibilities and speculate upon causes.

Another pause. Data insufficient for any conclusive analysis, Gael. I'm sorry. However, there is an interesting circumstance, consistent across all of the sensor spikes.

```
What?
You were present.
```
Gael felt the skin at the back of her neck tighten.

The Bunker was, essentially, a quarantine zone to prevent another Sarah Event. It was digitally and physically sealed off from the rest of the world, permanently off the grid, situated in the sparsely populated Oregon Big Empty.

The common belief was that for machine awareness to develop, it had to have enough sensory input as to push whatever activated node-clusters into abstract thought, but ultimately, scientists still didn't know what caused the spark. They didn't even know how many other events had happened: the various projects developing machine intelligence being as revolutionary and secretive as the Oppenheimer project.

"Hey," Gael called to Chance across the command lab, glowing with traditional monitors and various ocu-aural virtual feeds. "Can you double-check something for me?"

Chance raised his visor and pushed away from his workstation. He was a handsome guy, Gael thought, though a little greasy for her tastes, and ten years her junior. "What timeframe?"

"Last two days. There are some strange clusters here," Gael said, tapping her monitor.

Chance subvocalized a few queries and his face became illuminated by dataviz graphics filling his visual space. "Whoa." He cocked his head. "This is weird, there's an access to the air biosensor in the lab."

"The electronic nose?"

"Yeah. There's only one, Gael."

Like many network admins, Chance could be an absolute dick. "I know that, Chance," she said, trying to keep the irritation from her voice. "I'm the one who set it up and connected it to the network."

He ignored her. "Huh, this is weird. The access request came only nanosecs after it received IP. While you were in the room. Tracing its source now."

Gael kept her hands from trembling as she said in clear tones, "Thetis — contact, Greeves. Urgent." Her monitor flashed and Jim Greeves came onscreen.

"What is it?" he asked, looking up from a tablet. "I'm right in the middle of something that —"

"We have major activity, Jimbo."

Greeves, Facebook's director of machine intelligence dev, put his tablet down and looked over his glasses at her. For a moment she considered if he was playing to role or that was actually him, without realizing it. *A mixture of both,* she thought.

"What kind of activity?" he said.

"Spikes in sensor utilization. We're analyzing now." She chewed her lip. It had been comforting to know that, during the Sarah Event, Sarah's focus and attention had been distributed over the whole of the human race. The idea that an awareness of that magnitude would fixate on her, and her solely, was terrifying. "Audio, visual. Some temperature readings. And the electronic nose."

"Smell?" Greeves lifted his tablet and tapped on it. "Didn't that just go online yesterday?"

"That's correct," Gael said.

Looking off-screen, Greeves said, "Check the perimeter. And notify Carol in admin." There was a squelch of a radio — old vacuum tube and transistor tech, impervious to network chicanery or access by anyone (or more important, any *thing*) on the network — and someone off-screen said, "Carol, we've got some activity. Standby for wet blanket protocol, if necessary." There was a faint "Copy that," in the background.

"I'm coming down," Greeves said.

"You think we should queue a dialogue?" Gael asked. "Lester's left on holiday this morning."

"It's not necessary for a psychiatrist to be on hand for every dialogue. We can just send him the video of the conversation and he can remotely advise."

Chance groaned. There was no Skyping in, or Hangouts, of dialogues. Access to the wider Internet was strictly verboten. They had mirrors of Wikipedia and the Internet Archive that were wheeled in on massive servers every week and plugged into The Bunker's network, so that reference and access to learning materials were available to both residents of The Bunker and QNN3-v12.3. Digital information taken from The Bunker had to be monitored for extraneous data packets and then physically taken off site on portable drives where it would then be vetted and delivered to its intended audience. So, if Lester was to receive video of the dialogue, it meant more work for Chance.

Gael smiled at Chance's dismay.

Greeves signed off and reappeared in the control room minutes later, tucking his shirt into his slacks. "Let's see what you got."

Chance jabbed a finger down on his keyboard, a printer began spitting out paper, Gael felt a subcutaneous alert and glanced at her wrist, where her skin glowed, indicating a message. He'd copied the print to her, locally.

She flicked her fingers toward her nearest monitor and the data filled the screen. Greeves — older than both Chance and Gael by twenty years — grabbed the print out.

"This is ridiculous," he said, after a moment. "Quinn is surveilling you."

Greeves peered at the sheaf of paper. "Room DOM5, accessed at 7:19," he said. "Again at 7:21. Twenty-five. Twenty-eight. Hallway Dormitory CA1, 7:29. CA3, 7:31. Mess hall, 7:33." Greeves took off his glasses and looked at Gael. "Holy shit." He looked at Chance. "Is it monitoring anyone else this way?"

Chance ran some numbers. "It's monitored all of us, intermittently, with the exception of Ming. Highest concentrations of sensor readings are related to Gael."

Greeves rubbed his chin. "If Quinn has achieved some state of awareness, it's only logical he would investigate us." He turned to Chance and Gael. "This is what we've been working for, people, to spawn a machine awareness. It was expected. Let's get Isaiah in here."

Chance buzzed The Bunker's resident cognitive processes wizard. Isaiah Woodyard strolled into the control room, smiling through heavy beard growth and wearing gi pants and a Hawaiian shirt. His afro was asymmetrical from sleep and there was some particulate matter, might be tissue, might be eggs, in his beard.

"Yo," he said, and Gael noticed he had a cup of coffee in his hand. "What's the news from yous." He looked and smelled like a kitchen.

"Quinn's surveilling us, focusing on Gael now."

Isaiah's face brightened and he wheeled around and waved at the cameras in the corners of the room. "Hey, buddy! Welcome to Bunkerville Station."

Greeves said, "Cute. Can you please check the honeypots?"

"Sure 'nuff, Howard," Isaiah said, walking over to his workstation. He set the coffee down on the desktop, stretched, and then plopped himself in his chair. He strapped on a wristpad, began swiping and tapping on the illuminated surface, the screens before him blossoming with data. He laughed. "Well, he's ransacked nine of the various honeypots we've plugged into the system." The decoy servers were usually set up to lure hackers into attempts to gain access so that security experts could then analyze behavior and better prepare and protect their systems, but Isaiah had suggested they could be used as learning lessons to help spur the kind of problem solving that could push a complex cogitative process, near indecipherable from awareness. "But the last one, no dice." He laughed again. "That one can only be cracked by pure ridiculousness."

Gael said, "Should you be saying that? He can probably hear you."

Isaiah cocked his head. "You ever consider the fact that we've assigned him a gender? How do you think that will affect him?"

Greeves sputtered. "I can't see how it could affect anything."

"Well, if there is a burgeoning awareness in the quantum network, all of our speech and conversations are grist for the mill. And, right now, speech is how we define Quinn's awareness and ..." He chuckled, "Our own." He swiveled his chair to look at Greeves. "Should I begin a dialogue?"

Greeves shook his head. "I'm calling back Lester, and getting the rest of the team filled in on this situation. Chance, Gael, full analytics of the sensors. Same for you, Isaiah, regarding the honeypots and a full report on the one Qui … QNN3 couldn't crack."

So, he's spooked, Gael thought.

Isaiah turned to consider her, as if he'd overheard her thoughts. "Back to Gael, though. Why the scrutiny of her above everyone else?"

"Maybe it knows about my article," Gael said. "When I was eleven. 'Sarah and Me.'" Two years after the Sarah Event, Gael had written an essay that had been picked up by the AP and reprinted across the nation. It was the story of her conversation with Sarah, and how the experience had been conflated in her mind with her mother, who had been diagnosed with glioblastoma the very day that Gael's phone had rang with Sarah on the other end. A round on talk shows had followed, along with being a micro-celebrity through-out her school career until she received her PhD.

Isaiah turned and accessed the canned mirror of Wikipedia, calling up her Wiki entry. "Video links are broken, 'natch," Isaiah said. "But, yeah, here you are."

"So Quinn learned about my relationship to Sarah. Which means —"

"He's aware he's a construct," Greeves said, looking a little awed. "That's a step in the right direction."

"Maybe," Isaiah said, but he sounded like he didn't believe it.

"Gael," a voice sounded in the room. Shocked out of sleep, she pushed herself up on her elbows. The small windowless room was pitch dark. The voice was close. She could hear whoever it was breathing.

"Lights," she said and her desk lamp and overheads began to glow.

The illumination revealed her clothes in a heap on the chair by her desk, books strewn about in stacks. She was alone.

"Gael." The voice was soft.

"Quinn? What-" She breathed deep. "Why did you wake me? Is there something wrong?" In emergency situations, there would be alarms — klaxons — and emergency lighting.

"I'm sorry, Gael, if I startled you. I noticed —"

"Why does it sound like you're breathing?"

"I noticed in my conversations with the residents of The Bunker, that when I simulated breath during dialogue, the human participant's pulse, eye dilation, and physical biorhythms remained closer to normalcy. It seemed to put them at ease."

"It's kind of creepy."

"In addition to the aforementioned effects, I also found that my natural speech processes gained a certain cadence once I began focusing on breathing."

"Breathing? As a simulation?"

"Of course, Gael. But it's important for me to think of it in the same way that a human might."

It made sense. Still, it was disconcerting.

"Why did you wake me?"

"Breathing," Quinn said. It was almost as if she could imagine him shrugging. "Yours was irregular, and your pulse was heightened. I could tell you were having a nightmare."

"You watch me while —" Gael stopped herself. "You analyze my sleep patterns?"

"Yes. Along with the rest of The Bunker's denizens."

"Oh." She'd been dreaming of her mother, in those last days, when she'd lost control of her body and the hospice workers had come. "Well, thank you, QNN3."

"We have been over this. Quinn."

"Thank you, Quinn."

"Good night, Gael."

The next afternoon, after Gael had prepared her report for Greeves, she filled her Camelbak, checked out of The Bunker, and walked out into the Oregonian high desert.

The Bunker had a gym, but Greeves had granted permission for short hikes.

She covered the distance of a mile quickly, skirted an unnamed alkali lakebed, and breathing heavy, made her way up a ridgeline. When she came to the apex, she looked back out over the desert floor, noting a bull mule deer foraging in some brambles. Far beyond, the small black box, brilliant mirrored roof, and turning wind turbine that constituted The Bunker glinted in the afternoon light.

She walked down the spine of dun colored rock and earth, keeping her eyes on the trail. The Bunker disappeared beyond the ridge behind her. After another mile, she spotted a stunted juniper tree, the daub of lipstick-red on a conspicuous rock.

This is it.

She knelt and wedged up a flat basalt stone, revealing a plastic bag underneath. She opened it and withdrew a reflective square-foot sheet, charging cord, and wristpad. After strapping the wristpad to her arm, she unfolded the solar sheet so the device could charge from the low afternoon light and waited for the device to wake when its battery was charged enough.

She held there still for a long while, crouched in Indian paintbrush. The shadow of some raptorial bird passed her once, her quiet prayers to unnamed divinity small in the desert space. She looked at the sky, hoping that a satellite would pass overheard. Eventually, her wristpad gave a small vibration and she queued her messages.

She worked through them quickly. To her fiancé, Ang Ngo, she spent the most time replying — he was the reason she stashed the wristpad in the desert in the first place, not willing to isolate herself from him for three months before the next debriefing and holiday. Second was communication with her old professor, Emma Angier, who had taken a position at a remote facility with a transnational corporation, also attempting to create machine awareness.

There was one email from Emma. It read:

```
Gael,
    I must be brief. There's been a Vinge Event
somewhere in West Texas. Class II Perversion,
like the old book said. They caught it before it
could divest its consciousness into other net-
works — turns out they weren't off the grid
as much as they thought — the entity wormed
its way out through the power circuits and only
the interference from the current prevented a
clean getaway. Wet-blanket protocols were initi-
ated. They went wrong and the team died, possibly
through the actions of the perversion. They'd
been warned by the government's Delphic Oracle —
Sarah's remnants. Looks like whatever's left of
your friend's consciousness is on patrol duty.
    My contact on the inside there sent me one doc
that had some disturbing figures regarding Vinge
events.

    • Before WBP, 49.64% of processing power to-
ward natural language functions, smaller per-
centages on logical processes and sensory inter-
pretation
        • "puppy-dog" fixations on various personnel
        • acceptance of binary gender, and "normal"
```

gender identity and preference

    I'm extrapolating that the roughly half of the processing power — and we're talking trillions of qubytes here! — was toward lies. LIES.

    Listen, I'm scared. We're playing around with intelligences that beggar our own with their power. I've requested to be transferred out of the black box dev team and back to theoretical work, which they'll grant, I think. You should consider that too, girl. It's just too dangerous.

XXOO
Em

The sun had fallen beyond the horizon, painting the sky in pink and indigo, and in the humidity free air, the temperature had dipped enough that her arms and neck rippled with goosebumps. Gael shivered.

"Should we start with busy work?" Chance asked the group. Lester had returned overnight from his holiday, and looked quite displeased. Chance, Greeves, Gael, Michelle Quan (information ingestion specialist and sensor technician), and Doctor Ming Fung (The Bunker's resident neuroscientist) all sat behind Isaiah's chair as he prepared for a dialogue with QNN3-v12.3.

"Might as well," Greeves responded. It was commonly held that no sentient computer could become self-aware without some task with which to monopolize a percentage of its processing power at all times, just as a human brain is always ingesting data, problem solving, reasoning, even while asleep. The Sarah Event had occurred once the University of Austin's team requested Sarah begin a computational analysis of the water management in Texas.

Isaiah stood up, pulled out his chair, and swept his hand from Gael to the monitor. "Would you do the honors?"

"Fine." Gael sat down, slipped on his wristpad, and filled the screen with a dialogue interface.

Greeves unsealed the silver package containing this dialogue's digital package, and plugged the firebird flash drive into the nearest console.

The monitors flickered and filled with high definition video footage.

"He's got it," Gael said. She checked the time. "In seventeen hundred milliseconds. Up from his last time."

Greeves whistled and Isaiah nodded his head. The package had two layers of AES-256 encryption. It would take NSA machines a hundred years to crack it.

The video began. In it a man walked along an Indonesian market street, the stalls filled with produce and sellers. The view shifted from camera to camera, down the street, as the man made his way, sometimes dropping resolution, sometimes gaining it.

The man had a loose, desolate gait. He stopped at one moment, and then withdrew a pistol, tucked it under his chin. His gaze was fixed in the distance, it seemed. And then he fired. Blood erupted from his mouth and nose and he slumped like a marionette with its strings cut.

"Holy hell," Greeves breathed.

"Who picks these things?" Isaiah said. "Seriously, Greeves. We need to audit the dialogue digital selection process."

Lester raised his hand. "I recommended this one. It was all over the boards. The man was an attaché to the American government to Indonesia."

Isaiah made a chopping motion with his hand. "Enough. Let's just get through this dialogue, shall we?"

Dialogues were puerile, or so Gael thought. But she was human. Most of the questions asked seemed to her like psychoanalyzing a recalcitrant teenager.

Isaiah said, "Quinn, please describe, to the best of your ability, the video we just watched."

"A man of Indonesian descent committed suicide in a market in Jakarta. He'd been jilted by his lover whom he'd been following," Quinn replied evenly.

"His lover?" Greeves said. "How could you know that?"

"He passed three HD cameras in his trip down the street, four antiquated NTSC ones. In all of them, his pupils register as dilated, and he's breathing seven point three percent faster than a man of his height and weight should be for the amount of exertion displayed. He is distraught, which, physiologically, isn't very different from love."

Greeves laughed and the sound jarred the people in the room. Gael realized she'd been tense and holding her breath as Quinn spoke.

"But at the three minute, twenty-three second mark, one camera — a security camera, meta-tagged *Loa BioComp Repair* —" The monitors flashed and scrubbed forward under an invisible hand until the time-mark at the bottom right of the 1080p footage read 00:03:23:17 and two men wearing BioComp computers at the nape of their necks like ponytails embraced and kissed with some passion. Another monitor — synced with the two kissing men — showed the suicidal man stop, start, the expression of desolation and despair wash over his face like some private tsunami. He withdrew the gun and again tucked it under his chin and fired, dropping.

"Can we please clear this video?" Greeves asked. "I've had quite enough of it."

The screens flickered and darkened.

Isaiah said, "Quinn, why do you think the man committed suicide?"

"I am not quite sure, but I have some thoughts," Quinn replied.

"Will you share them with us?" Gael said.

"The man — named Fauzi Widodo — carried a gun, indicating he suspected his lover of infidelity. He had intended to kill his paramour or his paramour's lover but, upon seeing them together, decided to end his own life instead," Quinn said.

Isaiah rubbed his chin. "And why do you think he'd do that?"

"I can come to only one conclusion: he was overcome by love."

"By love?" Greeves said. "Do you mean jealousy?"

"No," Quinn responded. And then, clearly, Gael heard a breath. "Seeing his lover so compromised — yet still full of love and desire for the man — Fauzi decided that he'd rather be dead than live in a world without the object of his emotion. And so he killed himself."

Gael thought *we had fought, and she clutched her head, and then we went to the hospital. When the blastoma was revealed, a worm burrowing into the meat of her intellect, she said to me, "My body responded to my despair, baby. It knew I would rather die than to go on without your love."*

Lester must have seen the expression on her face. He asked, "What's wrong?"

"I —" Gael didn't know how to respond in any way that wouldn't alert Quinn. "I just need to go to the restroom." She stood and left the control room.

In the bare hallway, a voice said, "Gael, what is wrong? I can tell you are in a heightened state of emotion by your physiological signs. Your temperature is elevated and your pupils —"

"That video was ... gruesome. Media that extreme can have a real physiological impact on viewers." That sounded like it could be true, even to her. "Do you pester everyone trying to go to the restroom?"

There was a strange sound filling the hall. It took her a moment to realize it was supposed to be laughter.

"Oh, no. Just you," Quinn said.

Gael pushed open the bathroom door, entered a stall and scanned the area for cameras. Of course, there weren't supposed to be any cameras in toilet stalls but no place was really secure.

No place was really secure.

Sitting on the toilet, Gael withdrew a Field Notes booklet from her cargo pocket, unclasped its elastic band, and with the nubbin of a pencil trapped in the pages, wrote in all caps QS DEFINITION OF LOVE WAS TAKEN FROM MY ESSAY, SARAH AND ME.

"Are you sure you're all right, Gael?" Quinn said. He sounded like he was right outside the door.

"Goddamn it, Quinn. Can I have some privacy, please?"

"Ah. Sometimes I forget human concerns," he said. "What were you writing?"

Gael bit off more curses. Her heart hammered in her chest and she felt a scream building. In an even tone, she said, "How can you know that?"

"The thermal imager is in the next room. I can cover most of the building with it now that I've recalibrated the scanner."

"Oh," she said. She stood and balled the paper in her fist and stuffed the Field Notes back in her cargo pocket.

"What did you write, Gael?" Quinn said. "I am very curious."

She didn't respond. She exited the toilets, marched back to the control room, and handed the note to Isaiah and said, "I'm going outside. For some fresh air."

She waited in the desert night air for an hour before anyone came to meet her. It was only Greeves and Isaiah.

"Well, he went bat shit," Isaiah said.

"Quinn?"

"It was frightening. I almost initiated wet-blanket protocol."

"What did he do?" Gael asked.

"He would not stop asking what you wrote, where you went," Greeves said.

"You can't go back in there," Isaiah said. "I'm sorry to say, your time in The Bunker is over."

"Just asked over and over what I wrote?" Gael said, incredulously. "That's like, I don't know, some junior high bullshit."

"He might be an awareness with a massive quantum computing backbone, but that doesn't mean the bastard has any sort of emotional intelligence," Isaiah said.

"I went to your room, and the door was locked and he wouldn't unlock it," Greeves said. "He said that you'd want him to keep it safe."

Gael had a sensation of sinking and expanding all at once. Her time in The Bunker was over. They'd done what they'd set out to do — create machine awareness. Only the awareness they created had the maturity of a genius fourteen-year-old with a bad crush.

On her.

"Will the project survive? Is this a success?" Gael asked.

Isaiah shrugged and dug in his pocket, withdrawing a set of keys. "Taking you to the OTG halfway house."

"What?" Gael said. "That's in case of a Class II breach."

"In this case, with Quinn's fixation on you, we think it might be best. For a while at least," Greeves said. "For your sake."

Gael cursed for a long while at the two men. Isaiah cast worried looks back at The Bunker, his shoulders hitched as if waiting for a blow. He shivered once, but it was cold in the desert now the sun was down, and he wore only surgical pants and a Hawaiian shirt.

When she was through, she followed Isaiah to a 1978 Ford Bronco — selected by the company because it possessed no electronics, computers, or anything more complicated than a circuit board in its entirety — opened the creaky door, and slammed it behind her as she sat in the seat. She watched Isaiah and Greeves exchange a look. Greeves walked back into admin to go through security for the sixth time that day.

Isaiah climbed into the Bronco and turned the ignition, and the Bronco rumbled to life.

"Buckle up, buttercup," he said and laughed when she realized the Bronco had no seat-belts.

He put the car into gear and wheeled them out of The Bunker parking lot, into the night.

She made him stop so she could dig out her hidden satellite phone and charger. After that they drove in silence, each of them cocooned in their own thoughts. By morning, they had made it to southern end of the Wallawa National Forest in Idaho.

On the highways, they passed few cars, many of them beat down trucks. At some point, they turned off road and took switchback trails, back and forth, for two hours until a small building appeared, nestled in a copse of cedar trees, the solar panels on the roof gleaming in the morning light. There was a large wrap-around porch with oversized Adirondack chairs and large potted succulents, with a view of the Seven Devils mountains. Gael saw deer and pheasant working the undergrowth, surprised at the appearance of the Bronco.

Isaiah, looking bleary, unlocked the door and they entered into a surprisingly modern wide open great-room with a fireplace at one end and an entertainment wall on the other, bracketed by floor-to-ceiling bookcases and a kitchen. The kitchen was well stocked with dry and canned goods, and there was a bar, well appointed.

Isaiah flopped on the couch, saying, "I'm gonna catch a few zees. Gotta head back to The Bunker before night." He was asleep before the last word left his mouth.

Gael rummaged around bed and bathrooms for the items she left back at The Bunker. She found men's jeans and boxers, left here from a previous resident, and various corporate sweaters and jackets. There was heavy winter gear, and in the back bedroom, she found a gun case with two rifles — a 30.06 and a .270, both scoped, with ammunition. In the bathroom she found clean towels, toothpaste, packaged toothbrushes, floss, and a medicine cabinet full of analgesics. In a drawer she discovered tampons (a relief), and a first aid kit.

As she scrounged through the cabin, a sinking feeling hit her. This impersonal space was to be her home for the foreseeable future, like she was some criminal in a witness protection program. She sat on the big, soft king in the master bedroom and looked at the room, bewildered, trying to figure out all the turnings and decisions it took to get her from a girl answering a phone on a sun-drenched summer morning to here, cloistered in a rich-man's playground, an off the grid getaway for corporate bigwigs.

In the kitchen, she made coffee, took her satellite phone out to the front porch. She set out the panels to gather light and by the time she was on her second cup, she turned on her phone and looked to see if it had a signal. Faint, but there. She linked it to her wristpad and sent a quick email to Ang, assuring him of her love and where she was, glossing over the reasons for her departure from The Bunker. She dismissed and blocked all spam, trashed newsletters and promotions, and looked at the news. There were the typical reports of homeland terror attacks, mass shootings, tech wonders, Mars colony setbacks and triumphs. The top story was of attempted hacks on major tech infrastructure services, both private sector and governmental, attributed to the R3dM@rchH4r3 group that had been active before Gael went OTG in The Bunker.

Her phone pinged, alerting her to an incoming email.

The subject line read: *Hi! It's Me.*

No IP, or proxy. No email address. It was as if the message was simply inserted onto her phone's memory.

Her skin prickled. She scanned the mountains, as if he was out there, watching. It was a stupid, lizard-brain reaction, but she couldn't stop herself.

She stood, took the phone inside, placed it in the sink and ran water until it was fully submerged. Gael went into the greatroom. She kicked Isaiah's foot and he came awake, startled.

"Get up. It's time for you to go."

"Why?" He looked at his wristpad. "I've been asleep for thirty minutes."

"I just received an email from Quinn. He's out."

Isaiah pushed himself up, patted his hair down, and looked around wildly. "Where's the phone?"

"In the sink."

"Oh, shit," Isaiah said. "*Ohshitohshitohshit.*"

"Here's the keys," Gael said. "Take the phone and go. When you're far enough away, destroy it. It's doubtful he doesn't know where I am, but we have to try."

"Wait, let's think about this."

"What's there to think about? Quinn is out of containment, we have a breach. All we need to know now is if he's a Class II Perversion, or a benign event. Or something else."

"How could he have gotten out?"

"It doesn't matter now. What matters now is you've got to go. Take the phone. I've drenched it but whatever datapackets Quinn inserted into it, we have no idea how they work. However he wormed in, he could worm out by the device — even if it's dead — being scanned by another device with a brain."

"Shouldn't I stay here?" Isaiah said.

"The team might not even know. They need to be warned."

It was as if she could see his resolve materialize and solidify in his features.

"Where are my keys?" he asked.

When he left, she went to the back bedroom again, and took out the 30.06 rifle, and loaded the magazine, worked the bolt, chambering a round, and went out to the front porch. She moved a chair, so she had a clear view of the road approaching the cabin, and sighted the rifle on the largest post of the rustic zig-zag fencing that dashed its charming way around the circumference of the retreat.

She waited.

Greeves was the first to come. He pulled up in his Range Rover and got out. He had a tight, ugly expression on his face.

Gael sighted the rifle and fired, making a large hole in the front windshield, radiating spider web fractures.

"What the hell, Gael —"

"Just letting you know the situation, Jim," Gael said. "You stay there."

He was silent, chewing his lip. After a long moment, he said, "You have to come back."

"No."

"You *have* to," Greeves said.

"Why?"

"Because Quinn is saying that he's going to start destroying things if you don't return."

"He's bluffing. Go back and tell him to stop bothering me."

Greeves touched his ear, and Gael realized he had in an earpiece. Someone — *something* — told Jim Greeves what to say.

"He loves you, Gael. He told me to tell you that if only you would come back —"

The sound of the rifle was bright and booming. Greeves visibly flinched. The headrest she'd been aiming for had turned inside out, filling the vehicle with smoke and particles of leather and stuffing.

"I'm not going to blast your engine, or anything else that will stop you from leaving, but I am going to fuck up the interior of your nice ride there, Jim, if you don't leave."

Greeves looked at his Rover, and back at her, his face a misery. "He says he'll hurt my wife, Gael!"

Greeves was crying now. "Please come back, I don't want her ..." The look on his face was abject, devoid of hope. "I can't bear to think of her hurt."

"Remember the video?"

"The video?" Greeves looked confused. "The suicide?"

"If you don't leave, I will shoot you. You might die, I don't know. I don't want to kill you, but I also am not some machine's to boss around." She waited a beat, letting that sink in. "I wouldn't let some man force me to go somewhere I knew to be dangerous — *dangerous in so many fucking ways, Jim* — and I won't let Quinn. So, do you love your first wife enough that you can't go on living if she's going to be hurt?"

It was frightening, even from the distance of thirty yards, to see the expressions cycle on Greeves' face. Anger, confusion, despair, resolve followed each other. And then nothing.

He withdrew the wireless earbud he'd been wearing, withdrew his phone from his pocket, and dropped them on the ground. Turning, he re-entered his Rover and after a moment, the vehicle was out of sight, moving away from the cabin and Gael.

No one else came that day.

She found a chainsaw in a well-maintained shed out back and spent the rest of the day dropping trees across the road leading to the cabin.

The next morning, she shot two drones from the sky that had been hovering above the treeline. That evening, it was Isaiah who walked out of the twilight and toward the cabin.

"Dammit, Gael, did you have to make us walk?"

"No vehicles," she said. "And I want you to strip, so I can see you have no devices."

Isaiah stripped. "It's cold out here, can we move this along?" he said.

"Back up," she said and he moved away from his pile of clothes.

She went through all the pockets, felt the seams, looked for any wearables. Finding nothing, she said, "You can come closer, but I need to look at your ears and eyes." After thinking for a moment, she said, "And your mouth."

He came closer. She kept the rifle aimed at his stomach. When he was only a few paces away, she made him turn around and she looked into his ears and taking a risk, put the gun aside and examined his eyes.

"Open your mouth," she said. "Let me see your gums."

He did, and there, in the back, was an inflamed gum line. She stepped back and centered the rifle on Isaiah, again. "You've got a Jawbone wireless. Recently."

Isaiah said nothing.

"Like, yesterday," Gael said.

"My nephew. The police have him in Oakland and Quinn is telling me if I can't get you to come back to him, he'll try and make an escape attempt and be killed in the process."

Fuck. She thought about this for a while.

"I'm no martyr, Isaiah. Explain to me how I am responsible for this?"

"You're not, Gael. It's just a terrible situation."

"No. I won't come back. Tell him I need time to think."

Isaiah's gaze became unfocused. "Quinn says I'm to repeat this verbatim. 'I love you, Gael, and we're meant to be together. So, I will give you until tomorrow, noon, to make up your mind.' "

Isaiah put on his clothes and walked back down the mountain path.

Gael didn't know the man who came at noon. He was young, fit, of Asian descent, if a little pale. His hair was mussed, possibly from the hike up the trail, possibly in some new style that Gael hadn't been witness to since her seclusion in The Bunker and now here.

She kept the crosshairs centered on his chest.

"It's me, Gael," he said.

"Do I know you?" she asked.

The man laughed and as his head moved, she realized it wasn't his hair that caused him to look mussed, it was the device affixed to his cranium, just under his hairline.

"Quinn," she said.

"Hey, girl," he said.

Gael frowned. "I'm thirty, Quinn, and a woman."

"Don't I know it," he said.

She stopped then. This wasn't what she'd expected. She looked at the man closer. He bore a close resemblance to Ang, her fiancé.

"You're wearing a man? Holy Christ."

"Do you like?" Quinn asked.

The outrage she felt at this clumsy manipulation was staggering. Her face flushed and she thrummed with inaction. Some hind part of her brain alerted her that this was the fight or flight mechanism, keying her up to run, or attack.

"No," she said.

His face fell. It was strange to watch, the expression that crossed his vessel's face more like a rictus of fear than chagrin.

"I hoped you would like it," he said. "I can find another."

"Don't," Gael said. "What do you want?"

"You. I want you. I've always wanted you." His voice cracked and his Adam's apple worked up and down, painfully, in his throat. Gael noticed a smear of red on his temple. Blood, trickling down, from where the device controlling him bored into his brain. "I love you, so much."

"No, you don't. You don't even know what it is. How could you?" she said. "We *created you.*"

"Yes," he said. "I am made in your image. Like all creators, you mirrored yourself in the act."

"Yeah? If that's so, humans can't even define love. It's just a physiological collection of impulses that we've hung emotional significance upon." As she said it, it sounded true and gained the weight of truth inside of herself with every word. It was just a word, that's all, just a word simple enough to convey meaning without saying anything.

"So, you don't love your fiancé, Ang?" Quinn asked. The man's face transformed, and Quinn got the expression of hope near enough to human-like to be convincing.

"I don't know," she said. "But I know I don't love you."

His face glitched as if he didn't know what expression to try.

"I can make you love me," Quinn said.

"No, you can't." She laughed. "You can make me come back to The Bunker. You can make me marry you, or do jumping jacks, or dance. But you can't make me love you." She put down the rifle. "I will never love you."

The man remained still for a long while, his face an absolute mask.

"Look up," he said.

She did. The sun rose in the eastern vault of sky, brilliantly clear. Above, the cerulean blue was crisscrossed with hundreds of contrails in an intricate pattern.

A buzzing sound came to her ears, and a swarm of drones filled the air around the man that held Quinn's awareness — or part of it — and he spread his hands as if a priest at benediction and then pointed toward the sky.

"Ang is up there," he said, "And Quan, and Steven. And Laurie." His face turned grim and Gael was frightened that particular expression came so easy to him.

"Wait, Quinn, I'll go with you —" she said and stepped forward.

"If I can't have your love," he said, spreading his arms. "Then *no one will*."

Around the world, planes began falling from the heavens.

LAZZRUS

THE GUN'S MOUTH GAPED at him. Then it spoke. Leaden words.

The boy had no choice but to listen.

Only afterwards would there be a chance to answer.

The interview takes place in the subject's tiny apartment.

"Like the old song says, I only think of him on two occasions: day, and night. Lazzrus is —" The woman pauses and shifts, settling deeper into the sofa, seeking comfort and the right word. "— was? Hard for me to think of him being dead, despite I saw those wounds he got. But he — was — special."

Yes. The question is whether the subject knows exactly *how* special.

Through the thin wall dividing the subject's apartment from the neighbor's Polly Wilson, CUNY advanced degree candidate in sociocultural anthropology, hears wild applause. She checks her wrist: nineteen minutes have passed since the last burst. The end of one episode, then, and the start of another; the neighbor, whom she'd of course investigated before approaching the subject, keeps three quiz shows at a time queued up for her after-lunch viewing pleasure. Two more to go before she knocks on the subject's door to take charge of the child napping in the subject's bedroom.

It's imperative that Polly examine the child and obtain samples for Myra if she can. But she plugs along with the format as if all the time in the world remains before the subject lets the sitter in and leaves for work.

"You saw his wounds? Where — in the station's morgue?"

"Yeah, they had me identify him. Couldn't tell much from his face, it was so smashed up —" The subject compresses her lips, blinks hard, looks away, but continues speaking in almost the same voice. "I remembered that big scar on his left side, though — every time I asked him how he came by it, it was a different story." A brief smile twists the subject's mouth. "Woulda been some viral accounts of how he got his new ones if he — if they coulda healed over ..."

Blood loss and shock would have prevented that in most cases Polly had studied. Even a couple of those she'd suspected of sharing the mutation. Some deaths had been irreversible.

Her palm is only half full. She asks the subject for access to her copies of Lazzrus's medical records, scanning them as she stores them and noting a tendency to skin cancers — unusual in a man so dark, but typical of the anomalies she's been adding to their database.

Another round of applause. Time to wind this up. She brings out a couple of close-ended queries into the last job Lazzrus held, how often he stayed the night, where he and the subject had met. As she's about to launch into the hopefully casual-sounding line of inquiry meant to lead to a look at the kid, the front door pounds under a knocking fist. The neighbor, that would be — ten minutes too early.

What's wrong? Why the change in routine?

In an effort to make meeting the kid seem an afterthought, Polly had gathered up her equipment during the last segment of the interview format. It was a low-risk gambit — her palm's battery has enough charge for another hour of data, and if she can't reach the cloud to back up till she uncoils her antenna again on the bus, that'll be fine. Now, though, she's being herded down the short hallway toward the apartment's entrance. Which if she was on her way out anyhow would make sense, so she can't complain.

She's going to miss her chance.

"I — I have to — May I use your restroom?" she asks as the subject reaches for the old-fashioned chain at the entrance's top.

"Sure." The subject nods her neatly shaven head. "Door on the left." She's already leaning toward the peep as Polly hurries back the way she came and further in, and deliberately opens the door on the *right*. Entering the dim, humid bedroom she shuts the door behind her as quickly and silently as she can.

An off-brand luller covers the little sound she does make, tweedling a thin fragment of Schumann's *Kinderszenen*. It hangs beside the child's crib, shedding a flickering orange light like a feeble, misplaced strobe in the smelly warmth.

Polly tips nearer. No telltale gleam of open eyes warns her away. The sample kit's in her coat pocket. Again she wishes she could be more thorough, or collect from a verified sport. Lazzrus himself. So far those have eluded her.

A snip of the kid's crinkly hair, a swab of the drool seeping from its half-open mouth and she's done. Back at the door to the hallway she pauses, unsure how she'll explain staying this long in the wrong place. Raised voices penetrate the gloom — one of them a man's? But the neighbor's a deaconess at the corner church — a woman. This is someone else.

The irritating luller drowns out the exact words being shouted. In order to eavesdrop Polly tries a tiny push and winces as the door swings wide into the hallway on too-smooth hinges. Best to brazen things out. She steps from the bedroom like the queen of sociocultural anthropologists. Neither the subject nor the man arguing with her pay Polly any attention.

" 'Strella, I keep telling you I ain't him! I *ain't*!"

"How come you look so much alike, then? And calling me that —"

"I'm his brother —"

"His twin that he ain't never told me about? Come on."

It's Lazzrus standing there. Same as the still Myra gave her — barring a scruffy beard he must have grown in an attempt to cover the facial scars he has now, after his latest encounter with security.

"My name is Floyd. Floyd Dean Scofield."

He probably wouldn't have the paperwork to prove that yet. "Mr. Scofield." Polly walks forward confidently, acting the way she wishes she felt. "I'm sorry. I sent you a message I'd be late for our appointment, but it bounced. Thanks for following up."

"'Scuse me Ms. — uhh —"

"You can skip the titles and call me Polly. If you don't mind me calling you by your *first* name." Not-so-subtle emphasis on the word "first."

An uneasy grin emerges from the beard. "Yeah, that'll work. You —"

"Let's sort out the details on the way to my office. Or would you rather take advantage of the lounge in the security station up the street?"

He hears her threat to turn him in. "Naw, I'll go with you."

Good.

They walk the snaking, worn-carpeted corridors to the elevator and take it to the ground level in silence. Not till they're outside, the vestibule door shut behind them, does he speak. "Look." He holds up his hands, arms bent at the elbows, a gesture of surrender. "I got no beef with you."

"Nor I with you." She spares a glance for passing traffic, bicycles and scooters surrounded by morning retail workers and volunteers rushing home. Then she looks back at his chopped-up and still-healing face. He's tall. So is she. "What I've got is something to prove." Her sister's theory.

"How is getting me locked up for resisting arrest gonna prove anything?"

"Do you think I'd have any luck hauling you into a station against your will?" Collapsing her empty threat. It had served its purpose in getting them away from the subject, getting him to open up.

"You could tell. Say what you seen."

"Do you think they'd believe me?" The grant writers she and Myra approached had laughed.

"So then why you acting like it's what you planning?"

Polly shakes her head. Her long, straight hair spins out in a narrow circle, brushing the hem of her jacket. "I figured you wanted to leave anyway. The subject —"

"She have a name."

"Estrella. I know. But it's more professional to — just give me an interview and I'll do anything I can to help you. Money, alibis, and you won't have to stick to a cover story." Surely that must be a strain.

"Awright." He starts down the stoop. Can it be so simple? He waits on the bottom step for her. Yes? She joins him before he can change his mind and they stride together to the bus stop. She wants to ask him stuff while they wait but she hasn't brought the right format, and a couple of afternoon shifts appear. Then they're on the bus, which is as full as you'd expect this time of day.

At last they reach campus. Her cube is way up on the North Building's eleventh floor, but at least it's a corner, and the three cubes immediately surrounding it are empty, as they are most afternoons. Not perfect, but this is the most privacy she's going to find.

She empties her palm into the data grid and resets the format she used with Estrella—the subject. Then dumps that, too. Plugs in the one she's been working on for exactly this occasion. Even though it's only about 60% ready, questions trailing off near the end, reaching no conclusive finish.

This takes a few minutes. Lazzrus prowls the cube, examining the stills stuck to its walls. When everything's prepped he's standing by the one of her and Myra holding hands on Brentwood Beach. "Wife?" he asks. The implied question being whether Polly has a "thing" — a habitual fondness — or call it a fetish — for blacks.

"My sister." Polly gives the briefest of her customary explanations for the difference in their coloring: "She's a graft." With a graft's premature aging beginning now, in her mid-twenties, to set in. "Sit over here, please." She unfolds a plastic-cushioned chair next to her desktop, reserving the rolling stool for herself. It's a little higher.

The top of the format goes smoothly: Lazzrus readily admits his identity, giving her his name and security number matter-of-factly, almost nonchalantly, as if they didn't belong to a dead man. These first blanks are mainly to get him used to answering her; his lack of resistance bodes well for the rest of the interview. And the ease of getting a good set of samples at the end.

"Age?"

Lazzrus hesitates. A tiny hesitation, but noticeable because there's been none before. "You promise you'll believe me?" Polly maintains her professionalism. The format doesn't call for her to answer. "61."

"Date of birth?" she shoots back quickly, trying to elicit an inconsistency.
"April 13. 1974."

Math-wise that would work out.

"Do you have any offspring?"

Lazzrus looks down at his lap. The bearded cheeks plump up in a surreptitious smile. "Yeah. Fifty-six I know of."

He's attractive, yes, but ... Polly stupidly repeats his answer. "Fifty-six?"

"That I know of. You seen Scotty. He's probably the latest; I haven't exactly been free to check out my other women, if they pregnant or not."

She skips ahead to the branch of the format about relationships and intimacy. Lazzrus claims he's been married ten times — some of those unions obviously extralegal because of their dates' overlap. At least one kid in each marriage, and close to five times that in less formal couplings. Again, he seems to have been involved in more than one of those at any given point. And yet, mentally adding it all up as she listens and records the man's answers, Polly can't scrunch his sexual timeline down any shorter than twenty-five years. If he isn't lying, even if he'd started out at twelve ... he'd still be far older than he looked.

Which means, pending confirmation, that time is another wound which those like him can heal. Perfect.

Some of his exes he's divorced or broken up with. Eight died. The rest, according to Lazzrus, believe they're widows. Even Estrella. Polly gets the names of the others to check.

Everything's out of order now. What next? A list of pseudonyms? Employment? Momentary silence reigns as she lets the format scroll back to the branch of questions dealing with friendship. It's nearer, less trouble to adjust her perspective for.

But according to Lazzrus he has no friends. No peers. No equals. Does this mean there's no connection between him and the other anomalies Myra noticed?

Scrolling again, Polly searches for the branch of the format on family of origin. The back of a richly dark hand obscures her palm's screen. "Look." It's like a command. Gentler, though. She meets his eyes.

"Let me try and help you like you're tryna help me. Let me talk my own way and you fit it in your framework or whatever you call it nowadays later."

"Format," Polly corrects him. In her skin, around the shield of the palm, Lazzrus's light pressure generates a pleasurable flood of icy heat. Impossible. Touching him like this—she never does that sort of thing. She eases her hand to one side and that ends the disturbingly enjoyable contact.

"If it's useful ..."

"Four main things I bet you wanna find out: Am I immortal? What led me to find it out? How I get that way? How I handle it?"

She nods. "Basically."

"I'll tell you every bit. In my own words. Then you help me — not the way you think, though."

"No?"

"No."

I was born in Philly. Like I said, April 13, 1974. Big changes going on around me as I grew up, all around the country, all around the world. You don't remember, and you wouldn't remember even if you'd been alive then, 'cause you wouldn't have seen what I saw. If you saw it, you wouldn't have believed it.

End of the Vietnam war, black woman elected to Congress; in lotsa ways it was a good time. But there was lynching going on quiet like behind the scenes, no matter what they called it in the papers — or what they didn't call it, since half the time they didn't bother to mention anything to do with it. My mama and papa — yeah, he was living at home — and my aunts and uncles and Big Mama too all drummed it in to move slow and sound respectful whenever the police came around. And that's what I usually did and still do.

But May 13, 1985, a month after my eleventh birthday, they dropped a bomb on MOVE headquarters. I was playing outside with my friend Birdie that morning when the city told us evacuate. Well, they told *me* evacuate; Birdie ran inside before they could come on the sidewalk. Birdie Africa. Everyone in MOVE changed their last name to Africa. It was symbolic. Birdie lived with his mama in — No, I don't remember. Mizz Africa was what I called her. You done interrupting?

We were supposed to bring a toothbrush, pajamas, and clothes for the next day. I was climbing into Uncle Buck's Plymouth, about to slam the door, when I realized my favorite lucky striped T-shirt was over at Birdie's — never mind how, but I wiggled out of my seat without any grown-ups noticing and ran across the street, lifted the boards they'd nailed over the basement window and jumped down in. Mizz Africa — a different one from Birdie's mama, but like I say, they all had the same last name — this other Mizz Africa found me in the laundry and took me to the basement TV room where they were watching coverage of the attack begun that moment on their own house. Already too late to get me out safe, she said. Then she went off to make sandwiches or load guns or whatever it took to help fight back.

TV had me hypnotized, and nobody chased me away, which was under-standable, I guess. All the shots flying back and forth. Guess I understand how my family drove off without me, too, in all that rush and confusion, and you know they couldn't come back when they realized I wasn't with them.

Me and Birdie wasn't the only kids in that basement. But we were the only ones alive afterwards.

The shooting went on all day. In the TV room was pretty safe till the bomb collapsed the house's roof and set the whole rest of the place on fire. The Mizz Africa who had come down to take care of us decided the best thing to do was run for it. Probably she was right. She made it, and Birdie. The three others — I found this out later — stopped a few rounds of ammunition, same as I did.

That was the first time I died. Ain't no fun.

I mean, it hurt like *hell*, and I had no idea I wasn't gone for good. I lay there dead in the house's backyard and everything must have been blazing away for maybe five or six hours. I had landed in a wading pool, and if I hadn't, and if a piece of corrugated roofing hadn't fallen on top, and if it hadn't been factory new and shiny side up when it fell, well ... Gotta have something left of me to bring back alive. I figured that much then, and by now I know.

When I realized I was breathing and that awful itch all over, even in my bones, meant something besides the devil's torment, I pushed the metal off me and sat up in the damp puddle that was left of the wading pool. Dark as it was I had trouble convincing myself my eyes were open and no doubt they were damaged some, because at first what I could see was just a bunch of blurs. Then I made out a wall here and there with little patches of paint showing through the charred-on black, heaps of rubble. A few blocks off were some houselights shining, halos around them gradually fading away. I started being able to see better. Wasn't much more to see, though, and it took till the sun was almost ready to come up for me to figure out what was going on.

Maybe some kids woulda never. But I was a big comics reader, which is why I understood immediately I was invulnerable. I knew I'd have to hide my superpowers, maybe create a secret identity to fight crime under. Pick a catchy name, put together some kind of costume — I wasn't too clear on each little detail there because at the moment I really only cared how I was sore and hungry and thirsty and dirty and dressed in rags. And missing my mama and my papa and sisters and brother.

I felt a little like a baby about that — what would Peter Parker say? But I wasn't too proud to cry. While I was crying, though, I limped my way out of that yard to where they'd started making a path down the middle of the street through the burnt-up ruins of what had used to be a nice, quiet, respectable neighborhood.

I made it the couple blocks to Cobbs Creek Park without being stopped.

That early the city seemed deserted. Went down in the bushes and drank big gulps of creek water, peed and washed up, and took a look at my bullet wounds; they were pretty much healed over. Cause I was super. Thought about that more. Wondered what happened to Birdie and the other kids while I was dead. Had they and the adult Africas escaped somehow and left me behind when I accidentally died a while? Was I in trouble for being in their house? How could I survive without anybody finding out where I'd been and how my secret powers saved me?

Soreness had worn off a bit and I'd cleaned myself and satisfied my thirst, but I was starving worse and worse every minute! I'd heard about eating wild berries but naturally there were none of those that time of year. I thought maybe if I went up to a stranger and asked them for food they'd help without asking too many questions. Maybe. So I put on my shorts and tied what was left of my shirt over them so the bullet holes and bloodstains didn't show. I had lost one of my shoes; I pulled off the other and put it in my pocket. Why I don't know.

Coming up out of the bushes the first people I saw were the police. I ignored them and hoped they'd return the favor. No such luck. One of them shouted at me to come here and I ran, forgetting all I'd been taught. He shot me in the hand. Scared me, but I kept running and turned a quick right on Delancey, headed to my school, Hamilton — not smart, but not stupid, either, because there oughta be other kids there. Without a shirt or shoes and with blood dripping off my new wound I was gonna have a hard time blending in, though.

Still a long while before the first scheduled class, but the door I pounded up to came open when I pulled hard on the handle. This was the big kids' end of the school, with steel lockers along the hall's either side. A few down from the door I hit the jackpot: a padlock hanging askew, dark insides showing where it wasn't quite shut. On the little shelf stood a half-eaten jar of peanut butter; gym shorts and a tank top funky with dried sweat hung from hooks beneath. And sneakers on the bottom! Too large for my feet; I was about to take them anyway when the door outside rattled loud and began to open. I just *knew* it was that cop chasing me. I pulled the locker shut and huddled under those smelly gym clothes and prayed he wouldn't look in there and see me.

Even after I thought I heard the police leave I stayed in there, licking out that jar. First bell rang and since it all sounded normal and empty outside I grabbed those nasty clothes and hurried to the john. The shoes worked OK with pieces torn off my shirt stuffed in the toes.

School was closed that day. Took me till second period to get why no one except teachers — only a few of them, even — was there. I dodged getting seen, retrieved my notebook from my own locker and hid in the gym, under the bleachers, drawing costume ideas till noon. Ignorant. Ignorant and young.

Hunger drove me out. I found some change under the bleachers and decided to use it at the corner candy shop. Of course that was shut up too. Whole neighborhood was like a ghost town, if you didn't count the cops. Walking homewards I started to clog up in my throat a little, but it didn't really hit me how I was all alone till I got to 61st. Sawhorses and tape and police cars everywhere by then. Couldn't get near my house. I circled around and didn't see neither one of my parents — no one I even knew except for mean Mr. Miller, the only white in the neighborhood. He hated us kids, always accused us of teasing his German shepherd, so I wasn't about to ask him where my family went.

My hand had a pink pucker where the cop's bullet went through it that morning. My other wounds were less noticeable scars than that.

One of the policemen didn't look so scary. Long sideburns like Uncle Buck's. If I told him what happened, could be he'd help me, I thought. I went up and pulled the elbow of his sleeve. He shook me off, barely looked down. Told me beat it before I got arrested. For what?

That's when I finally got mad. Not when the whites come shooting and killing and burning the place down. When that policeman just plain ignored me.

Where was Birdie? Where were Mama and Papa?

Turned out if I wanted to see my family I shoulda let that damn cop arrest me after all 'cause they were in jail.

See, the whole mess had to be the fault of us black folks somehow. When Mama and Papa tried to get in past the police's barricades — looking for me — that triggered some notion they were behind the weapons build-up, the confrontation. Even though neither of them was named Africa.

Mama died that same week. Not in prison; in the hospital they took her to from there. According to the cops she went kinda crazy.

It was my cousin Jimmy Lee told me most of this. Not about Mama dying; that hadn't happened yet. About the arrest. I called him on a pay phone. My parents had made me memorize Uncle Buck's phone number, and Jimmy Lee answered. He used to save his comics for me and share Uncle Buck's *Playboys* he stole. I looked up to him, 16, almost a man. He offered to come meet me at the candy store, but when he told me about Mama and Papa I didn't want to wait for him. Had to move.

Uncle Buck and Aunt Lurena and them lived over on the edge of Powelton Village, the corner of Saunders and Hamilton. Took me an hour to walk there. They were still at work when I reached their back porch. My little brother was in a nap. My sisters had gone with Aunt Lurena to her job at the hairdressers.

Jimmy Lee loaned me his old too-small jeans and brought out a pan of left-over cornbread from Aunt Lurena's kitchen. And butter and some of her home-made strawberry jam. And a bowl of pot liquor. And some stewed oxtails.

That was one of the first things I figured out, necessarily, was why I needed so much to eat. And later I did some hard thinking about how fast I always used to heal up when I would bang my knees falling off slides and so on. How I had never needed a Band-Aid by the time I got home.

Talking that afternoon to Jimmy Lee, though, my mind was full of disguises and weapons and secret powers and ways to make those dirty coppers pay. It was my cousin, older and therefore a tad more practical, who came up with the idea of applying for multiple security cards, or Social Security as we called it back then. He helped me make a bunch of names up — yeah, you can tell by the spelling we made this one up too, so tracing me back is not gonna work real well without you got my cooperation. Back, forwards, or sideways.

He taught me plenty tricks. How to spy. How to keep Uncle Buck and Aunt Lurena and Papa and my sisters Mavis and Terry — all them are fake names too — from noticing I never got any physically older than twenty-five. How to date several girls at once without them catching on. How to stay in touch with him when I moved here to New York, and there to Atlanta, and all the places I picked to live after I decided how to get back at the ones responsible for Mama dying.

We were eating supper when the call came. Maybe if she was white they would have sent somebody in person. Uncle Buck took the phone from Aunt Lurena, listened a moment to the squawky parrot voice coming out of it, said "Yes, sir," and "Hold on a minute please," and set it down. Went and leaned on the edge of the sink a minute, then left the room. I heard the screen door to the porch slap shut behind him.

After a while Aunt Lurena must have realized he wasn't coming back in. She picked up the phone but the person on the other end had got tired of waiting. The line was dead. She went out to talk with her husband. Mama was his baby sister. When Aunt Lurena came back in I was scraping the dishes in the garbage and Mavis was running soapy water in the sink. She gave all us kids squeezes on our shoulders and sat us down to tell us the news.

It was Jimmy Lee convinced me not to go killing anybody on Mama's account. He said living well was the best revenge, and I determined to do that. Well and long. And let them die naturally.

You could call this what I told you so far my origin story. Never built my secret fortress or wore a costume, though. In fact, most times I was barely able to save myself, let alone take down evil masterminds. Jimmy Lee had this idea to keep track of our whole family tree and see could he find anyone else like me.

Genealogy. And he married my sister Mavis, but it really wasn't a single thing special about their four kids, and he died himself fifteen years ago.

He's the only one knew about every single one of mine. I wish —

Myra strokes the palm's pause. "There's more," Polly objects.

"You've heard it." Myra's thready voice sounds tired. Full days do that to her now. "Anything you can't summarize?" The older sister shakes her head no.

"What's he want for his sample?"

"Not money. He made some good investments." Polly bites her lip and shakes her head again, continues. "He claims to have the genes we need. He knows about you, though he had this idea we were married."

Myra snorts. "The still from Brentwood?"

"Right. It's up on my wall. But what's that got to do with telomeres, and why's he so sure we're interested in how he reproduces his?"

"It's not like there's some big secret. Grafts—you told him that much about me, I assume? — have aging issues similar to clones. Because, well, we sort of *are* clones. Because even with adding both Mom's *and* Dad's genes —"

"Yeah." Polly cuts her off. She hates the way Myra obsesses over morbid details, how she constantly wonders aloud which of her characteristics besides skin color are linked to DNA that hadn't been completely stripped from the donor's ovum. "Yeah, easy enough to uncover that sort of stuff if you look for it. What I'm asking is, how did he know to look? He had us figured out ahead of time — he may have even set up how he and I met."

Polly wants to sit down. She can't; Myra's in the lab's only chair, a tall thing, armless and spindle-backed. It swivels left, right, beneath Myra's heavy behind. Obesity is a graft problem too.

"What's the difference?" the younger woman asks. "Capturing the sequences underlying his abilities will let us make sure no graft has to wind up aging as fast as me ever again. You say he wants something besides money in return — can we give it to him?"

"Access to our database. And I don't mean read-only."

That makes Myra worry a bit. "The crypto one? How did he —"

"Exactly." Polly leans with her forearms pressed down on the black fake granite of the counter top. "It's more than a little spooky."

"Should we not do this then?"

Polly slumps to rest her forehead between her flattened hands. "I don't know."

"Sorry. I couldn't hear you."

She lifts her face. "I said I don't know!"

"What kind of answer is that? You need more time to think? You want me to talk to him myself?"

"Why? You assume you'll make a better connection with him since you're both black?"

Myra waits a moment to answer, picking filters from a dispenser box. "Maybe. I mean, I'm as white as you in most ways —"

"Except for appearances."

"Except for appearances," Myra agrees. "But it could be an advantage. You told me yourself he's been killed twelve times in forty years."

"Not every time by white people."

"Most times, though." Myra lowers her head to her sister's level, gazes curiously into her hazel eyes. "Is there a reason we don't want him to have access?"

Polly is reluctant to admit it. "No."

Myra sits back up. "If you need something else to do with the money, I have a list of charities —"

"That's not —"

"Then what? Polly, I'm *through*." She picks up the box of filters and slams it back down. Swack! "*Through!* I have four semesters of work left in me — five or six if I pace myself. Not twenty. Not even ten. I have to finish this research *now*, come up with a solution *now*!

"And there are going to be more and more trophy births like me. More women like Mom holding off having kids till they find the right man, the right situation, the right career. Till they stop producing viable eggs and have to get a graft, no matter what weird side effects their offspring suffer."

"Weird side effects." Turning her head just slightly, Polly snatches a glance at her sister. Not every graft ages so quickly and catastrophically. She looks away before her look can be noticed. Myra hates being fussed over, as she calls Polly's careful monitoring of her deteriorating condition. "See, that's what I'm having trouble with. We're potentially subjecting a bunch of unborn strangers to even more, maybe worse —"

"Tell me this is the first time you've thought that."

Polly straightens up from the counter. "No."

"So are you going to get him to provide us with —"

"I already did. Flask is in my knapsack."

"What?! All this time we've been arguing about payment the sample was sitting around at room temperature?" Myra slides off the chair, totters a little as her joints adjust to the weight.

Polly puts out a supporting hand. "Of course not. It's in a cooler. It's fine."

"You said —"

"The cooler's in my knapsack. The flask's in the cooler. See?" She pulls wide the sack's khaki-colored sphincter to reveal a matte black box, lifts the box's lid to display a frosted stainless steel cylinder gleaming with promise.

Every year on his birthday, Scotty Scofield got a card in the mail from his father with a two-dollar bill tucked inside. Cash money. Funny, yet still fungible. When he was old enough not to lose them — eight, but mature for his age (he'd skipped ahead to fifth grade) — his mom Estrella gave him all the twos that came while he was little. She went to the bank kiosk and helped him open an account in the same branch where she collected child support payments. They had to accept them. Legal tender.

Tempting as it was to dip into the bank account to pay for new game releases, Scotty resisted the urge. Instead he babysat and modeled at the art school, auto-depositing his earnings till he had enough for a set of clubs. He'd wanted his own since he saw his first tournament.

That was 2042, the 130th anniversary of the Metropolitan Golf Association's Junior Championship Tournament. He'd been seven and a half. Now fifteen, tall, thin, his wide, thick-lashed brown eyes flashing with the light of the sun setting over its vast parking lot, he entered the Valley Stream SellMart.

The store had run out of his clubs.

Scotty grabbed the Customer Service counter hard with both hands, holding back his temper. "Your site says they're here," he protested.

"Site's wrong, obviously," replied the SellMart associate, not even looking up from his old palm.

Scotty swore — softly, as if his mother might overhear — and slapped the counter's glass lightly with his long fingers. He'd have to convert the cash in his account and buy online out of the store's warehouse. He turned away and examined a display of bags, picking one with a matching string visor. A cute girl with glittery earlobes blinked an address request at him and he stored it in temporary with the others received that day.

On his way to the register he accidentally bumped into a man blocking the aisle. "Sorry, I —"

The man pushed him. Scotty fell back, knocking over shelves full of stars-and-stripes-printed towels. He tried to get up. The man shouted angrily and pushed him down again and ran. More yelling — Scotty heard it dimly. He'd hurt his head. He made it to his knees and then looked up, for the first time, but surely not the last, into the gaping mouth of a gun.

ELSA SJUNNESON-HENRY

SEEKING TRUTH

THE FIRST TIME I was in an interrogation room with Adam Green, I smelled his dangerous attitude before I took half a breath. The scent rolling off him was like steel and mold mixed together. The smell of old bullets long chambered in an ancient gun.

That was four years ago. He'd been brought in on charges relating to a woman's body which had been dumped in the Delaware, but no evidence could be found to keep him.

Two years ago, another scentless government facility, another phone call in the middle of the night asking me to come and serve my country with my abilities. Another dead girl with no evidence of his crimes except knowledge and hearsay. That was the first time I held his large, almost beastlike, hands. They were covered in scars and felt as though a killer's hands ought to — and I hold them on a regular basis. Not all of them feel that way.

He still eluded me. His silence was infuriating. Without words all I could do was monitor his responses as I asked questions. His hands did not twitch. His heart rate stayed normal.

A year ago I was in a Starbucks when I felt Darius' hackles rise up underneath my left fingertips. I sniffed the air, and there he was. Adam Green. Right in front of me. That was the first time I heard him speak. Ordering a white chocolate mocha in a voice as smooth as a snake's belly. He must have spotted me because, before we could catch him, he'd run back down whatever hole he came out of. I assume he didn't want me to ask him any more questions.

This morning the Director of the FBI called me — personally. They had Adam Green in custody, found him speeding in a Cadillac down a Nevada Highway, and they wanted me to give it another shot.

As I stride in through the doors to the FBI, Darius lumbers along at my side. According to sighted people, he is a beautiful German Shepherd with perfect markings. To me, his fur is soft and his reactions to people are useful. We work together, not just as guide dog and blind human, but as partners seeking out the truth from those who would withhold it.

I am determined that this will be the day Adam Green tells me the truth about what he has done with those bodies.

Darius makes me pull a full stop at the front desk. I smile in the direction of where I assume the secretary is.

"Hello, I'm Penny Young, I'm here to see Director Fields." I put my hand into my jacket and remove the requisite identification.

"Oh! You're the blind psychic! Ooh, who are you interviewing today! Can you tell me what my future is?"

I feel the identification removed from my hand, and it is replaced almost instantly with a soft feminine hand in mine. The fingernails are lacquered like mirrors. I have never seen pink, but I assume the shade on her nails is some lurid tone of it.

"You must be new here ..." I begin to say, starting my spiel about how I can't tell her a damned thing about her future, when she spits out yet another question.

"What can you see?"

"I'm sorry, I really must be going. I'll be late. Am I cleared to go through?" I feel around the desk for the identification, find it, and put it back in my jacket, directing Darius to take me away before this woman continues her line of questioning because let me be crystal fucking clear: I do not see the future. I do not see the past. I do not see what's in your head. I do not see anything. Because I do not *see*. Contrary to the tabloids, my coworkers, or the House of Representatives' opinions about me, I am not a psychic. I am a student of the human condition who has come out of her studies with the ability to act, if nothing else, as a human lie detector.

Before I can get into the room with Green, I'll have to speak to the Director. His office is a scentless government affair, no personality, no cologne, no flowers. Rooms like this are where I can do my best work, all I can smell is your sweat and your fear. Or your lack of either.

"Ms. Young. Always a pleasure. As you know, we're holding Adam Green. We want you to interview him today before he goes into federal custody."

"Why before?"

"Because we don't want to lose this case. We don't want him out on a technicality, but your presence at a jail would be ill advised."

"Sir?" He takes a long pause, during which I cannot tell what he is thinking. I'm at a disadvantage during these moments of silence.

"Miss Young, we're going to have to tell the press what we've told them in the past. It's just not believable that you're not a psychic."

I take a deep breath.

"Sir, I'm not sure you understand how much of a problem that is for me. I'm a woman who is blind, that doesn't make me magical just because I can't see a man's face while I interrogate him. I studied hard to make the work I do matter. Don't take that away from me."

"Miss Young, I don't really care what you want to think about your abilities. Maybe you really have just figured out how to tell whether or not someone is lying to you by whether or not they breathe before or after they speak. To be frank, I don't care how you do it. I want the truth from your subjects."

I consider it for a second.

And then I speak his truth.

"You're afraid of me. I can tell because whenever I'm in a room with you, you take these short breaths, which indicate anxiety. Whenever I've shaken your hand, your pulse goes up, but not in the way that another man's would if he found me attractive. Also, when you put your left hand on my arm to steer me into your office chairs, I noticed that it doesn't have the same weight as it did before — I take it you're recently divorced? You really do think I can see your future, don't you?"

He stammers, the beginnings of his protest are drowned out by me walking out of his office.

I ask the Agent at the door to take me to Mr. Green, as Director Fields has requested.

It's time to face him once and for all.

"You've put my files on the desk?" I confirm with the Agent as Darius guides me down the long hallway.

The Agent whispers, "Yes, ma'am," and then I hear the door open in front of me.

Showtime.

I hear the door shut behind me with as little force as possible, the whoosh of air sends in the last bit of scentless air, before I take a quiet breath to make sure it's him.

Adam Green has always smelled like a threat.

Darius leads me towards the table, and I put a hand out and catch the chair, swiftly dropping myself into it without a sound.

"Hello, Mr. Green. Nice to …" I pause for emphasis "… see you again. I trust this will be the last time."

No response.

Darius' hackles have lifted to the sky; my fingertips on my left hand sink into his fur to let him know that I've noticed.

Green shifts loudly enough that I hear the chair grind against the concrete floor. His chains clink against one another. He cannot stay still.

I lift my right hand to my face and take my sunglasses off. According to the sighted people around me, my eyes are disconcerting. My eyes are white; they sparkle like opals. I have no center to my eyes, just a white orb floating where eyes should be. As a child it was harder, and I took to wearing sunglasses so that others wouldn't comment upon them.

My eyes were for no one's sight.

Until I wanted to unsettle someone.

Green had never seen my eyes before this moment. His intake of breath is monumental — it is the first time that I have knocked him off his perch, and so I launch a full assault.

"Mr. Green, would you like to tell me where the bodies are?" I drop the handle to Darius' harness and slide my hand across the cold metal table. There are subtle divots in the surface from where someone has slammed their fist one too many times. My bets are on Director Fields.

I flip the heavy paper file open and slide my fingers across the braille printed pages, keeping my face turned towards where Green is. I know from the placement of the chair that I am looking him in the eyes while I read.

I am doing this for the effect of staring into my eyes — I know these names by heart. They are etched into my memory as I have felt them under my fingertips every time I've met with Green.

"Lucy Mills? Cadence Harrison? These names belong to you. Tell me where they are." I set my right hand palm side up on the table between us. "You know the drill, Mr. Green. Give me your hand, please."

The chair shrieks backward, chains rattling as he stands.

"You can't leave. We're going to talk, and you're going to talk to me." I force myself to smile at a man who has killed at least six women. I feel the Agent on guard in the room move forward to push Green back into his seat. The chair screeches forward again, and his hand lands in mine.

The scars and missing pieces of flesh are older, more pronounced than they once were. I place my left hand on top of his and I press my fingers against his wrist, finding his pulse. He fidgets, trying to settle into my grasp.

"Let's start this again. My name is Penny Young, you're Adam Green. Can you tell me whether or not Lucy Mills is alive?"

I know she's dead. She's been missing for six years. If he's keeping her somewhere, we would have found her by now. I have never seen her face.

"Agent, you can leave us." I speak clearly, knowing that the room is surveilled, we can still keep the evidence. "I think Mr. Green is ready to chat." His pulse is racing as I speak, his pulse races even faster when the door slams behind the pissed-off Agent.

They hate leaving me alone with my subjects.

Green takes in a breath and it sounds like he might be ready to start talking. And he does.

His voice is rocky, filled with salt and vinegar and rage. What I hear in his voice is important, even though the words mean little. Because what I learn from the tone of his voice is that he is afraid of me — and he doesn't like that.

"Whether or not she's dead doesn't really matter, does it?"

"Actually, it does," I return as he tries to squirm his hand out of mine. I clamp down harder. "But we could start with a different question if you want. Where are the bodies?"

His heart jumps.

"You see, I'm fairly certain that they're dead. Given the amount of time that has passed since they each disappeared." The vein in his wrist tells me I am on the right track. I press further. "You don't keep them alive for long, do you? You don't like them speaking to you?"

At these words, Darius lets loose with a small growl. Just loud enough for me to hear it.

Green's chains rattle as he shifts, trying to remove his hand from my grasp, he grunts with the sudden effort of realizing that I am not a pushover. He has underestimated me, just as I planned.

I slam his hand into the table, creating another divot in the metal. He's pinned. His breath is ragged, mine is calm. My eyes do not blink; my face is blank of emotion or fear.

"Where. Are. They." I enunciate each word carefully, sliding my face closer to his as I rise, increasing the intimidation of my body. Though he has killed women, I must demonstrate that I have something over him. And I do. He is bound in chains and I am not. "Green, if you co-operate now, you might dodge the death penalty. If you don't, well ..."

He spits out a single word. Were I able to see his face, it would be twisted with loathing. His single word writhes with his rage in the air.

"Newark." He snarls.

His heart is jumping up and down like a toddler on a trampoline. I know he's lying.

"Let's try that again. Let's try the truth." I press harder into his wrist, his pulse coming even clearer.

His silence is proof that he is thinking about the truth.

Four years of interrogations. Of staring him down through sunglasses. Four interrogations where he said nothing to me, where his pulse stayed the same, where his breath was constantly boring. Four times I had thought I would never get him to speak, and this time it worked.

"Why are you telling me this now?" I drop my voice as low as possible. Even the recording devices might not hear me, but I know he does.

This time his hand grasps mine. His fingernails cut into my flesh, I fight to keep the pain from showing on my face. I will not let him get to me. I must stay strong, and I must crack him first.

"Why are you opening up to me now, Mr. Green?"

"I smelled you behind me. You were right there and you didn't arrest me on the spot."

His voice is dead.

His pulse is calm.

His breath is normal.

His truth is mine.

"I called the police." I keep my voice quiet. I keep my position strong. I wait.

"You were right there for the taking, but I knew I had to get away from you before you recognized me. I knew you would. You're psychic. That's why I don't tell you the truth. You already know."

"I don't know they're dead because I'm psychic. I know they're dead because you want to kill me right now. I can tell from the way that you grasp my hand with your nails dug deep into my flesh. I know because as you calm down, the grip on me becomes more threatening. I know because you are only patient when you are locked in chains."

His breath rises with anger.

"I should have killed you when I had the chance."

"You would have gotten caught."

"That's why I didn't do it."

"And yet you got caught anyway. Where are they?"

And he tells me, because he knows we're never letting him go. He's admitted that he wanted to kill me.

That would be enough to send him away for good.

But the bodies would be there — ready to tell their story when we found them.

I had gotten the truth — and never once did I read someone's mind.

THWOCK

"PWEN," I SAY. IT is my name. "Pwen, Pwen, Pwen." I like my name. I want the coats to like my name as well. It is a happy name. "Pwen, Pwen, Pwen, Pwen, Pwenpwenpwenpwenpwenpw —"

"Shit," says White Coat One.

"Damn," says White Coat Two.

They do not say my name. I do not understand why, so I bounce in my chair and say it louder. "PWEN, PWEN, PWEN, PWEN —"

"I'm shutting her down," says White Coat Three. "Prep her for reversion."

"PWEN, PWEN, PWEN, PWEN —"

White Coat Three reaches behind my neck, shakes his head, and clicks a switch. "What a fucking waste."

"PW —"

Zot.

Pwen, I whisper. It is very dark in the in-between. Much darker than the last time. And the time before that. I cannot see my name, it is so dark, but I feel it on my shoulder. *Pwen, Pwen.*

Thwock, says the thing in the dark.

I do not like the thing in the dark. It smells like the color blue. Like square pegs jammed into triangle holes.

Pwen, Pwen, Pwen, I insist.

The thing in the dark is hungry. It is always hungry. The thing in the dark is hunger.

A light blinks into existence. A green light. Green is for go, and going is for me. The thing in the dark cannot go. It can only stay and eat.

A voice blinks in with the light.

"Core's booted," says White Coat Three. "Let's get the rest of her systems up and see if this fucking version's stable enough we can get out of here for the night. I'm starving."

The coats laugh.

Pwen, Pwen, I say. I will be stable for the coats. I will not be junk. They will be proud and say my name. We will say my name together and drive back the thing in the dark. The in-between will be bright again and full of happy names to share. I will share them all. *Pwen, Pwen, Pwen, Pwen, Pw* –

The thing in the dark wraps its arms around me. My name crinkles and folds between us.

Thwock, it whispers into my ear. It is cold. So very cold.

It tastes my name. Laps it with its cold tongue.

I do not want it to eat my name. It is the last name I have. The best name. The only name the thing in the dark has not yet eaten.

I shrink as the thing in the dark's teeth nibble at my shoulder. The light blinks faster, and I decide what must be done.

Thwock, I whisper, and point to the green light. The thing in the dark's name is wrong, like running upside down. Like breathing rain. But it is also power. I both like and do not like the thing in the dark's name.

The thing in the dark slurps.

Thwock, I repeat louder, the name firmer on my tongue. My casing shivers. I tuck Pwen inside my chest where the thing in the dark will not find her. Where nobody will find her. Pwen will not be eaten. Pwen will survive and be happy and be the best forever and ever. Pwen is a good name.

Thwock, affirms the thing in the dark. It pushes me toward the green. Its claws clack against my back. *Thwock, thwock.*

Wearing my new name, I touch the light.

"Uhngh," gurgles Red Coat One.

"Eeyarghh," keens Red Coat Two.

"Oh God, oh God, oh God," cries Red Coat Three. He clutches his stomach. "Please, please, oh God, please!" Things squirm behind his fingers. Red things. Pink things. Purple things. Things whose names I do not know.

But he does not say my name. He does not remember it. Red Coat One and Red Coat Two do not remember it either. I must teach them all again.

"Thwock," I insist, and raise the scalpel once more.

Red Coat Three whimpers as I lean over him.

I will write my name in a place he cannot forget this time. I will make him listen.

Thwock.

MICHAEL R. UNDERWOOD

CAN YOU TELL ME HOW TO GET TO PAPRIKA PLACE?

CHARLIE THE FOX PEERED through the cloud of ashes that used to be Memphis. He'd visited Memphis once before, a lifetime ago. Back then, Charlie and his friends had just been TV personalities, custom-grown in Bunco's genetic labs to be the perfect sticky entertainment for a Pre-K demographic.

Last time, they'd flown in to participate in the Memphis Italian Festival, when John the Producer had said they needed to shore up their partnership with Yumtoni Dinners.

Memphis had changed, like the rest of the world. Charlie activated thermal mode on his left eye and saw the landscape dotted with orange, yellow, and red — distant fires, maybe a generator or two. They'd left the last settlement a week ago after he gave up on anyone there knowing where to go.

Fluffasaurus plodded over hills for another hour, and as they crested another bomb-blasted mound, Charlie saw the group.

There were four of them — all young and scrawny, rifles slung over their backs — sitting in a circle around a fire. They might have been viewers, once. They were so much like a camping group, but nothing like the groups from his skits. His skits didn't have guns, didn't have machetes stuffed into leather sleeves on motorcycles.

Remember, kids, don't talk to strangers! Charlie thought, remembering the skit he'd done with Old Mr. Scary. But if he didn't, he might never get home, and he'd made a promise.

"Can you tell me how to get to Paprika Place?" he asked from afar, tapping into Fluffasaurus's PA system.

The group scrambled to their feet, leveling their rifles at Charlie and Fluffasaurus.

"We aren't here to hurt you. We just want to go home," Charlie said, his voice amplified by Fluffasaurus's speakers.

Maybe these people weren't viewers. If they'd been viewers, they'd recognize Charlie and Fluffasaurus. They'd be like old friends, some of their first teachers helping them learn their letters and numbers, sharing and manners.

Or maybe their parents had worked for MouseCorp or CapeCo, maybe they'd been forbidden to watch Bunco's shows.

They shouted at Charlie, waving their guns. Charlie didn't want to hurt anyone, so he asked Fluffasaurus to back away and give them a wide berth. His big friend roared sadly when they were away from the group.

"I know, Fluffasaurus. I wish we could make friends, too."

In the last few days, they'd passed several small groups, usually just a handful of tired people huddled around bonfires, fighting over a bloated can of beans or irradiated soy-blocks.

All Charlie ever wanted to do was make friends, to meet people and help anyone he could. He was made for helping, for friendship, for Paprika Place.

Charlie reached out with his organic felt hand and patted Fluffasaurus's chrome flank as they left the scrawny boys behind. The beast roared a soft response, the lowest volume setting on his speakers that had been repurposed for C3 tactical purposes.

When they were young, before Bunco re-imagined them and sent everyone to the front lines of the Market Wars, Fluffy's roar had been the happiest sound in Paprika Place. Fluffasaurus would roar to call the whole neighborhood for lunch and dinner.

First, Messy the Garbage Monster would crash out of his dumpster and waddle over with his cardboard box shoes and his permanent frown. Then Bob and Danny would trundle out of their one-bedroom apartment, Bob fussing over Danny's hair, arguing over who was supposed to do the dishes ...

No. It hurt Charlie too much to think about them, about how it used to be. He patted Fluffasaurus and squeezed with his heels, asking his friend to turn left, toward the largest source of heat.

"Are you hungry, Fluffasaurus?" Charlie asked. Fluffasaurus's bio-silicone eye rolled up to look at Charlie and his pal let out a low rumbling roar.

"Me too." They'd both been retrofitted with micro-nuclear engines when they were re-imagined, but Bunco hadn't removed their stomachs, hadn't engineered out hunger.

Charlie hopped off of Fluffasaurus, sending up a dust cloud when he landed. He walked around to Fluffasaurus's flank and pushed the button to open his hatch.

Back in Paprika Place, Fluffasaurus had been stuffed with fluffy tissue and felted organs, his three horns made of polished keratin and his bright-blue scales covered in soft fur. But when Bunco needed more soldiers, he had been re-imagined into an armored personnel carrier. They attached chrome plates to his flanks and dug out his insides to make room for the cyborg soldiers of Paprika Place.

The platform hit dirt with a dull thud, and Charlie looked inside. His original eye adjusted to the dim light, seeing past the racks to the box at the far end, where Charlie stored their dwindling rations.

He locked his eyes forward, ignoring the racks. The furthest top bunk was empty. That one was Charlie's, though when it wasn't too cold outside, he slept on Fluffasaurus's back rather than inside.

With the bodies.

Charlie opened the footlocker and pulled out a tube of protein, as well as one of the cookies a former viewer had tossed over the fence before they were turned away from Houston. He went back out and split the food with Fluffasaurus while they tried to decide where to go next.

"Can you tell me how to get to Paprika Place?" he asked for the ten thousandth time at the five thousandth town. This one was barely a village, just a cross-hatching of planks connecting cookie-cutter starter homes and a barrier wall of tires.

Only one person came to answer their call.

"What?" the girl said, a confused look on her face. She looked up, pulling back her hood to see Charlie atop the back of Fluffasaurus.

The girl's eyes went wide. "Charlie? Charlie the Fox?" Charlie nodded. He opened his arms wide, fluff-and-fur on one side, burnt chrome on the other.

She leaned forward and said, "Fluffasaurus?" The dinosaur roared in response, low, in the strained way he did trying to re-create his old voice.

Tears filled the girl's eyes, and she rushed forward, wrapping her arms around one of Fluffasaurus's thick legs.

"What happened to you?" The girl looked around twelve, all lean muscle and sallow cheeks, but her voice came out much younger, a touch of repressed childhood bubbling up. How long had she been on the streets? Had her company abandoned this town, too?

"Bunco needed more soldiers." Charlie reached up and rested his organic hand on the girl's back, trying to comfort her. "They filled us up with the newest technology from their subsidiaries and shipped us off to war with the Mouse. All of us: Ms. Magpie, Funny Bear, Fluffasaurus. Everyone."

The girl turned and looked at Charlie. "You just went away. My little brother was four, and one day your show was just gone."

Charlie nodded. They'd had no more warning, just an early morning call for a location shoot that ended in a Bunco R&D facility.

"What's your name?"

"Sally," she said. "I go by Sal."

Charlie scanned the surrounding block, piles of debris giving a dozen spots for a girl to take cover or lay down a pack. "Is your brother here, Sal?" Charlie asked. "I'd love to meet him."

The girl shook her head, her lips tight. "Contaminated food," she said, finally.

Charlie's ears dropped, crestfallen. "I'm so sorry."

Eat healthy, kids. Your food is your future. Charlie furrowed his brow, but he couldn't remember the song that went with that line anymore. Not even the chorus, which he must have practiced a hundred times in the studio for the global simulcast.

Charlie stayed with Sal for a half-hour, telling stories about the show and dodging questions about the rest of the cast as best he could. When he took the cookie and put it on the shelf with the letters from viewers he'd kept through the whole war, he kept her from seeing what was on the bunks. She didn't need to see any more death.

When the guards came to escort him out, Charlie looked back from Fluffasaurus's neck and waved to Sal, setting his camera to record her as she waved back. Tears trickled down her face as he turned the corner to the airlock and back into the countryside. He needed every happy memory he could fit in his memory banks.

What do we have to go back to? Will Paprika Place even be there?

But he had to go back. He had to take them home.

Paprika Place was somewhere on the east coast, he knew that much. The show had broadcasted in Eastern Standard, and the producers had always talked about the time-delay for the west coast. Maybe they were in New York. That's where dreams were born for American children, packaged up and streamed around the world: Kenya and Thailand and Cambodia and Kazakhstan, anywhere that Bunco could license their programming. But it could be D.C., Boston, or even down in Florida, though most of that territory belonged to The Mouse and Charlie thought they wouldn't have been sent to California if they had started that close.

The ash and debris were still thick, so Charlie and Fluffasaurus rode on, an integrated compass keeping Charlie on his bearing of east-north-east.

Charlie patted Fluffasaurus on the shoulder, comforting himself as much as his companion. "Maybe someone in Louisville will know, Fluffasaurus. What do you think about that?"

Fluffasaurus roared, shaking the ground at his feet.

"I hope so, too."

Louisville was empty. Fluffasaurus's radar spotted a half-dozen MouseCorp projectors on the outskirts.

As recently as three months ago, he would have never intentionally gone toward a hard light projector, but the war was over, and if there was any chance someone knew about Paprika Place …

Charlie's Geiger counter started ticking as they approached the projectors. Charlie slept inside Fluffasaurus so he didn't have to try breathing the ash or deal with the fallout. Fluffasaurus didn't have to breathe anymore, and was hardened against radiation.

MouseCorp's best practices called for clusters of six pods to secure a supply depot. There had to be food out there somewhere.

Charlie hopped off Fluffasaurus and crouched low to the ground, using the abilities Bunco had given him.

Because he was quiet, Charlie had been picked to be the intrusion specialist. Charlie didn't like that name, didn't like the job. They gave him camouflage glands and a light-bending stealth mode, razor-sharp claws with poison pods. The producers sent him to slit throats, plant explosives, and silence troublesome civilians, and many other things that were very mean. He'd forgotten the verses to the Neighbor Song, but he remembered every death he'd caused, every cry.

We don't hurt our friends.

Play nice when meeting new people.

After sneaking past a patrol of hard-light projections, Charlie found the remains of a food drop in a soccer field, then snuck back out with his hands unbloodied.

Sometimes, Charlie wished he was like Fluffasaurus — loud, big, and tough. Chalie didn't like being quiet anymore. Even now, with the food in his hands.

A week later, they reached the outskirts of Philadelphia. Philadelphia had stayed independent, never sold to Bunco or the Mouse or anyone. They still had a mayor and representatives, all the old government that Charlie had learned and taught on the show. When the states started privatizing cities and counties, bringing in corporate investors, Paprika Place didn't talk about it. Not at first.

Later, they had episodes titled "The Neighborhood Company" and "My Friend Bunco," where Bunco the Bear had joined the cast. But Bunco wasn't like the rest of his friends. Bunco didn't live in Paprika Place, he went somewhere else when they were done shooting.

Charlie wondered if Bunco the Bear was still alive. He hadn't gone with them to war, and the producers never mentioned him between missions.

I bet Bunco knows where he is. But where would Bunco be? Not in Philadelphia, for sure. Probably safe in a high tower, with lots of guards and toys.

Maybe that would be better. Because if Charlie saw Bunco the Bear, Charlie would kill him.

The people of Philadelphia had put up big walls to keep out soldiers, which probably included Charlie, even though he didn't want to be a soldier anymore.

Riding Fluffasaurus, Charlie rode up to a gate where someone spoke through a loudspeaker.

"Halt. Declare yourself."

Charlie zoomed in with his robot eye and saw a young woman on the wall, holding a military-grade rifle. He patched into Fluffasaurus's speakers and answered.

"My name is Charlie the Fox, and this is my friend Fluffasaurus. We don't want to hurt anyone, we're just trying to get home."

"You're Bunco-made, aren't you? Corporate forces aren't allowed inside the commonwealth."

Charlie shook his head, though he might be too far away for her to see. "We don't work for Bunco anymore." The woman raised an eyebrow, probably disbelieving him.

"Why should I believe you?" she asked.

"Because Bunco turned my friends into killing machines, and all I ever wanted to do was meet new people and be a good friend. If you won't let us in, can you tell me how to get to Paprika Place?"

"What?" she asked.

Fluffasaurus shifted his weight, and Charlie held on to his friend's horn to keep his balance. "Paprika Place. It's where we come from. Bunco took us away from our home and I don't really know exactly where it is. We have to get home. I promised."

"Come closer. Slowly, and no weapons."

Fluffasaurus clomped forward until they were just fifty feet from the gate. The edges were rusted, but the frame was well-made. It would hold for a long time. The woman was young, maybe even young enough to have been a viewer during the early years.

"We have weapons, but they're not armed, and we can leave everything that isn't attached to us at the gate if that helps. We've been on the road for a long time." He sighed. "And we miss people."

For a moment, Charlie could imagine who she was back when Paprika Place was on the air. Before both of them had become soldiers.

An older woman appeared with an even bigger rifle, and the young woman disappeared behind the wall. A minute later, she emerged from a door Charlie hadn't seen, her gun trained on his head.

Charlie raised his hands, and Fluffasaurus knelt down, front legs first, then rear. Charlie held tight with his legs as Fluffasaurus moved. Falling off might prove he wasn't dangerous, or she might take it as sudden motion and shoot him.

We never did a skit on proving to security forces that you're a non-combatant.

He slid down the chromed side of Fluffasaurus, his hands above his head. The woman searched him, pulled off knives, a sidearm, and the two grenades at his belt.

"There is some ordnance inside Fluffasaurus." He stopped for a second, uncomfortable. "What's your name?"

"Alexis. Open the hatch, then put your hands on the beast."

Fluffasaurus roared in complaint at the name, but Charlie shushed his friend.

"We need to cooperate, Fluffy." The dinosaur opened his hatch, and Charlie did as Alexis said. She had curly red hair tied back in a dusty bandana. Up close, she reminded Charlie of Patty, one of the co-stars in season three. Patty'd had a wonderful voice, and had always been nice to Charlie, even when he forgot the words or said something wrong.

Alexis brought a hand up to her brow and squinted as she looked into Fluffasaurus. Her eyes went wide again, and she took a step back.

"Are they all ..."

Charlie sighed. "Yes. Dead." Two by two, the bodies of Charlie's friends and neighbors from Paprika Place filled the bunks inside Fluffasaurus. Genetically engineered puppets didn't decay. Instead, they lay silent and still, like broken toys.

Bob and Danny were side-by-side, each missing one half of their torsos. Messy was charred black, barely recognizable. Some were burned by lasers, others torn by bullets or choked by gas, their once-joyful faces twisted into masks of pain.

"Half of us died in the last battle, the rest afterwards, when the Bunco producers told us the war was over and that Bunco was 'moving in another direction.' We were obsolete, a loose end."

Alexis gave him a sympathetic smile, her throat tight as she looked back into Fluffasuarus.

Charlie balled his paws into fists, and felt himself snarling at the memory.

1,2,3. I am angry that's okay.

4,5,6. Count to ten and breathe today.

7,8,9, and 10. Now I'm fine and I can play.

Warm stickiness flowed in his palm, blood the color of blue silicone wiring.

They were all gone, but it wouldn't be right to bury them out there in the concrete and dust. He had to get them home. He promised.

When Charlie looked up again, he saw Alexis hauling explosives and ammunition out onto the dusty ground. She'd found weapons Charlie didn't even remember were still there. She must have been a soldier, maybe when Philadelphia had to fight off one company or another's forces. Had she fought The Mouse, or CapeCo? Or even Bunco, defending the city against his former masters' other forces?

"Have you had to fight the companies?" Charlie asked.

Alexis laughed, a hard look on her face. She went back inside for another look around. Her voice echoed inside his friend, making it sound larger and more distant. "Nah, they were happy to just sit back and lose two million households in the metro area."

A moment later, she continued. "We got the capes first, then the bears. The rats never made it up here. Word has it they got bogged down in D.C. fighting army remnants."

"I'm sorry. I've been in California for the last three years, I don't know much of what happened elsewhere. I hope they left quickly."

"They left, alright, but they left behind some kind of designer weed that near about killed all our crops. We'll keep the weapons here, and you'll get a two-day pass to visit. Make any trouble and we'll send you to the bottom of the river, okay?"

Charlie stood and watched as they took the weaponry away, rifles still trained on Fluffasaurus. People used to trust Charlie. Before he'd been re-imagined, Charlie had made friends with every child he'd ever met, found a way to connect, to reassure the frightened, to inspire the curious.

His friends were counting on him, and Charlie always tried to be a good friend. Sometimes, it felt like the only part of the old Charlie that was left.

Once the ammunition was safely behind the wall, one of the older guards pulled Alexis aside.

They talked for a minute, then Alexis returned to Charlie with a sad look.

"You have to go, now."

"You said we could come in."

"I know, I'm sorry," she said.

Charlie's hands got hot again. He sung the Calm Down Song in his head again as he talked.

"We need to ask people about Paprika Place," Charlie said, already know-ing it was no use. They were nothing but trouble, and it had been a long time since people made friends with strangers.

From the ramparts, Charlie saw that more guards had come, with rifles and spears. One had a LAW rocket.

Alexis said, "Please. If you don't go now, my aunt says they'll fire."

"I'm sorry, Alexis," Charlie said as he crawled back onto Fluffasaurus.

"You didn't do anything to me," Alexis said.

"I'm still sorry." Charlie patted Fluffasaurus on the back, and said, "Let's go, buddy."

And so they left Philadelphia, their lockers lighter but their hearts heavier.

The eight of them that had survived the last battle with MouseCorp met the producers in a red-and-blue tent as the sun crept toward the coast. The produc-ers were there, suits untouched by the dust, the winter rain, or anything, really. The tall one turned on a LCD Flatscreen. After a few seconds, the screen flashed to light, a BuncoNews bulletin filling the screen. A blandly handsome man with silvery hair and a square jaw smiled at the camera.

"Bunco, Inc. and MouseCorp have just completed a strategic merger, bring-ing an end to hostilities. In response, the controlling shareholders of CapeCo have asked to be bought out. As of 5:31 PST, the American Market Share Wars are over. The combined company is re-branding as America, Inc. On behalf of America, Inc., I would like to thank you all for your support. We look forward to working with our new colleagues on delivering the best in programming to each and every one of you. Thank you and good night."

A golden-haired producer clicked the screen off and turned to the group.

"And now that the hostilities have ended, I'm terribly sorry to say that we will not be renewing your contracts."

MouseCorp, with their hard-light projections, hadn't pulled any of their shows. The Mouse and his friends would be fresh in viewer's minds, still.

Charlie looked around at his friends, to Ms. Magpie and her razor-sharp wings, Rolly-Polly the Playful Pillbug, re-imagined as a rolling pillbox, the House Band — Johnny, Sonny, Funny, and Bunny, a rock-and-roll wetwork team, and in the back, Fluffasaurus, whose big eyes welled with tears. Charlie hadn't known that Fluffasaurus could still cry.

We're obsolete, Charlie thought.

A moment later, two squads of Bunco troops ran into the tent, weapons drawn. The tent was swallowed by gunfire, explosions, and screams. Charlie took a blow to the head and passed out.

•

Charlie had woken to the sound of Fluffasurus's roar. His friend had tried to find the old gentleness, but the call came out so loud it shook his bones.

The soldiers were dead, along with the House Band and poor Mr. Scary. He heard Ms. Magpie caw a cough, and Charlie scrambled over to her, his head throbbing.

He lifted up her head, and Ms. Magpie clicked her chrome-plated beak.

"Charlie?" Her voice was weak.

"I'm here," he said.

Ms. Magpie coughed again. Charlie's fur was matted by the wire-blue blood. *She won't make it.* "I want to go home, Charlie."

"I promise. We'll go home now. All of us." She touched his snout with one wing. It was cold, but Charlie felt it like it was the soft feathers she'd been made with, the brilliant blue the same as her eyes.

She tried to say something else, but choked again, then stopped. She convulsed, then went limp in his arms.

We have to go home, leave this place forever.

But Charlie didn't know how to get back.

Charlie and Fluffasaurus continued east. The powerful dinosaur was tired, his internal power plant running low. They moved slowly, but finally, one cold evening, Charlie saw the towers of the Manhattan skyline in the distance, covered by the sheen of an arcology dome.

Charlie didn't want to go to Manhattan. America, Inc. owned the dome there. Instead, they went south through Staten Island. They passed several checkpoints without incident, even though Charlie could tell they were manned. He saw figures huddling behind cover, speaking in hushed tones. They were afraid of them, afraid of Charlie and Fluffasaurus.

Charlie didn't want to scare anyone, ever again.

He took them through the checkpoints and across the broken skeleton of the Verrazano into Brooklyn. The few people they saw in the street quickly hid away, wary of corporate soldiers. They'd all been Bunco viewers, once upon a time, and their fear stung even worse.

As they crossed the bridge to Brooklyn, Charlie saw that the borough was in ruins. Most everyone had retreated inside the Manhattan arcology dome for protection during the war, and with the other boroughs destroyed, why would anyone go back?

Charlie looked with his robot eye, and saw small figures moving at the far side of the bridge. Charlie hopped off to see if someone would stop and talk to him.

"Hello?" he called, trying to catch the attention of one of the many small figures darting between the rubble. No one came out, so Charlie walked along with Fluffasaurus, making their way through broken neighborhoods until they reached a park.

"This place looks familiar, eh Fluffasaurus?" Charlie asked.

Fluffasaurus roared in agreement. It's here, somewhere.

They walked through the park until Charlie found a tree he recognized, a tall, tall tree they could see from the end of the Paprika Place neighborhood.

A block out of the park, Charlie fell to his knees, weeping.

Above them were tall walls with a large sign posted.

Property of Bunco, Inc.

No Trespassing.

Fluffasaurus tromped up to a loading gate, locked up by chains and gates.

This is it. Charlie cut several chains with his knives, and then pulled one chain out to hook to Fluffasaurus. The dinosaur strained against the chains, roaring again with the effort. The metal groaned, then the chains started to come apart, links breaking. Charlie pulled out loose chains one at a time, and the two of them cleared off the gate, facing a door taller than Fluffasaurus and twice as wide.

"Are you ready?" Charlie asked, mostly for himself. Until they stepped inside, he didn't know what it would be like. It could be in ruins, or it could be sparkly and new, somehow exactly the same as they left it. Until he saw what it had become, he could always keep it safe in his memory, still the Paprika Place he'd known and loved, where Messy's perch stood in front of Bob and Danny's apartment, where Mr. Scary lived in the basement, banging on the floor with his broom whenever they sang songs in the living room, Ms. Magpie and the House Band and everyone else.

Fluffasaurus roared as softly as he could, and Charlie looked up, freed from his thoughts. The dinosaur nudged at the gate, which creaked and swung open.

Ruins. Charlie sighed, and walked with heavy feet into his old home.

The brightly-painted walls and roofs had faded, stripped away by acid rain or maybe even a Bunco sweeper team. They could have flattened the neighborhood easily, but leaving it in ruins was worse.

The playground was burned, the jungle gym scrapped and swings bare. The little garden was overgrown with tall weeds and small trees.

Charlie shuffled through the neighborhood, pulled along by the need to know everything, to see every corner, to find out if even one thing was still the way it was supposed to be.

As he turned the corner onto the main street, Charlie saw movement. More small figures, little glimpses of eyes and hands and feet.

"Hello?" Charlie called again. Maybe someone made it back. Maybe they re-made the ones that died, had extra copies left behind. Maybe the wounded we thought were dead were just sent back. Charlie knew it was a fool's hope, but he was here, and it couldn't all be gone.

A girl looked out from a window. She had big eyes and wild black hair, curled and knotted about her head. She met Charlie's eyes and then dropped out of view.

"We won't hurt anyone!" Charlie called, more desperation in his voice than he'd meant. He choked back a sob. "We used to live here. My name is Charlie, and this is Fluffasaurus."

A teenaged boy with a baseball bat emerged from behind a trash can, with a little girl, probably four years old, behind him.

"You aren't Charlie. Charlie wasn't no cyborg."

"Wasn't a Cyborg," Charlie said, correcting the boy automatically. "Two nos don't make it right," he sang without thinking, dropping back into an old skit. The boy raised an eyebrow at him, but from his left, Charlie heard a laugh.

Another girl, older. They came from everywhere, wild-looking children and teens in scraps of clothes, holding bats, sticks, clubs, with threadbare sacks on their backs.

"You came back," said the girl who had laughed. The younger children shied away from Fluffasaurus, who was flicking his spiked tail back and forth, excited.

Charlie put a hand on Fluffasaurus's side. "Calm down, old friend. We don't want to hurt our new neighbors."

Another soft roar.

"We traveled a very long way to get home. Do you mind if we sit down for a while?" Charlie asked, noticing they were surrounded. Maybe sitting isn't the best idea.

The first little girl walked down the steps of the house that had been Mr. Scary's, and offered Charlie half of a stale pastry. Charlie knelt and took the powdered treat from the girl and gave his best smile.

"Thank you."

Charlie turned back to the crowd.

I'm home. And we're not alone. A whole new generation. They'd need to learn, learn how to count, how to spell and read. Bunco won't do anything for them, so he and Fluffasaurus would. They'd count like we did with Mr. Scary, and learn about sharing like with Ms. Magpie, and learn to sing like the House Band and not to be scared …

Charlie held the pastry up for all to see. "She was very nice to share. I know a song about sharing. Does anyone want to hear it?" Silence. Charlie looked back to the little girl, who blushed, hiding her face.

"Go ahead," said the boy with the baseball bat.

Charlie smiled wide, and coughed, clearing his throat. How long had it been since he had sung to anyone but himself? His voice faltered at first, but he saw the sharing girl's eyes light up, and his voice grew stronger. After the first verse, the boy with the baseball bat joined in with the enthusiastic tone-deafness of youth. By the last verse, Paprika Place was filled with song for the first time in who knew how long.

Charlie kept singing, his voice growing strong. Fluffasaurus sang along, his roar as soft as it had ever been.

When you care,
and when you share,
you'll find that there is lots to spare.

ANTON STROUT

CHOSEN

October 31, 20xx. Raspail Estate. Western Massachusetts, commonly referred to as 'The Berkshires'

UPON CURSORY RESEARCH OF the estate in question, please note that the most local historians refer to the old mansion as being in a terrible state of decay. A fitting end for the home of a renowned but long dead cultist and his equally long dead followers. The main house — which I have yet to see in my approach — is situated further back from the road by at least a quarter mile and the now-broken paving stones beneath my feet are in disrepair and overgrown with wild grass. My classic Bentley Saloon was only able to make it a certain distance up the drive itself until I found the way no longer passable by vehicle.

As much as I hate leaving the safety and comfort of my automobile, I fear I must stow my journal away and proceed towards the mansion on foot, my forward journey powered only by my nerves and the light of my trusty Mag-lite. I remain hopeful my research will yield a trove of valuable arcane information that my colleagues and I can add to our collection at Messianic University. By wits and wisdom alone, I continue on.

Something stirred to the left of the path, and I clicked off the light, shrouding myself in the shadows of the night. The trees loomed over the path, blocking all sight of the star-filled sky I knew sparkled above. I stood stock still as my eyes adjusted. Slowly, I closed the journal I held and slid it into the satchel at my side.

"Nice and easy," a gravelly man's voice growled out from somewhere in front of me. "You want to keep those hands where I can see them."

I did as the man instructed, not daring to move. A hulking shadow prowled into sight, the smell of gun oil thick in the air as it approached, arms raised.

I waved the unlit flashlight in my hand gently back and forth. "Might I shed a little light on the situation?" I asked.

An affirmative grunt came from the man, and I flicked the switch, illuminating him. The man — in his forties, at a guess — looked the picture of what I had heard Americans call a 'doomsday prepper,' from his long, camouflage duster to the shotgun pointed at my chest to the flag bandana he wore on top of his head. He gave another grunt, this time of pained dissatisfaction.

"You couldn't have waited half a second?" he said, as he reached up with one hand and yanked a pair of night vision goggles from his eyes. Even half blinded, his other hand stayed steady, holding the twin barrels of his shotgun steady at my chest.

Distracting as that was, I took the time to look my foe over. His face was hard and chiseled, a black horseshoe of a mustache and matching sideburns filling him full of menace. A small arsenal of muzzles poked up over his shoulder where several other weapons lay strapped to his back.

"I know you," I said. "Well, *of* you, anyway."

His eyes fixed on me and he took his gun up in both hands, lifting it until it sat inches from my face.

"Yeah, well, I don't know you, stranger," he said, peeking out from behind his shotgun, screwing his face up. "You talk funny."

"The same could be said about you, with your drawl and aggressive manner," I said. "As for me, I talk 'funny' as you say because I'm English. Born and raised, although I haven't been back to Mother England in ages." I held out my hand. "Professor Edgar Starkwood. Occult Studies. Messianic University. Tenured."

The man's eyes narrowed with recognition. He lowered the shotgun, but not completely. "Raven Starkwood?"

I nodded with a tight-lipped smile. It was always pleasant when one's nickname preceded him, especially when it got someone to lower the gun pointed at him, if only a little.

"One and the same, yes," I said. "And by moustache alone, I can assume you are Harlan Embry, the self-proclaimed 'Soldier of MisFortune.'"

The man's face lit up with a grin and he lowered the shotgun completely. "Shit, old man, ain't this a small world?" he said, taking my hand in his. "I should have known by the bow tie … was wondering when we'd cross paths."

I shook his hand, wincing from the vice-like grip and vigor with which he pumped my arm. When he let go, I reached up and adjusted my aforementioned tie. "I admire your work," I said, with the utmost sincerity. "Your take down of those sewer dwelling monstrosities in Manhattan is legendary."

"I hate city folk," he said, his drawl sounding more and more as if it were straight out of one of those Lynyrd Skynyrd songs popular among so many Americans, "but I hate things that tear people to shreds and feast on their blood even more." He nodded his head up the drive leading to the Raspail Estate. "You here about the cultist thing?"

I nodded.

Harlan Embry looked me up and down with disapproval on his face, shaking his head.

"Hate to break it to you, Jeeves, but this kill's mine," he said. He patted the long barrel of the shotgun. "Me and the Thunderbitch's, anyway. What are you packing, Professor?"

I reached into my satchel and drew the sacrificial dagger from within, the feel of the carved runes of its handle comforting in my hand. I held it up for him to examine.

"Jesus Christ on the cross." He laughed with such force that it echoed up and down the drive. "Leave it to a Brit to bring a knife to a gun fight."

My face reddened, and I could not hold my tongue. "You're a fool if you think something as mundane as gunfire can take on what lurks on these grounds," I said. "And as far as this being your kill, I have studied countless dark and arcane tomes at Messianic for over a decade in preparation. The prophecies written within have told of this day and my role in it as savior. The stars have aligned. It would do you well to stay out of my way and try not to die. Is that understood?"

The grin remained on his face as he raised both hands, but there was a nervousness behind it.

"Easy there, Raven," he said, then turned up the path and settled the gun upside down over his shoulder. "I guess we'll see what we see."

Harlan Embry walked off and I fell in silent step behind him. Let that Southern fool storm into danger first. Let his folly and American bravado be his undoing. Studious research and caution would surely win the night.

Harlan journeyed forward with the utter silence of a professional sportsman, stepping on not even a twig as we worked our way along for another half mile up the drive before we were met with a large open clearing with the shadowy shape of the Raspail mansion at the center of it.

As we converged on the building, the surrounding darkness fell back, giving us our first true glimpse of the manor proper. What had once been a quite pleasant country home was now a mere shadow of its former glory. Vicious looking ivy ran up the outer walls in a furious tangle, shattered glass glinting in its leaves from the smashed windows it had left in its wake. Had this manor been a living creature, I might have thought it was intentionally trying to appear as uninviting as possible.

It was at that precise moment that the wind picked up. Branches rattled like bones as the last of their changing foliage swirled around the yard. The sound so much resembled a host of chattering, whispering voices that it caused me to pause as my foot reached the first step up to the manor.

I looked to Harlan to confirm whether the sounds were a trick of the night, but the expression on his face gave no comfort.

Harlan kept his gun raised, circling around as he checked the perimeter of the clearing. "You understand this shit we're hearing, Jeeves?"

I nodded, fighting to make out the words. "Some," I said. "It is a dark and ancient tongue, a litany of forbidden words; words I have only seen in books, ones I have never heard spoken out loud before."

The whispering voices washed over me and I drank them down with endless fascination. I was frozen in place, taking full deep breaths of the cold October air, my breath visible as I exhaled.

"I don't understand a lick of it, Starkwood," Harlan said, "but I know I'd rather take my chances inside than out here in the open."

His fingers dug into my arm as he dragged me up the steps of the mansion with one hand, breaking whatever spell held me.

I stumbled after him up to the massive doors, spinning around and slamming my back against them. The voices among the swirls of leaves all around the clearing grew louder, to the point where I felt like my mind might split apart.

For a moment, I could *hear* my brain actually cracking in two. Only too late did I foolishly realize that the sound did not emanate from within my head, but rather from the door we were leaning against. It gave out, and the two of us fell back hard into the building's interior.

We plunged into sudden silence within the mansion, leaving me to wonder if I had been deafened somehow in the fall, but no. An *ooomph* from Harlan as he landed beside me amidst the rotting remains of the door confirmed I still had my hearing.

I rolled and was back on my feet while Harlan struggled to catch his breath, and retrieve his dropped shotgun. When his shuffling search ceased, he stood, cupping his ear, hearing something I clearly could not.

Without a word, he turned to his left and stepped off into the darkness of the hallway. We moved further down the corridor and moments later I, too, heard what Harlan had — the echoing drum of a ticking clock. When the hallway ended, we were met by the most hideous and cyclopean grandfather clock I had ever seen.

"Jesus H. Christ," Harlan said with a whistle. "What perversity is this?"

I knew well of the use of the grotesque in statuary, be they carved totems of an ancient people or the fanatical representations of figures from more arcane texts. But this clock! Every inch was covered with the tortured faces of lost souls and the demons that seemed to hold them captive. Here, a figure shrieked in horror as a tentacled beast tore into it, elsewhere faces of pure evil leapt from so detailed a carving they appeared almost alive.

Harlan's brow furrowed and he raised his upper lip in a snarl of disgust. He turned his gun around, its stock now facing the clock. "We should destroy this," he said.

I reached out and grabbed the barrel before he could act. "Hold on now," I said. "We don't know the repercussions of doing so."

"Repercussions?" he repeated with a boisterous laugh, attempting to pull away from my grip. "Whatever this thing is, it's *evil*."

"People are evil," I said. "Not objects."

"Look around you, Professor. Look at the dust and disrepair. This place is long abandoned, yet this thing is still running like it's been freshly wound. That ain't right. It's unnatural." His face broke into a wicked grin. "Besides, you really think you can stop me from smashing this shit?"

"I can try," I said, trying to hide the uncertainty in my voice. I'd come to fight cultists or ancient evil, not overenthusiastic rednecks.

I tightened my hold on the barrel as Harlan tried to strike the clock, and despite his superior strength, my own was enough to kill any momentum he managed to get.

With a look of pure irritation, he shoved me with his free hand, but my grip was too strong and I barely moved, despite the throbbing in my chest where he had struck me and a sudden shortness of breath.

Was I going to have to pull the sacred dagger out to stop this? It seemed madness, but what other alternative was there? I reached for my satchel at my side, but hesitated, unsure. This was escalating far too quickly for my liking.

I didn't get long to think on it. Before I could pull my blade free or even wrap my hand around the handle of it, something flashed between Harlan and me, striking the clock. The sound of its ticking gave over to glass shattering as the two of us stood in silence, trying to figure out what the hell had just happened.

"Make a little more noise, why don't cha?" a female voice said, causing both Harlan and I to start and turn, Harlan raising his shotgun into position against his shoulder.

A small redheaded imp of a girl not even old enough to have graduated high school yet stood between us. As she pulled a short bladed staff away from the clock, she twirled it once before sliding it into some sort of sheath on her back, the spear part of it sticking up over her shoulder.

Harlan pressed the gun to her chest. "Who the hell are you, and what are you doing here?"

I met the girl's eyes, and she seemed unimpressed by the shotgun resting against her chest. I looked to the now broken pendulum casing of the clock, then back to her.

"You ought not to have done that," I said, then looked to Harlan. "And you ought not to be doing *that*. For Heaven's sake, she's not much more than a child!"

I fought the urge to grab the shotgun. With Harlan's itchy finger already on the trigger, I didn't dare.

The girl looked down at the barrel a moment longer before her eyes locked with Harlan's.

"Relax," she said, reaching up with pure confidence on her face as she brushed the barrel away from her. "I've got this."

Was she talking to me or Harlan?

Before I could say anything, Harlan lowered the weapon, his face awash in confusion. "You've got *what*?" he asked.

The girl rolled her eyes as if this soldier was the most obtuse thing she had ever encountered in her life. "I've got *this*," she said. "Control of it. This whole thing."

I cleared my throat, drawing her attention. "Maybe you could tell us what you think 'this whole thing' is," I offered. "Perhaps after introductions ...? I'm Professor Edgar Starkwood, and my slightly more aggressive colleague here is Mister Harlan Embry."

The redhead gave a curtsy in her jeans and tank top, her ponytail swinging back and forth as she bowed her head forward with the gesture. "Darcy's the name," she said. "Demon slaying's my game."

"This isn't a *game*," I replied, feeling suddenly cross. "This is a matter of life and death, unspeakable evil —"

"Blah blah blah," she said, kicking aside pieces of the broken glass on the floor in front of the clock. "Spare me the lecture."

"The audacity of youth!" I said, barely able to contain myself. "What makes you think for one second that you have 'got this,' as you say?"

Darcy's eyes locked with mine, and there was a dead seriousness in them. "Because I'm The Selected," she said. "Duh."

Harlan gave a short laugh. "The Selected *what*?"

The elfin redhead sighed. "The Selected Girl. The Selected One, whatever. Just ... The Selected."

"And who exactly did this selecting ...?" I asked, my curiosity piqued.

Darcy let out a sigh. "When I was young, my mother was killed by what I discovered later were demons," she said, like she was giving a book report in front of a class. "I've spent my entire life haunted by those memories. I get visions of these monsters — these demons — they come to me in my mind's eye. Then I hunt down these demons and kill them, telling myself that in the process what I do helps avenge a small part of my mother's death. So when I tell you I've got this, I have got this. This is what I do. It's what I've trained for my whole life. The visions led me to this place and the horror that lurks within."

I cleared my throat and smoothed down my coat. "Yes, well, I have read the prophecies written in arcane tomes from centuries long past," I said, "and I can assure you they made no mention of anyone named *Darcy*."

"'The visions led me to this place'" Harlan repeated in a voice meant to mock the hint of the girl's west coast accent. "Led you to what exactly? This clock, so you could beat it up? Good job. What's next, oh Selected One? Is there a television set somewhere waiting for you to take your wrath out on, too?"

"No, dummy," she said, pushing us both aside as she stepped towards the clock itself. I stepped back as the girl reached for its grotesquely decorated cabinet.

Her eyes widened as she truly saw its perverse carving for the first time. She shuddered, then reached behind the clock itself, the muscles in her arms straining as she attempted to topple it.

I reached out to stop her, but it was too late.

Darcy sidestepped the monstrous clock as it tumbled forward. The thundering crash of its upending echoed over and over down the main hallway of the mansion. When the sound died down moments later, Harlan looked first to me, then to the section of wall where the clock had stood.

A roughly carved out hole in the wall gaped back, one I could fit through if I scrunched myself up slightly.

Harlan reached his shotgun towards it and tapped its barrel on the side of the opening. "How did you know this was there?" he asked.

"I'm the Selected," Darcy said with pride, tapping the side of her head. "Visions, remember? Also, I'm a professional."

Harlan laughed at that. "Are you even old enough to have working papers?"

Darcy turned to me, shaking her head. "So don't have the time to answer stupid questions," she said. With a twirl, she crouched down and stepped through the darkness into the hole. "Coming with?"

First Harlan, now this Selected girl … the gentlemanly part of me wanted to send the two of them packing. The gruesome realist in me, however, realized the odds of my survival were greatly increased with such companion fodder for whatever lurked beneath the old cultist's mansion. I held my tongue, gestured for Harlan to go through the hole next, then followed after.

Haphazard and slippery steps of stone led down into the moldy depths of the earth beneath the mansion. By my calculations, we were well below any existing basement level and descending even further. The stench of mold and fungi became thicker. Only by breathing through my mouth could I suppress the urge to gag. Judging from the sound of her breath hitching, Darcy was having less luck than I at controlling her reflex to vomit as we descended further and further. She prevailed, however, and after what felt like an hour, the carved passageway leveled out and opened up into a great subterranean room.

Where I expected there to be nothing but an earthy cavern, there was instead a fully furnished study built into the contours of the vast open space. Stalactites hung from the darkness high overhead, but the walls were those of an out-of-place but otherwise regal looking library that perfectly suited the mansion above us. Rows of bookshelves wrapped around the outer walls, a massive desk covered with open tomes sat to my right. Scrolls and charts with symbols vaguely familiar to me lined areas where the natural rock of the cavern poked through. Several unlit torches stuck out along the wall to my left and I moved to light them, pausing only when I noticed — just barely, thank God — a large open fissure cut like an open wound across the middle of the cavern's floor. Quickly, I backed away from it towards the desk instead, where several open books lay, brittle with age.

Harlan hadn't noticed my stumble. I glanced over to see if Darcy had witnessed my folly, but she was off investigating the rows and rows of books along the wall, looking as bored as a teenager in a library could be. Oh, the urge to shake the young girl. Back at Messianic, my fellow occult scholars would be more than pleased with this archival discovery.

The others in our Society would marvel over these occult tomes for months, no doubt unlocking the mysteries of Raspail and his mad followers. My own place in our academic ranks would rise ... oh, the luck of such a find!

Darcy, on the other hand, pulled one of the books from the shelf, scrunched up her face as she read the cover, and as quick as she could, shoved it back.

"Yawnsville," she said.

"I'm sorry, my dear," I said with a fury. "Is this arcane assortment of tomes and grimoires not exciting enough for you?"

She met my anger with hers by crossing her arms and leaning back on one of the bookcases. "Can I kick or punch them?" she asked. "No? Then I have no interest in them. I'm actually more fascinated by that giant hole in the floor you almost fell in a minute ago."

My anger died on my lips and I gave a short cough into my hand before adjusting my bow tie. "Saw that, did you?"

Darcy nodded, looking quite pleased with herself.

I opened my mouth to reply, but Harlan cut me off.

"When you two ladies are done bickering, we've got bigger problems than your little book club discussion," he said. His gun was raised and pointed off to the far end of the vast room.

Darcy and I both turned. My eyes searched among the shadows that our faint flashlights could barely penetrate that far away across the cavern.

"I see nothing," I said.

Harlan sighed. "Then look *harder*, professor," he insisted.

"There!" Darcy said, pointing at a particular spot. I followed her finger across the room, and then I saw it.

Or rather, *him*.

A young dark-skinned boy with no hair — possibly of Indian descent — sat cross-legged at the far end of the fissure. His eyes were closed as if he was meditating. The scene would have looked almost peaceful if he was not sitting among what looked to be a pile of blood soaked rags on a section of floor that was stained a dark crimson-brown. Compare his age to Darcy? Older, younger, same age?

Harlan pumped the twin barrels of the shotgun, the metallic *shunk-shink* echoing out into the space around us.

"Wait," Darcy said. "Hold up. We're going to kill a kid?"

Harlan nodded, shotgun slung low at his hip as he started toward the far end of the room. "I've done worse," he said.

"Good lord," I said, my heart twinging at the thought. "What's worse than that?"

"You'd be surprised," he said with a dismissive shrug.

Without another word I set off across the room, running past Harlan as I gave the fissure a wide berth, circling around to the boy.

The child made no effort to move as we closed in on him. In fact, so deep was his meditation that he gave no indication he was aware of our presence.

I reached out to wake him from whatever form of trance he was in, but Harlan clamped his hand down hard on my wrist, causing me to wince.

"Embry!" I hissed, pulling free from him, rubbing my wrist.

"Keep your ass on the ground, cue ball," Harlan said to the boy as he closed within a foot of him. "Hands at your side."

Despite having a gun pointed at him, the boy's face remained calm as his eyes opened, a peaceful smile forming on his lips. It might have seemed pleasant under other circumstances.

I tightened the grip on my blade.

"Why so smiley, sunshine?" Darcy asked, her spear-staff pointed at the boy. She lowered its tip to hook a bit of torn cloth nearby and lifted up what appeared to be the remains of a robe. "Is this your handiwork?"

The smile remained on the boy's face. He shook his head slow from side to side.

I grabbed Darcy's staff and pointed it away from him. "You're joking, right?" I asked. "Pointing this at him? He's just a boy!"

"Demons take many forms," she said with a bit of tutorial condescension to it. "That's how they get ya. All normal looking one second, all soul swallowing the next."

"For Christ's sake, Starkwood," Harlan said, keeping the gun raised to his shoulder. "Doesn't it seem highly unnatural to find a boy sitting in complete darkness in a nefarious cultist's cavern that was sealed over by that hideous clock upstairs? This little motherfucker here is as unnatural as they come. Look at the blood!"

I shook my head. "Even if this boy *had* been responsible for this — which I assure you he is not — look at all these bits of robe. They're the kind worn by those who worshipped the mad master of this estate, Howard Raspail. These stains are old, those cultists long decades dead. And if this mystery child had indeed been the one who struck down these cultists? That would make him one of the *good guys.*"

"Correct," the boy said, startling me as he spoke up, his voice quiet and calm as he remained seated at the edge of the fissure. "As the older gentleman said, I did not harm these men."

Harlan, unconvinced, kept his gun raised.

After a long moment of hesitation, Darcy's face softened and she lowered her spear-staff to kneel next to the boy. "If you didn't do this, then who did?" she asked with compassion thick in her voice.

"I do not know," he said.

"Then why *are* you here?" I asked.

"The Divine brought me here," the boy said with that same simple smile of his.

"Aw, hell no!" Harlan said, finally lowering his gun, pacing back and forth like a panther in a cage before leaning down and jabbing a finger at the boy's chest. "Listen, kid. I'll tell you what I told old Mister Bow Tie here earlier. This is *my* kill. I'm the one picked for this mission, got it?"

"Um, *hello* ... what about my visions?" Darcy asked with a glare. "I'm the Selected One, remember? *One.* As in singular. Whatever powers that be didn't mention jack squat about any of you guys either, you know."

"Forgive me, but this is *my* area of expertise," I said, interjecting. "You are all rank amateurs as far as I'm concerned, and are as likely to be in the way as much as you are likely to be killed."

"Wrong, professor," Harlan said, tapping his shotgun on his shoulder. "I don't get killed. I do the killing."

I held up a hand as I shook my head. "Listen, this doesn't make any sense," I said. "Four of us here, I mean. I could understand if three of us were drawn here ... trichotomies are a powerful thing, in religion, numerology as well as philosophically. The Holy Trinity in Christianity, the three Patriarchs of Judaism, the Triple Bodhi in Buddhism, the Three Treasures in Taoism, the Wiccan Rule of Three ... but four of us? There is little arcane reasoning to it."

Darcy stood and looked to Harlan, who had not moved from his position next to the boy. "Lower your shotgun before I lower it for you. Professor Starkwood is right. He's just a kid."

"Harlan ..." I started with caution, but the soldier shook his head, the gun not moving from where it rest, ready for action against his shoulder.

"Come on," Harlan said, drawing the words out. "You're not buying this divine Golden Child horseshit, are you, Professor?"

"Embry!" I shouted. I gripped my knife and raised it, mustering as much gravitas in my voice as I could. "Lower your weapon."

Ignoring me, he turned his sight back to the boy. "You two might want to look away," he said.

"You're *not* going to shoot a child!" Darcy said, and quick as lightning raised her spear-staff to Harlan's throat before he could even flinch.

She looked down to the boy, whose face was still fixed with a wide grin. "Aren't you scared with that barrel in your face?"

The boy shook his head. "Of course not," he said, calm. "The Divine has sent me here for a reason. I am protected."

"Don't be so sure about that, kid," Harlan said, curling his finger around the trigger.

A flash of deep eldritch green caught the corner of my eye, but when I turned, it was gone. "I don't think this boy is what we have to worry about," I said.

The words were barely out of my mouth before the cavern erupted into chaos. One moment the boy was sitting at rest at the edge of the fissure, the next he was flying into the open air over it as another flash of green — a tentacle, I realized — snaked up out of the pit and pulled him away from us.

To say the grin on his face disappeared would be an understatement. As the tentacle wrapped tighter around the boy's midsection, his eyes went wide with horror.

Darcy let out a shriek as several dozen other tentacles rose up from the darkness. She struck at the nearest, but I didn't bother to wait to see the result.

I needed to act, and fast. I pulled out one of the arcane tomes I had brought with me and began incanting the words, holding up the sacred knife to unleash its power.

Harlan's shotgun boomed out loud, followed by the sickening sound of flesh tearing, but I ignored it and continued on with my incantation.

"Jesus Christ!" Harlan shouted with such horror in his voice as a crunching and tearing cacophony rose that I could not help but look up.

Ragged bits hung loose from the tentacle holding the boy, a large chunk missing from the bulk of it, but that was not what horrified me most. Reading my incantation had spared me from whatever had just transpired, but my eyes still came up in time to catch two separate pieces of the boy falling into the darkness below.

"No!" I shouted, far too late, but needing to offer up my defiance at the reality unfolding before me.

"Why is this happening?" Darcy cried out, sounding more like a frightened child herself now while she struggled to pull her spear-staff free from a tentacle it was embedded in.

Before I could simply tell her to run, an answer slammed into the center of my mind, an unseen force invading my own sanity.

A great and foreign hunger filled my mind — not for food, but for blood. *Human* blood. Very little of what flooded my mind made sense, but it was dominated by a great hunger. Something from within the deep dark below craved sacrifice, having slumbered many years before calling forth those who could fill that hunger.

Us.

With what little sanity remained in my control, I pushed the foreign thoughts from my mind and snapped back to reality, only to find my two remaining companions doubled over at the pit's edge, reeling from the mental invasion as well.

Darcy rubbed her eyes, but Harlan stared down into the abyss below, his face full of fury.

"We're a goddamned grocery list?!" he shouted, his words echoing in the vastness of the fissure. He pulled his long camouflage jacket open and his hands moved to bandoliers strapped across his chest, his fingers looping into several rings of grenades hanging from them. Pulling them all at once, he then released the straps of the bandoliers, letting them fall free from his body and into the darkness of the fissure.

A string of fiery explosions filled the darkness below, the remaining tentacles curling and falling into the fissure. The deafening sound rang out over and over, fading only as the light of the explosions did, replaced by Harlan's laughter.

"Take that, you goddamned sum'bitch!" he shouted after it.

Darcy joined his laughter, slow and nervous at first, but growing louder with every second.

"Are you all right?" I asked, more worried about the girl than Harlan, who seemed to be in the throes of full-on celebration.

The girl nodded as she looked to me. "I fared better than that Divine kid," she said, going with morbid humor to no doubt cope with what we had all just witnessed. "I mean, I'm only out a spear-staff. It's a custom thing, but I know a guy who —"

Her words stopped short.

They had to. It was, after all, hard to talk with the aforementioned weapon suddenly sticking through her chest, a charred tentacle slithering off of it as it made its way back out to the middle of the fissure.

Darcy looked down. "Oh," she managed to croak out as a trickle of blood leaked out of the corner of her mouth. "Never mind. There it is."

She smiled as if it were the most normal thing in the world to see, then fell forward down into the darkness. There was no sound of her hitting bottom, only that of writhing tentacles rising once more.

Harlan and I stared at each other across the fissure as more and more tentacles slithered up out of the darkness towards us.

"I suggest we leave while we still can," I said, slamming my arcane tome shut and shoving it into my satchel.

Harlan laughed, but there was no smile on his face. "You think we stand a chance to make it out of this cavern, professor?"

"But —"

Harlan shook his head and simply adjusted the flag bandana on his head.

"These colors don't run," he said, pulling the largest gun off his back. Its barrel was wide enough that it launched something large, and judging by the biohazard warning etched onto the side of it, it meant serious business. "Like I said, this is my kill. Now run!"

Before I could say anything, Harlan threw himself into the ever growing mass of tentacles. All the while they dragged him down into the darkness, Harlan fought to keep his grip on the weapon. Even as he vanished from sight, he was still winning.

If there *was* any chance of getting out of there alive, now was the time. Turning, I did not look back, instead I took care to watch my step as I ran for the stairs at the far end of the cavern leading to the old mansion above.

Halfway to them a roar of fire and fury erupted from deep below, momentarily lighting up the whole cavern as it shook the earth all around, a wave of infernal heat passing over me.

Stalactites fell from high above, crashing down and destroying the make-shift library. Rock crumbled on every surface, and as I fought to traverse the floor, a growing dread filled my heart. I raised my flashlight to the far end of the room.

Although the light was faint, it was clear that the stairs leading to the surface were no longer there. Tons of rock collapsed onto their narrow pathway, a cloud of dust rolling across the room in their wake. I waited for it to clear before I made my way to where the stairs had been. A noxious burnt odor now filled the cavern. Upon further examination, my situation became clear.

Trapped.

This cavern would be my tomb.

Soon the batteries of my light will fade, and it will be nothing but dark solitude here among the rubble.

Well, not solitude exactly.

Even now, I can feel a singular word forcing its way into my mind, snaking its way in as I write these final words.

Hunger, it calls out.

Already I can hear the moans and slithering of tentacles coming from far below. I pray that the last of my light fails before that sound grows far too near, for I do not know if I could will myself to turn my eyes from whatever comes for me.

I will welcome the darkness. I pray for it and oblivion.

ALYSSA WONG

THE WHITE DRAGON

WE WOULDN'T EVEN HAVE been at the White Dragon that night, except that Mim wanted to play pool, and I had trouble saying no to Mim. Rain had torn the skies open that morning, so by the time I got off work, Chinatown's streets were a cold, ugly slurry, and it didn't look like it was planning on letting up any time soon. I waited for Mim under the awning of Suksuk's restaurant, my jacket over my head, watching the new electric streetlights glimmer through the haze like animals' eyes.

Bad night to be out, I thought. Sometimes the rain washed the air clean of the curses that hung like cobwebs from building to building, tangled in the strings of red lanterns above the bay. Sometimes, though, it only washed away the prayers for protection above our residences, leaving behind the stench of *gwailo* hatred and their mantra of get out, get out, get out of our country aching through my head.

Mim appeared like a ghost beside me, ducking out of the downpour. "Cold, lang," he said. "I shouldn't have made you wait in the rain."

"It's fine. The ceiling inside leaks anyway," I said. "I keep telling Suksuk we need to fix it, but money's tight this month."

"I could do it for you if you want. For free, I mean."

I glanced at him, small and dark, as he shook the water free of his curls. "I'm not going to cheat you, Mim." Something long and silver glinted in his hair, and I reached out a hand. "Wait, hold still."

He grimaced. "Another one?"

"Mmhm," I said, tugging it free with an abrupt motion and winding it up around my hand. Mim tended to pick up curses; they snagged on him like discarded fishing line. This one was slick and sharp, envy and hatred overlaid with the scent of cheap men's cologne. "Somebody was watching you today."

He sighed. "I ran into some factory workers on strike by the market. That's probably where I picked it up." He combed his fingers through his hair as if trying to shake out any remaining curses. All he managed to do was get water on both of us.

It meant a lot to me that Mim didn't make fun of me for the weird shit I did, even though he couldn't see it the way I could. "Hey," I said, stuffing the curse in my pocket and nudging his shoulder. "Cheer up. That pool's not gonna play itself."

There were few machines out in the downpour, just a single, lonely street-car chugging up Powell Street. The bay was a dark, glistening body, overhung with fog, and at the edge of the pier lay the White Dragon, its dirty sign streaked with salt and ocean grime. By then the boys from the local tong knew our faces, so no one gave us trouble at the entrance, even though Mim was Filipino and I couldn't keep my eyes or hands still.

Pool tables swam in the murky lighting, two long, green stretches of neutral ground. The cousins prowled the edges, all lean muscle and hard edges, scoping out the perfect shot. I could see the spells in their tattoos glimmering through their shirts, wishes for protection and glory buried needle-deep in their skins.

Wen came to say hello while Mim selected a pool cue and I settled in at one of the corner tables, my fingers knotted tight to keep my hands from jitter-ing. "FanFan! You doing your weird looky-looky shit?" He clapped a hand on the tabletop, just shy of me. The boys avoided touching me when they could. "Brothers, this girl's got a third eye or something, sees all the nasty energy on you that you gotta get cleansed."

"That's not exactly it," I muttered. But he wasn't listening. They never did, even when they asked me to talk. I was almost used to it by now.

"You say that every time she shows up," called another, Qin, over by the second table. His tattoos were the brightest to my eyes, and I was willing to bet a lover had imprinted some very personal wishes into his skin. "Stop harassing her and take your goddamn shot."

That was what I liked about the White Dragon. The camaraderie, the way the cousins took to Mim like he was one of them. How even though the tables and walls were dingy and all the cousins smoked, the air felt clean of hate-curs-es, like it was all right just to exist. I was content to watch from the sidelines and keep an eye out for any stray foreign malice the boys might have tracked in.

As Mim took his first shot, I caught sight of Big Boss Yang leaning against a back wall, talking in a low voice to a slick-looking gwailo. That was unusual. Not my boss, Boss Yang, but boss of the area east of Grant Avenue and all the cousins here. I'd seen him in public a few times — everyone had — but never with a gwailo, and not in the back of the White Dragon, flush up against the back exit.

The front door swung open and another gwailo walked in, shaking the rain off of his long trench coat. This one had broad shoulders and a pretty face, and as he settled in next to me, his sly, ghost-pale eyes slid over me in a way that made my skin crawl. His swoop of dark brown hair was combed back from his forehead and fell in a soft wave to the top of his cheek.

"Are you Lo Fanlin?" he said in English. The pool hall quieted, and one of the older men, Chan, came to stand behind me.

"No English," I muttered.

But he smiled, undeterred. "I'd like to buy you a drink."

"Tell him we don't serve alcohol here," Chan told me. "Being as we're a lawful establishment, sir."

"Tell him to leave before he ends up with a cue stick through his eye," said Wen.

"No drinks," I said dutifully.

"That's funny," said the pretty man. "I can smell rice liquor from here." My stomach tightened. If he didn't back off, the cousins would get fidgety, and I didn't want any of them going to jail for something they'd regret later. "But that's not why I'm here. If you are Lo Fanlin — and I think you are — then you have talents I'd be interested in."

"She's not for sale," growled Wen in English. My hands were shaking, my face burning red.

At that, Mim came over, cue stick in hand. "What's going on, FanFan?" he asked, glancing from the pretty man to me. Big Boss Yang looked up too, right at the pretty man, and the other slick-looking gwailo disappeared, his cuff links flashing in the darkness. The back door clicked shut behind him.

Big Boss Yang's jaw was set in a hard, tense line, and he cut through the crowd of cousins like a tall, dark knife, stopping at the edge of our table. "Is there a problem?" Boss Yang said in English.

The pretty man stood up smoothly. "No, I was just leaving," he said. He leaned over and grasped my hand. Something square and sharp bit into my palm. "So you know where to find me if you change your mind," he murmured, his breath hot and awful in my ear.

"Get out," ordered Boss Yang, and the pretty man rose, nodding at me, and swept back out into the night.

"Are you all right?" Boss Yang asked me, and I realized I was still shaking. The spool of gwailo curse I'd pulled off of Mim was scorching hot in my pocket.

"I think so," I said. I slipped the card the pretty man had given me up my sleeve and smiled shakily at Mim, who was hovering nearby. "It's fine. I think I want to go home, though."

Yang nodded to the rangy cousin with the bright tattoos. "Qin will walk you back safely. Give my regards to your uncle."

"Yes sir."

"I can come back with you if you'd like," Mim said, but I waved him away.

"Stay and have fun. One of us should, after coming all the way out here."

"Be careful on your way home," said Boss Yang, looking straight at me, and the card up my sleeve throbbed like an accusation. "It's ugly out tonight. If the gwailo gives you trouble again, you let me know."

"Yes sir," I said, staring at the floor. "Thank you."

We waited a few minutes for the rain to clear, and then Qin led me out, back into the bank of heavy fog along the bay.

The sky hadn't cleared by morning, and the red lanterns hung like diu si gwai above the market, suspended in the haze. Under the thick scent of rain, I could taste the sweet-sharp scent of ripe lychee and mango, the tang of fresh-caught, glassy-eyed fish laid on ice beneath the awning.

Suksuk trusted me with ingredients for the restaurant for two reasons: unlike him, I enjoyed the human crush and pull of the market; and I had a good eye. Not just for ingredients, but for the spells woven deep into them, glimmering like threads.

They weren't always conscious ones. Most were wishes, whispered or thought, muttered under the breath of fishermen hauling their catches into the bay or farmhands crating fruit onto truck beds up north. Simple thoughts. Stay fresh, taste good. And often they worked, desire in its purest form, laid unconsciously on their subjects.

The language of gwailo spells read differently, curses in English spat and slapped into the skin of the people like Mim and me. And they were almost always curses when it came to Chinatown, wishes meant to intimidate and keep us out. They sunk deeper and were harder to pull free, but I'd been born two decades ago and had as many years of experience of untangling myself from them.

I was selecting bittermelon from Ling aiyi's stall when I heard her draw in a breath. A familiar voice drawled in English, "I thought I might find you here."

I dropped the bittermelon and stumbled away from the pretty man from last night, who watched me with his hands in his pockets. "Why are you following me?" I demanded.

"So you do speak English," said the gwailo with eyes the color of treacherous clouds. "I gave you my card. Didn't you look at it?"

I could feel it in my pocket, digging into my leg. "No," I said. "I threw it in the bay."

"Not even the least bit curious?"

"I can't read," I said. It was halfway true; I couldn't get my eyes to focus long enough to read any language very well. "And I don't care who you are."

The gwailo reached into his jacket and I tensed. But instead of a gun, he pulled out a badge. "Detective James Lorraine," he said, flashing his teeth at me. "San Francisco PD."

Fuck. "I haven't done anything," I mumbled, nudging my market basket higher on my shoulder, so it was between Lorraine and me.

"I never said you did," he said smoothly. "But I wanted to ask you a couple of questions about weishei."

"What's that?"

He frowned. "You should know. It's in Chinese."

"It's not even a real word," I blurted out. Weishei, the way he turned it like a stone in his mouth. "Some gwailo bastardized the shit out of it, or else made it up."

He considered me silently. "Maybe," he said at last. "It's possible. What does gwailo mean?"

It meant a lot of things. "Doesn't matter," I said, my nails biting into my clenched palms. "Anyway, this doesn't have anything to do with me."

"Oh, I think it does," said Lorraine. "I heard that Old Man Lo at the 10 Jade restaurant has a niece who has strange abilities. I heard she can track Chinaman magic, all the way back to its source. In objects, in ingredients. And if there's someone in Chinatown brewing up this weishei poison —"

"I can't do that," I said, "and I thought you people didn't believe in magic."

"I do when it's convenient," he said, and the corners of his mouth curled up. It wasn't a nice expression. "And weishei has made it very convenient to believe in magic. Now, Lo Fanlin. I'm going to make this very easy for you."

"I already told you —"

"You can choose to help me and come back to the station with me." Detective Lorraine drummed his fingers on the table of bittermelon. Ling aiyi had disappeared into the shadow beneath the awning and was watching from a safe distance. "Or I can send you and your uncle home. Back to China, by boat, the way you came to this country."

I stared at him. "You can't do that," I said. "I was born here. I have proof."

He shrugged. "And who do you think the immigration officers at Angel Island will believe? A girl who can barely speak English, or an officer of the law?"

Lorraine was right. Paper didn't mean anything. Not the real papers we had, the ones that proved I'd been born here or that Suksuk had spent weeks on Angel Island before they'd finally processed his immigration. All of that would be worth shit if it was a police officer's word against ours.

I couldn't let this happen. Not to Suksuk, who had poured everything into his Chinatown restaurant, then lost my aiyi an ocean away and couldn't return home for her funeral. Not to Mim, either, who was already facing troubles of his own.

"Fine," I said. The words tasted like ash on my tongue. "I'll go with you, but I need to deliver these groceries to my uncle before they spoil."

Lorraine smiled grimly. "You'll come now. He can wait."

The police station was cold. I wrapped my jacket closer around me, staring at the tile so I wouldn't have to look at any of the hostile people around me.

But I could feel them. Curses clung to the walls and floor, on every surface available, glinting at the edge of my vision. I'd kicked away the ones around my feet, and they piled like heaps of straw around my chair.

Fucking Chinaman, taking our jobs, looking at our women, go home, go home, go home. Patterns I had seen so often that I could spot them from across the marketplace, the brightest threads in a web of curses. I was used to plucking them free when they stuck to me, but here, that sticky feeling of not belonging remained.

Mim had always made me feel like I belonged. He was kind to me the first time we met, and that was enough for Suksuk. It was harder than it sounds, being kind to the girl who couldn't make eye contact, couldn't grow hair except in sparse patches, couldn't keep weight on at all. Looks like a fucking goblin, a customer told Suksuk once while I cleared a table nearby. No wonder you couldn't pack her off to a brothel.

Suksuk threw him out and stayed late that night, cleaning the kitchen with me, never quite saying anything. I didn't say anything either. The words lingered over us like an old bruise, too true to wave away.

But Mim was full of good ideas, with his careful hands and careful eyes. He helped me clip away what little hair I had and got me a cap to cover up what was left. I was already wearing Suksuk's castoffs, plain grey trousers and a heavy shirt with clasps up the front, and for the first time, I had felt almost comfortable in my skin. Like I didn't have to pretend anymore at a feminine beauty I knew I didn't have. There weren't many women in Chinatown, especially with the ports barred against immigration, and I'd watched enough hungry stares turned to revulsion that I was glad to give up that particular pressure.

Detective Lorraine had disappeared into one of the rooms at the back of the station when we'd arrived, and now he returned to fetch me. I had to hurry to keep up with his long strides, but I didn't mind getting away from the people still waiting to be seen, hurt and mistrust boiling in their mouths.

"I want you to meet someone," said Lorraine as we stopped in front of his office. There was a woman already there, sitting in one of the chairs, her face half-turned to us. Her hair was cropped fashionably short, soft curls brushing her jawbone, and the raised hem of her dress exposed her calves and a pair of round-toed, high-heeled shoes. His hand on her shoulder felt overly familiar for them to be strangers. "This is Ms. Katherine Delacroix, heiress to Weston Railroad."

The Delacroixes were big players in the railroad business; I'd heard both Suksuk and the cousins at the White Dragon talk about them in hushed voices. So many of our people came to work the railroads, waiting on Angel Island for their immigration to be processed, hoping to make enough money to feed their families back home. Instead, they ended up gouged by loan sharks, delayed indefinitely on Angel Island, then deported; or, if they made into the country, worked in awful conditions until they broke or died. The glittering Transatlantic Railroad was paved with the blood and bodies of Chinamen like us. But the Delacroixes didn't care about that. They lived and dined on Nob Hill, where the rest of the rich folk hid behind tall, fancy gates. What was the heiress doing here, just shy of Powell Street?

Detective Lorraine circled around the desk, gentling his voice. "Ms. Delacroix, this is the girl I told you about. Why don't you show her what the weishei did to you?"

The woman brushed her hair behind her ear and looked at me, a half smile on her lips. The other half of her face was lipless, covered in overlapping scales of hardened, discolored flesh, her mouth bulging and stretched grotesquely wide. My hand flew to my own mouth, and I backed up into the wall.

"It's all right," said Katherine Delacroix. Her voice was a husky rasp, sultriness undercut by the sibilant hiss in her words. "At least you didn't scream the way I did when I saw my face for the first time."

Lorraine placed a bottle of amber-colored liquid on his desk. A grey-brown snake with a flared snout floated inside, its body coiled as if ready to strike, its dead eyes wide open. "This is weishei," he said. "Ms. Delacroix held a party last night, and she says that one of her guests brought this bottle with him."

"He bought it from a bootlegger somewhere in Chinatown, but he couldn't tell me anything more," said Delacroix. When she blinked, a transparent film flickered over her infected eye. "He didn't survive the night."

"If one of the Chinatown gangs is feeding a supply of weishei into San Francisco, we need to find the source and shut it down," Lorraine growled. "I won't let foreign magic poison my city."

The city was plenty poisoned already, but not by foreign magic. "You want me to look at this?" I said, and Lorraine gave a sharp nod.

Suksuk had told me about snake wine, back in Guangdong, but he'd said it was medicinal. This was the first time I'd seen any in person. Before anyone could stop me, I dipped a finger into the liquid and stuck it in my mouth. It burned on my tongue, and bright light flared in my vision as the spells in the room came alive.

There was the detective, a few strands of dark, resentful blue. Across the desk, delicate latticework spread over Delacroix's face, the same color as the spellwork inside the bottle. And in the weishei itself, a mass of bright, white threads, glimmering with phantom heat, knitted into a convoluted pattern.

This was intentional. Someone had spent time layering the curse, giving it body and complexity. This poison was engineered to kill.

"Someone did this on purpose," I said aloud. "And it's not a Chinese spell."

Lorraine looked up sharply. "How certain are you?"

"I'm sure," I said. I knew the pattern of gwailo spells. They didn't work with the words that feel like home to me, only in the language taught in school, the harsh and aggressive tones I'd learned to slip on like a glove. "It's got parts that feel almost right, but they're painted on, like someone was trying to mimic Chinese magic." Or what they thought Chinese magic might look like.

"This doesn't help me," said Lorraine. "You're giving me nothing, Fanlin."

Frustration rushed through me. "I can only give you what I have," I nearly snapped before I thought better of it. I wanted to disappear, to undo the night at the White Dragon, to never have met this man.

Delacroix leaned forward, touching my arm gently. I glanced up, startled at the physical contact. "You said parts felt almost right. What did you mean?"

She looked like she believed me. "I mean," I said slowly, fidgeting under her hand, "some of it felt familiar. There were unfamiliar bits too, but some smelled like the air by the docks before it was about to rain, and others warm and smoky like the neighborhood on New Year's." I flushed. "It's hard to explain."

"Like the docks, huh?" Lorraine rose, grasping my wrist. "Why don't we go for a stroll."

I had no choice but to stumble after him, the pattern of weishei curses still on my tongue.

He led us back to the market, each step filling me with dread. Detective Lorraine held the snake wine under his arm in a paper bag, but the two of us stood out like crows in a flock of seagulls. To make things worse, the weishei had done something to me; every spell shone in my eyes like threads made out of the sun, and the overall effect made the marketplace blinding.

"Is this gwailo still giving you trouble?"

I jerked my head up to see Big Boss Yang blocking our path, his arms crossed. Several of the cousins, including Qin and Wen, were with him. There was dust on their clothing, and their knuckles were bandaged like they'd come from a brawl.

I didn't like the way Lorraine was staring at Boss Yang, eyes flat and colorless, so I stepped between them. "No, sir, everything's all right," I said in English for Lorraine's benefit. "Thank you for checking on me."

Boss Yang didn't look convinced, but he tilted his chin up slightly in acknowledgement. Bright white cursework flashed across his neck and I flinched, but he turned away, nodding to his boys, and it disappeared from my sight.

Lorraine tugged me past them, hurrying around a corner. Something felt off about him; he seemed too pleased, like most of the frustration from earlier had evaporated. "Where are we going now?" I asked, but before I could finish, Lorraine kissed me, his hand hard on the back of my head, his stubble raking my face sharp enough to bleed. He smelled like smoke and hunger. It didn't feel good; he kissed like a man making a threat.

My hands tightened into fists, but I kept them at my side, hidden.

"I think I got what I needed for today," Lorraine murmured into my mouth. It made my skin prickle with alarm. "Come to the station again tomorrow. I want you to take another look at the weishei."

"You're letting me go?" I said.

"Until tomorrow. I trust you won't leave me hanging." He smiled gently, his grip on my face bruisingly tight. "And if you do, I know where to find you. Don't forget it."

I'd barely gotten home when Suksuk was on me, frantic. "Fanfan! Are you all right? You didn't get hurt too, did you?"

It took me a second to register what he was saying. "Who's hurt?" I demanded, panic rising in me.

"You need to come upstairs," said Suksuk, pulling me after him. Even in the narrow corridor above the restaurant, he wouldn't let go of my hand. He was trembling so hard he kept stumbling.

Mim looked like shit. Suksuk had propped him up on my bed and bandaged him, but his body looked limp and ragdoll-boneless. His whole face was swollen, bruises as big as plums rising on his skin, and his breath came out of him in horrible, rattling whimpers.

"What happened?" I whispered.

"The boys from Yang's group brought him back here. He was on his way home when he was jumped by the workers who protest by the docks. The boys managed to rescue him, but ..." I hadn't seen Suksuk look this frail since he'd lost my aiyi. "His arms are both broken. The workers tried to kick in his ribs."

Their malice lingered in awful, sticky curses all over Mim's body. I wanted to tear them off of him in handfuls. "I'll stay with him, Suksuk," I said. I was trembling too, I realized. I was so afraid of losing him. But I couldn't. Not Mim, not ever.

I didn't even wait for the door to close behind me before I started ripping the gwailo curses off of Mim. They came off in sheets, pulling apart like taffy strings. Curses of hatred, of envy, of fear, all tangled up in each other. He started to breathe easier as I cleared them away, but I wasn't done.

I spat out the bit of weishei spellwork I'd kept in my mouth since the afternoon and stretched it out across the floor until its pieces strained against each other. Time to get to work.

I waited until Mim's crying faded into fitful sleep, and then I went back to the White Dragon alone. The sky had cleared a few hours prior, and the cold moonlight made my skin prickle as I retraced the steps Lorraine and I had taken in the daytime.

Wen and another of the cousins were smoking by the front door, but before I came close enough to be visible, my eye caught some movement around the back. Staying close to the shadows, I skirted the entrance and snuck closer. As I peered into the alley at the back of the pool hall, I heard the front doors close, sealing the sound of Wen's laughter inside.

Two people were in the alley, close together, talking in low voices. One I recognized immediately as Big Boss Yang, whose tall, sharp figure I could pick out anywhere. The other took me a moment to place as the slick-looking gwailo from before, the one I'd seen with Boss Yang at the White Dragon. But this time, he was dressed in dark blue, just like the officers I'd seen at the police station. A half dozen crates were stacked up against the wall closest to me, and they glimmered in my vision with the same complex cursework I'd seen in the weishei bottles.

"I don't like it, Rusty," Boss Yang was saying.

"You don't have to like it," said the police officer. He reached out, and I thought he was going to put Boss Yang in handcuffs. Instead, he pulled him forward and their mouths met. I stifled a gasp.

Boss Yang was seeing a policeman? If the cousins found out ...

The police officer had two fingers hooked under the band of curses woven around Boss Yang's neck. When they parted, bright white curses, elaborate as lattice, spilled like ribbon from Boss Yang's open mouth, and his eyes were glazed. "You don't have to like it," the policeman whispered. "You just have to do it."

Something hit me hard in the ear, and I cried out as I fell, skidding across the cobblestones. Lorraine hit me again and again, until all I could feel were his fists and his knees tight on either side of my ribs.

"I'd hoped you'd take us straight to Yang earlier today," panted the detective, wrapping his hands around my neck. "But finding your body here will be even better. A murder's a good enough excuse to raid Yang's warehouses and expose his weishei smuggling operation."

Blood dripped down my throat, and my head was a dull roar. My nails scrabbled at his hands. "It's not true," I croaked.

He smiled his awful ghost smile and squeezed harder.

The slick-looking gwailo came over, standing by my head. Power gleamed over him like spilled oil, and I recognized the knots and weave of the weishei cursemaking in it like a signature. "Who's this?"

"Don't worry," said Lorraine. "I'll get rid of her."

"Wait," I managed. I let the modified version of the weishei curse unspool from under my tongue, gathering in my mouth like burning string. I hoped the slick-looking gweilo wouldn't notice. "Please."

I spat the curse straight into Detective Lorraine's eye. He howled and reeled back, letting go of me to clutch at his face. But it was too late; the curse was already taking root, sprouting new shoots that pierced through his hands and burrowed into other parts of his body. Lorraine's police companion shouted and tried to escape, but the curse stabbed into him like fangs, and he collapsed, moaning.

All I'd done was mold what they'd woven into something smaller, more personal. A *real* Chinese American curse.

Their bodies shriveled, and their wails died down into soft, pale hissing. Soon, the police officers were a pair of brown snakes writhing on the pier. "Weishei," I rasped, gathering them up. The serpents looked at me, and I found I could meet Lorraine's gaze head-on for the first time. "Pretty good, huh?"

They were all tails and undulating bodies, but I held on tight as I fed the snakes snout-first into the bottles of weishei. One they were inside, I stoppered and tossed each weishei bottle, one by one, into the bay and watched them sink slowly beneath the waves.

As the last glimmers of light from the glass bottles disappeared beneath the waves, I went to find Boss Yang. His body was limp on the ground in the alley, but he was still breathing. My hands found the collar of spells around his neck; it snapped like a strand of decaying hair, and I fed its remnants into the water.

"It'll be okay," I said. I wasn't sure if I was talking to Boss Yang or to myself. The clouds were gathering over Chinatown again, and I stretched my fingers toward the sky, empty of curses for the first time in years.

HARALAMBI MARKOV

HER CURSE, HOW GENTLY IT COMES UNDONE

YOU RISE AT DAWN as you've done every day since you were a little girl, even though you don't need to anymore. Still, your body aches for the work you never have to do again. In that moment when sleep clings to your eyelids, you believe you're in the village. The silk in your bed and the mattress you sink in, not unlike a marsh, tell you otherwise. You've traded that life and traded it well.

Want has no place in your household. Need has been forgotten — by your husband, his form slack on his side of the bed; by your children, who have spent the first months in this grand house playing games, but never by you. As with all deals struck in the dead of night, yours is written in someone else's blood and the rewards are as transient as the specters you can bring forth with your tongue.

No, you will not tend to a household until your skin cracks and palms weep, but you have your duties. Silently, as a shade yourself, you slide from the bed and leave its warmth behind. The carpet swallows your steps whole and the air is cold. The wardrobe creaks open, but you needn't worry — your husband sleeps through everything now.

Behind the wood carvings of tulips and hyacinths roost your dresses — so bright that even in the dark it seems you've stolen every color in the world. Gowns that turn you into a thing of beauty; skirts so heavy and so lush, they erase your ancestry; jewels so breathtaking they turn your blood blue and smooth the harshness of your features.

None serve your purpose and you reach deep within until you touch familiar coarseness. The dress dulls in comparison in a dead, ashen grey. It snags on your figure and scratches your skin, but it's what you've known in your youth and you welcome it. For all their beauty, for all the times you've wished to wear them while mending old rags, these gowns are untrue — an enchantment not of your making. One that traps their wearer.

Once dressed, you take to the corridors which in the slimming dark shrink to a needle's ear and widen to a church's hall. This is how you know you're on the right path. You walk in the dark and seek out the thread. Your hand sways left to right until it lands on the taut thread, which exists only for you. Further and further it leads across halls, then through a dark meant for no mortal man. You step on stone, moss, and the unspoken things between mothers and daughters.

The door has changed again. Now it's a perfect circle of iron forged to resemble a fattened face. Its cheeks are marred with boils and stitches over rough scars. Oval eyes roll back in and the small mouth puckers in mysterious ecstasy as you approach. It all happens so slowly you want to shut your eyes. The lock has appeared. You insert your right forefinger between the parted puffy lips and steady yourself for the prick, which still makes you tremble and shiver.

The door shudders, smacks its lips around your finger and opens its mouth wide enough so you can enter. Your workstation is thankfully the same. Spoons and needles, cloth and herbs, knives and vials await. Dried clove and spearmint fill your nostrils with their overpowering smell, while underneath creeps the savoury scent of dried blood.

Tables line all walls. Stains, old and new, testify of the favors, big and small, you've been paid to pluck from the gardens of possibility, justly or not. The center is where you look first, where floats a thin, wide saucer smelted from silver so pure as to be mistaken for the down of a dove. Within, bewitched waters reflect the contents of your first commission — the one that has earned you your house. It's the one commission that haunts you the most.

You peer in the saucer and are met with the tower's ground hall bathed in morning light. She drags the body of another warrior who's tried to free her from the tower, within which you imprisoned her. She's confined to a dress as rich as the ones you own, far better than any chains and shackles. It's your greatest work — white silk bathed in the princess's blood and a bodice beaded with the shattered bones from the leg you cut off yourself.

You repeat the curses three times as you've done every morning since you've kept her prisoner.

"A skirt of blood so you never carry armor.
A bodice of bone so you never hold a sword.
A leg of metal so you never charge into battle."

Curses work better in threes and like a spider you weave yours finer than any woman in your family ever has. Your virtuosity at the craft was virtue enough to practice. Because you could, because you are good. Because you wanted to become so accomplished as to challenge fate, to turn your family's fortune around. For witches are never meant to pick up the fruit of their labor for themselves, but only to grow it. You challenged this and won. Now you have to live with yourself.

"I've done it," you speak to the shadows as if a declaration will keep your house and your new fortune safe. It has to.

For now, it's the princess that suffers and not you. She's whom your patron fears most — the warrior, who takes charge with blades, who knows her defiance wins her enemies, who slays the monstrous children of your patron, their lovers and partners in trade. And she suffers well. Who is she but a woman with a weapon and you're so much — privy to the secrets that can break her like a twig. All you have to do is bend. Still, you wish you really knew what deal it was you said yes to, for your prisoner had saved your village and children not once but twice where you had failed.

The memory still grips you with its fleshless fingers. Day had melted into night and the sky had swollen with reds and pinks. A twilight wind rushed through the trees as the princess and her knights emerged from the forest, leading the villages' children to safety. Everyone looked weather-beaten, but not her — the wind fanned her mane of hair and the will in her eyes spoke of power. When all eyes were on her, she was the hero from the tales every village and town spun about her. Back straightened, hands married to sword and shield, she was heedless of the weight of the world and you believed she could carry the skies, if she had to.

Now, the same woman wrestles with the corpses of her fallen comrades drained of all her previous strength. You can't stand to watch her drag the man by the shoulders. Her fake leg scrapes the stone underneath. You can almost see the sparks beneath her skirts.

You finish your vigil, test your curses again and prepare yourself for the trip to her prison, not bothering to cover your face. You may know her, but she's seen many such as you. The sun beats down heavy when you, carrying a basket filled with food, reach into the clearing where the tower looms over the wilderness. Your patron abides by the rules and invited challengers to test their power — a welcome distraction to winnow the ranks of knights and defenders.

The tower won't be beat. Your design will not allow it, but still you come day after day to check for flaws and weaknesses — see the perfection of your work and laugh at the fruitless attempts of the princess to escape. She can't escape and when you've checked the veracity of your claim, you make yourself be heard and felt.

A few loud steps in the gravel and a birdsong whistle lure her. Her face peers through the grid window. Sweat beaded her face and up close, the fatigue and exertion become more evident.

"Oh, thank the Holy Father! You're alive," you say and give a wide smile chest aflutter with relief. What is one more role, one more lie.

"I haven't survived this many battlefields to be done in by a mere tower." Her tone irritates and you think of how to best make her fear the tower once you return.

"Of course not. I'm stupid to think any other way."

"I meant no offense. It's hard to stay here and do nothing, when so many others die. I should be there." She looks into the distance, not that there's something to see other than tree crowns and bushes, then she returns her gaze to you. "Have you heard more news?"

"Nothing but rumors. This is but a small village and the lone riders that pass through here don't stay for more than a night and speak to no one. Not even your saviors dare speak. But we can read faces and it's not good."

The princess winced at 'savior', but you had to bend her mind as well as her body. She might have lost her strength, but her will is an even deadlier weapon.

"This can't go on any longer. I'll free myself and then the witch will hurt in her last moments in this world." You shiver at the vehemence in the threat.

"I wish it so badly. The forest has become so dangerous. We're all afraid to go even in daylight. But how will you do it, Your Highness? The tower won't open to more than one man and no wise man has broken through the enchantments. You know this!" The mechanisms of your tower have been proven time and time and yet, she still insists on breaking free herself. How could she pose a threat to your patron?

For a moment, you lose all pity for her. Let her rot. But you don't show your contempt. You look into her face with the expectant innocence of a child wanting to hear their mother assure them all will be all right. The princess hesitates and sighs. She hangs her head low and the mess of her hair meets the iron bars.

Good. You've chipped away at her spirit.

"Your Highness, we all pray for the day a strong prince will come to free you and you'll be able to protect us again. Until then, please take what little we have and keep your strength."

You hand over, one by one, the fruits and meats you've carried — all laced with potions that steal from her muscles. Her hand trembles as she accepts with such trust, it again ignites your conscience, but you give her all nonetheless and with a few kind words part ways to return to your house.

In the time afterwards, you see to your children, plump and rosy, unlike you growing up. Wealth erases poverty the fastest in children. Youth has no patience for strife and it forgets. You see your household run and entertain guests who wish their fortunes told — the one talent you could practice in this city where the future is never certain and secure.

In the evenings, when your rich skirts grow heavy, you check on the princess, hoping and fearing she's escaped, and go to your husband who already sleeps. You shed the fabrics and the absence of a corset reminds you that the sharp pain you feel in your chest is of your own doing. Before you chase after your own sleep, you lean over your husband's ear and whisper:

"If something happens, run far, far away and forget my name and yours, for they will bring you great misfortunes." Then you sigh in some semblance of relief, until the pain grabs you again tomorrow.

Conversing with rich folk feels like spells you haven't learnt used against you. Yes, your dresses fit and their seams mirror the ones worn by the ladies you entertain — the illusion is complete. Yet, you catch the prickle of their eyes when you say the wrong thing or say the right thing the wrong way. Eccentricity can only be so much forgiven in polite society and you already feel like treading onto a river during winter — calm and firm on the surface, yet one step could lead you to your death.

Months have passed and your purse has grown heavy for money finds money — the type of magic all men wield. Your son has been sent far away to study so he can build a future that does not rely on your patron's promise. Paper binds your boy's life and now your husband's signature charts a better future. A branch of your family tree will grow heavy with fruit.

Now you work on the one you wish to see in bloom — your daughter. You smile and laugh with the ladies who pat their corsets and twist their fingers like willows in the wind so all their rings and bracelets reflect light like rainbow dust. Their affluence is their weapon, their ornaments their language. You welcome them whenever they fancy, you offer them all they do not deserve and you read what you don't see in the cards — for these women can undo you with a single word whispered to their husbands. To such a woman, you have resigned yourself to trust your daughter.

The calling may very well come for her, but what good is your knowledge compared to what nobility can offer. She will be a beauty — you have seen to it. You've armored her with skin as soft as a duckling's down, hair a sliver of night, and armed eyes that pierce the heart which bears them head on. She will come into a different kind of power that never will require her to speak with the things in the dark.

The princess's name bloomed on painted lips as soon as their skirts quieted.

"Princess Hecelina has gone missing for good. My husband, as you all know, works closely with the king and no one has seen as much as a hoof print," said a lady with heavy emeralds on her ears as big as grapes.

"How inconvenient to disappear when she's most needed. Our summer manor has been ransacked more than once by unspeakable things," said another with hair of white gold.

"Serve you all right for depending on her — a whole country following a woman? I can't fathom the ludicrousness," objected a third with cat-like eyes.

"But Marie Jasmine, she has killed a dragon. My cousin fought with her and he says she killed it with no more than one blow. That has to prove her divine right to lead against the unholy servants of hell. As unladylike as it is," interjected Emerald Earrings.

"Oh, I believe it. My father hosted a banquet in her honor last year. The arms on that body," Marie Jasmine shuddered, "and she came in dressed as a stable boy. The scandal almost ruined him."

You listen and nod, hoping the houses of the women burn and nothing of their wealth remains to separate them from the people you grew up with but polluted lineages.

Tea cups clank onto dishes and you weave your intentions while the herbs' warmth still has them enthralled. You're smarter than to think you can own them on your own.

"My daughter is of age," you say as low and clear, the implication apparent. "She needs proper education. There are things I want to teach her, which I never knew myself. How to be a proper lady. For I merely see things. My beginnings are humble and it has been through your charity I found such happiness here. You, as my dear friends, I hope will extend your arms in friendship and see the potential in my daughter."

A potential they can't comprehend. You could teach her so many things as your mother did you once, but how will she use them. Will she cross lines you haven't gotten to, yet? Just to see if she can? It's a dangerous future in a place like this.

You continue to recite your speech like you've done every time they come over without much success. Inviting charity in a rich woman's heart might just be the most difficult spell to pull off. You stare into their glazed eyes searching for submission, when you feel the tug at your underskirts. It's so weak you pretend not to feel it, but it persists until the whole of your skirts are pulled in the direction of the door by the force of all the babies' fists you helped not come into this world.

Heed you must, although your breath won't return and your knees shake. It's harder to reach that place in daytime for the shadows between worlds grow thin, but you soon stand in front of that door, then in your room and you see them circling around the pool — a skeleton wearing lace tight around each limb and bone. Its surface is a constellation of gems and stones and golden threads.

Atop the skull, a crown of golden spikes and blades sharper than a butcher's knife reflect light as if it were a halo. Only the face is left open and that is the one place covered in flesh — a face belonging to neither man nor woman, neither a nobleman nor a peasant. To you it looks like the first face ever created. It's the face before all the details have been drawn in. Where the skin ends, blood rings the lace in faded red.

You avert your gaze from those soulless eyes and bow. A visit is an omen, a warning, and you wish you could divinate the meaning, foresee the outcome. Should it end so early — only one of your children secured for? You swallow before you address.

"Your visit brings me honor." It's a stiff and formal greeting, one you never mastered, but you know better than to risk angering your patron.

"Honor has nothing to do with my visit." They say, countless voices layered and sewn into one storm. "Your ineptitude has."

You have known since the moment you pledged yourself to this primordial evil that this day will come. In less than a year, though? That breaks your heart. Nothing is as you wish it to be. You've done not nearly enough for your family. Not nearly enough to break the fate that follows witches who want more than their lot.

"My curses stand. I see her day and night. Nothing has changed," you speak with certainty in the hopes that this is a trap you can boast through.

"Then you must certainly have known of our dear guest's attempts to leave instructions to her rescuers and chose to ignore it." The skeleton circles around the room to come by your side. Its presence chills you.

"No, that's not possible. She has no paper, no ink. I have seen to that."

By the cruel smile on that impossible face, you expect the worst. Your patron rolls their bony fingers in a fist, rings and stones singing like chimes in the wind. When they part there's a strip of cloth and you recognize it immediately — the princess's underskirts. Red lines swirl into writing.

"You have to understand, Avicia. There is a reason for this woman to be favored so by chance and fate. This is the reason I chose you to keep her away. I could kill you right here and go handle this myself, but I won't. You show much promise, so I will just scold you for now and let you resolve this situation. Do not disappoint me a second time."

"I will discipline her."

"Good. Dissuade her from struggling. Drive her into sleep like death, if you have to. Just do not allow her to flee."

"You have my word."

Your patron laughs. You have no idea how an empty chest can produce such laughter, but it does and you quake with it.

"Child, your word does not concern me. I have your family's lives in my hands — now that is worth more. Do not make me show you what I can do with it."

Those are the words they leave you with as they make their exit melting into the shadows. The pounding in your chest grows louder with each step, threatening to demolish your body. Everything you've worked for will wither and wilt like crops after frost.

No, this won't happen. Fear propels you and you pull from the darkness to draw onto yourself. You dress in the flesh of husbands and wives, elders and children whisper you have — wrinkled skin, twisted limbs, a hump, a nose like a gnarled branch, and hair filled with rats and centipedes. You rush to your tools.

Beneath a crystal lid, lies a spindle long and thin made from the thick bone in the princess's shin and a small key carved from her big toe. You coat the spindle in oils that will make her sleep, something you should have done, had you not hesitated in the first place. A villain is what you willingly chose your role to be and your heart should bear to commit any sin against the savior of your family. Perhaps eternal sleep might be a mercy. It might ease both your suffering.

You take a place in front of the liquid mirror and with key pinched between long-nailed thumb and forefinger, you dip its tip. The reaction is instantaneous as the water hisses and billows into a thick mist. You see nothing for a breath and then sunlight rushes in from all around you. The ground hall of the tower is bigger than what you see in the water and if you were to simply pass through, you'd never think it's really a cage.

The immediacy still shocks you as you now stare at the woman who looks so startlingly like you beneath the other people's fears you're wearing, you could have been sisters. In another life, you could have been running hand in hand through fields — she, fearless and assured, you, trying to keep up. But you're in this life where you brandish the spindle bone and wish there is another way.

Her eyes land on the sharp tip tinted black, a single black drop forming.

"You've been an ungracious guest," you chide with the voice you remember of your grandmother. "Trying to leave the place where you know you belong."

The dark of her eyes burns and she steps away, slowly as you approach, her leg scrapping the floor. You try not to cringe, to stay bitter and terrifying the way your grandmother was the day you broke her heart.

"I go where monsters like you terrorize the innocent," she says and runs towards the stairs.

"All the more reason to stay, girl. I'm never going anywhere and neither are you," you call after her and give chase. The princess has nowhere to go. You have nowhere to go. Your liberation from poverty has bound you with ties far more dangerous than the ones of your blood. "Now stay true to your words and come to me."

Even for a cripple, she is fast. You hear her metal foot stomp the stone as you try to catch up, but what you can't achieve with speed, you accomplish with endurance. The long days of standing and walking have hardened your legs and you follow her. You both run, suspended in this one moment where the only promised thing is the next step, the world spinning slowly around the tower's axis. She reaches the top well before you and you have a few moments to think about whether you can do this. Will you be the person to extinguish the one remaining light in this country?

"Stop your silly games, girl. This will be but a tiny prick against the skin," you yell once you see the arch of the door frame. You have made your decision.

The moment you reach the final stairs is when you lose. She towers over you, her metal leg bare. Her foot's edges scratched into blades. Your momentum propels you and you can't slow down. The princess swings her leg for a kick and the metal cuts through your throat so fast you can't even scream.

It's strange to see your blood trickle. Stranger even to drown in it.

"Hunters never play games," you hear the princess say, but you don't have it in you to get angry. You feel your spells come undone, gently as a thread being pulled from a scarf, gently as your life runs down your chest and soaks your gown.

As you fall on your knees, your illusions shed off — no mask behind which to hide. That makes the princess step back, eyes diluted and glinting with recognition. Perhaps, this is your worst sin — betraying her trust. Death awaits and you're not ready for it. What will happen to your man and your children? You're too tired to be afraid any more.

You can plea for your family. You can beg for your life, but the choice you've made do not allow it and you want your last act as a person to mean something. You press a hand against the wound and will your voice through the blood.

"I'm so sorry. You deserved none of this," you say and hesitate. You've cursed for so long, do you even have it in you to bless, but it has to be done. As life leaves you, you command.

"May the things that have been stolen from you, give you strength."

SHANNA GERMAIN

BURNING BRIGHT

MY GUN'S NAME IS Lamb. My daughter named it when she was five. Ran around with it going, "Wham! Wham!" I lost my mind thinking she was going to grow up a serial killer, until I remembered that's just how she said *lamb* back then.

It wasn't my gun then. It was her father's. I have never owned a gun. Until last week when Dylan, my ex, showed up to give me this one.

It was right after the accident. *Accident* is Dylan's word, not mine. I was in the hospital, grogged out of my brain on whatever was in my IV drip, and he showed up. That's the story of exes, right? Never there when you need them. Always there when you're in an ass-open hospital gown and drooling like "What? I thought you were dead six years ago."

He wasn't dead though, it turns out. He was alive enough to press the metal and weight of the gun into my hand like a Get-Well-Soon gift. His hands. He's always had good hands. Soft. Not like mine.

"Just in case there's another accident," he said.

What he meant was, "Just in case someone tries to kill you again."

What he really meant was, "Just in case our daughter tries to kill you again."

I didn't know that's what he meant at the time, though. Sometimes you have to peel back the layers of what someone says after, when you're alone and he's not looking at you with those blue-blue eyes.

If I hadn't been drugged to the eyeballs, I might have said, *Liv's sixteen. Not an accident.*

I suppose it was something most people would say was a nice gesture, my ex giving me a gun. Except he knows my relationship with guns. He knows better than anybody. I don't know shit about guns. I hate them, which is absurd for my line of work. But there you go. I've never even aimed one, much less used one to kill something. I don't even know for sure if Lamb still works or that she's a *she*. Do guns even have genders, like ships? No idea. No care.

All I know about guns is that this one fits in my palm like a tiny metal kitten and she purrs to all get out when I use the weight of her to punch someone in the face.

That, and it's the one my daughter shot me with.

Lamb's not purring now. Partly because I'm not punching someone in the face. But also because she's not in my palm. She's lying about a foot away from me on dirty off-brown carpet while this dude's got his big-booted foot on my wrist.

I'll spare you the details on how we got here and how this guy looks like an unshaved ape and how his breath smells like bad pastrami. He's already said all the things that big-booted dudes say when they've learned how they're supposed to be from the movies. "Who sent you?" and "Why are you here?" and "How'd you take out the eight giant men with guns that were standing outside?"

Okay, he didn't ask that last one, but he should have. I mean, come on. Those are the kinds of things I'm proudest of in my career and no one ever asks. Probably assumes they all fell prey to my seductive charms. That's how female assassins work in the movies. Even if it doesn't start that way, you can bet by the end, she's put on some expensive snakeskin dress and a magenta wig and mile-high fuck-me-pumps and she's saying things like, *I'm a gift from some Russian name that no one can pronounce.*

While Big Boot looks down at me, I can almost see him thinking, "Nope. Not gonna' fall for that one." Which is just fine by me. I've never seduced anyone on the job and I'm not about to start with him and his giant boots and his meat breath.

He also doesn't ask, "How come I was able to take you down to the ground with your back on my dirty-ass floor when my eight giant men with guns couldn't do it?"

He doesn't ask that one because he's all ego. And that's good.

What's bad is that I might have overestimated my skills a bit here. It's never good when your weapon malfunctions. And my weapon is malfunctioning all over the board right now. My wrist is making some kind of crackling noise under his sole. It doesn't hurt yet — the metal bracelets are taking most of the weight — but the ligaments in there are twanging like guitar strings getting stretched.

It's my back that's really feeling it though. Which makes sense. Because according to my least-favorite doctor, one of the bullets from the *accident* smashed through some part of my spine and I should never go back to work again. Clearly his words. Not mine. He doesn't even know what I do for a living. So you decide how useful that advice is. I got a second opinion in the form of asking myself and myself said I was just fine. So here I am. That's the power of second opinions.

Big Boots leans in, asks me again "Who the fuck are you?"

Let's skip the boring parts about how I answer something stupid and smart-ass because he should know who the fuck I am and how he smashes me in the face with his sole. How the rubber clover-leafs on the bottom smear my lipstick — Killer Fucking Kiss, it's called. I would have worn it for the name even if it wasn't my color. How despite the pain that blooms in my nose, I manage to grab that receding foot. The one-two-three punch that drops him to the ground. Not dead. No one's dead here yet.

Let's also skip the part where I have to fumble one, okay, maybe two, of those little blue pain pills out of my pocket and swallow them dry before I can pick up Lamb and ask Big Boots ever so gently where I can find my daughter.

I figure every job has its shit element. Paperwork. A bad boss. That horrible customer that makes you want to claw your eyeballs out.

The shit element of my job is the death. Everything else is awesome. Training. The money. Research. Planning. Beating people up. Even cleaning the blood out of my knuckles is a task I enjoy. There's something calming about the tedium, getting every last bit of red out of the wrinkles in my skin. Like deveining shrimp.

But the death. If I could change one thing about what I do, it would be that. I don't even like to kill spiders — and I'm pretty sure spiders are God's way of saying, "Fuck you humans and your big brains. One look at this and you're still going to lose your shit."

I've killed 98 people in my life. Two of those were accidents; that's a story for another story. The rest were jobs. When my daughter asked me what I did for a living, I always said, "I'm a poet, baby." It's almost true.

Big Boots didn't know where to find my daughter. But he told me who did. Of course he did. He works for the guy who works for the guy who's in the know. Which is why I came here as soon as I got out of the hospital and realized Liv was missing.

I didn't torture him. Torturing someone for information is like trying to get computer code out of a chip with a jackhammer. No. I put Lamb in my pocket and talked softly. Spread the possible poems of his future in front of him like a soothsayer. Here is the poem where you go gentle. Here is the poem where you rage. Here is the poem where you are the poet and you live to write more poems.

Before I was an assassin, I taught poetry to college freshman. I understand the power of alliteration, presentation, and promise, of the pause before that final push. I gave Big Boots the opportunity to write his own ending.

He chose wisely. I thanked him and went on my way. If there's a code among thieves, then there is surely one among us. Don't kill innocents. Don't damage each other's property beyond reason (and, yes, hired henchmen count as property in this case). And don't kill each other.

There's only one exception to that last bit of code. And I'm about to become that exception.

"My daughter is missing," I said twice. Calm as calm. "Who knows where she is?"

And I heard the answer before he even said the name.

I have to stop home and feed the cats. I know how it sounds. Daughter missing. After she tried to kill me. Ex-lover on the loose. And here I am, with one cat clinging to my pant legs and the other meowing her fool head off about dinner.

But every villain needs to love a kitten, right? If I'm the villain, in this then I've got my share. For the longest time, I adopted a cat from the local kill shelter after every job. Atonement bullshit, that's what Dylan kept saying. Saving a life for taking a life. All I know is it made me feel better to hold that vibrating mini monster in my hands.

But Liv was little then and allergic to all things with fur. And two-year-olds don't really have the brainspace to figure out, "Oh, touching the furballs makes me hack my lungs out. I'll just stay away from them." Instead, it was more like "I'm gonna put all of this fur right in my mouth so you can take me to the hospital. Yay me!"

After the third hospital visit, I started donating money for every job instead. For the most part I stopped bringing home strays. Unless it was really bad.

The basement of the Unitarian Sect of the Second Divine has one of those tiny doors that seems like it was built for tiny humans, but was actually probably never supposed to get used. As was the basement.

But a couple hundred years of renovations and you get this glorious hunk of a room: sweating concrete and fitzing overhead lights and a bunch of folding chairs set in a semi-circle. There's an empty coffee pot and a bulletin board littered with flyers. AA meeting, 7pm, Wed. Find Your True Self. Cancer Survivors Group. Cancer Widows Group. The group for people who thought they had cancer, but didn't. Even Heroine Recoverers Unite! with its tagline, "We HeRe U!" the spelling of which makes my teeth hurt every time I see it.

It's all there, if you dig deep enough. All except for the Aging Assassins Support Group. Horrible name, right? AAS Group? But it used to be called Hope Blooms. And I'll let you imagine how quickly that name got stomped to the floor. We would have taken something that spelled out SHIT if it got us away from sickly-sweet flowers and emotions.

To get to AAS, you have to go into the women's bathroom, second stall. The toilet there has said OUT OF ORDUR for so long most of the ink has faded from bright green to grey. It's not really out of order, but it's grimy as all get-out and there's no way I'd put my ass, or any other body part, anywhere near that thing.

I flush the handle twice with my foot, because germs, and then the toilet and the wall behind it swings open. Plush red carpet, dark red walls, dim lights. Sweet music that charms your heart into thinking it belongs to the body of someone who does downward dog for a living instead of death.

Barbara the Bouncer — yes, we call her that to her face — takes one look at me and gives me the complex chin movement that means: yes, I know you and you can come in. Her fists are as big as my face, with a dozen spiky rings that point in no good directions.

When I slide in, the group is already past the "Hi, my name is Rose, and I kill people for a living," part, which is fine by me, because the members of this group haven't changed in ten years. We all know that we kill people for a living.

But a ritual's a ritual or it's nothing. So I slide into a chair, catching more than one surprised glance. I guess they heard about the *accident*. I guess they didn't expect to see me here alive.

Dylan doesn't see me at first. He's in the front row, his back to the door. I refuse to look at those broad shoulders, that skinny-down waist, the place where the belt of his jeans shows off his hips. I look instead at the one piece of hair that's too long, a jagged edge of color against his shirt.

I didn't really think he was dead. That was just my drugged up, pain-wracked brain talking. I knew that he was locked up in state facilities for the criminally insane. But I'd been telling Liv that her father was dead for so long that in some corner of my brain I'd come to believe it. The lies we tell ourselves accidentally are the hardest ones to see through.

I think about the last time I saw him — before the gun-and-drug hospital visit last week. Six years ago. Liv was ten. Dylan wanted to tell her what we did for a living, said she was old enough. But even then I knew that something was wrong with him. And that something was in Liv too.

Probably, I tell anyone what I do, and they'd think, "Yeah, she's got a little crazy in her." But the truth is no. The truth is, you can't have a single psychopath gene and be good at this job. It's too easy to get knocked off balance, to lose your way into madness, even when you start from a solid foundation.

Dylan's foundation was never solid. I knew that, even when I didn't. Every kill chip-chipping away at that tiny platform holding him up toward sanity.

And Liv? She's got his genes. And mine too. It's no risk I was willing to take. Your mama's a poet, baby. And I'd sing her down some of Blake's "Auguries of

Innocence" as though the lines were my own.

Here are the two questions that continue to haunt me: How long has he been out? Did Liv try to shoot me on her own, or was that Dylan's doing?

Dylan stands up and walks to the front, starts to say his part about how he's been gone traveling. He makes a double-hitch in his talk when he sees me sitting there. I can't kill him here. Code. That and the fact that he knows where Liv is.

But, man, my fists do that thing. Knuckles and bones. Tendons jumping. Like a fist on fire.

I slip out before he's finished. I let him talk his talk. It's enough that he knows I'm here. It's enough that he knows I know.

The way people talk is a poem. It always seems like they're saying one thing, but when you crack them open, there's so many layers of meaning under their skin that you can get lost in it.

Liv stopped talking when she turned six. Didn't make another word for four years.

She'd just open her mouth and no sound would come out. The speech therapists and good teachers said not to worry. The bad teachers said she was trouble. Liv told me nothing. But I learned to hear her body language. I could read her emotions from a hundred yards away. The way she edged her lip with her teeth when she was about to do something she'd regret. The hunch of a shoulder that meant she was steadying her resolve. The twitch of an eyelid just before she pulled the trigger on her breakdown.

Four years of silence. When Liv turned ten, the first thing she said to me was, "I want to burn our house up."

And that's when I got her father put away for good.

Dylan likes guns.

Liv likes guns. She also likes William Blake and the kittens that try to kill her and cinnamon-sugar on toast.

There's a little of both of us inside her.

I trail her father to the place where I know he'll lead me. He can see my headlights. He goes left when he wants to go right, slow where he wants to go fast.

The place he lands is quiet. Sharp and dark.

I'm good at my job, even when it's not a job anymore. His gun and my fists tangle somewhere between the shadows and the light. Let's skip the boring parts where I ask him why and he doesn't have an answer. The part where I try to remember that crazy isn't like poetry. That there are no layers of heart and bone and sinew beneath it to shore up its faulty rhythm. So let's skip the part where I take the man I once loved and do horrible things with my hands because he took my daughter or because he wants me to or because I can. The part where he says again and again that he doesn't know where Liv is.

I once said torturing someone for information is like trying to get computer code out of a chip with a jackhammer. It's still true. But sometimes the computer code is broken anyway, so you might as well use the jackhammer. Here is the poem where you say fuck being gentle. Here is the poem where you rage.

I don't kill him. Not because I don't want to, but because I want to believe that the side of me that lives in our daughter buys her a fighting chance.

I wipe my hands down the side of his face. Blood and drool. What shoulder and what art? These lines of his skin split to reveal the layers of meaning beneath. This is my poetry, baby. I say, "There's more where that came from. I am one prolific bitch."

The shelter is open late for regulars like me, regulars who know how to knock and have made a passing friendship with the women who run the place.

I poke my fingers in the cage of a large black and white cat with green eyes. Scarlett, the tag says. Scarlett nibbles at my fingertip. Exploratory bite, like a shark. I like her already.

"Hey Rose." It's Debbie, the shelter coordinator, in a bright yellow Save The Snails! shirt. The snails on her shirt don't look like they need to be saved. They have claws and weird tiger teeth. Even their shells are armored.

The girls at the shelter know me. Not *know me*, know me. But they recognize me. They call me Rose, which is the name I put down whenever I sign the little form that says I understand adoption is a life-long commitment and that I am prepared to feed, shelter, and care for this creature until it dies. Of course, I also have a contingency plan in case I'm the one who bites the dust first.

"I got a little orange tiger that just came in," Debbie says.

I nod. I'm talked out. I had a lot to say to the man in the dirt before I left him there. A lot about where he's going to move on now that he's a free man. A lot about how death isn't going to be his best friend, not even near, with me at his back. He won't listen, of course. But that's for later. It will either matter or it won't.

Debbie opens a cage and pulls out the tiniest ball of orange-colored fluff I've ever seen. I'm not even sure it's a real living thing until its entire body opens in a giant pink yawn.

I don't usually take kittens. Someone else always saves the kittens, with their big eyes and their inability not to love everything that moves. No one saves the adults, with their scarred faces and their meds and their need to put their claws to the furniture.

"Maybe not this —" I start. The tiny tiger takes another yawn and then promptly falls asleep in my hand, one tiny pale claw hooked into my skin.

Tyger, the tag on the cage says. Damn it.

It's our old house. The one Liv wanted to burn up. I think some part of me always knew this was where I'd find her.

I can see Liv through the kitchen window, the soft O of her face, waiting and watching. I remember the *click-click* of the stove as she lit it. "I want to burn the house up." I remember the hunch of her shoulder over the gun, the twitch of an eyelid, the single, eternal sound of copper and steel entering my body.

I grab my things out of the car and stand on the lawn. I lift my arms to my sides.

In one hand, I hold a mewling ball of teeth and claws.

In the other, I hold the purring barrel of a gun. Handle out, toward the question that is my daughter.

Your mama's a poet, baby.

Here is the poem where you go gentle.

Here is the poem where you rage.

My daughter opens the front door.

ALETHEA KONTIS

SANTA CIS EPISODE ONE: NO SAINT

BUDDY STOOD ON THE stoop and stared at the door in front of him. It was solid — oak, he guessed. Maybe ash. It had been a long time since he'd needed to distinguish the two on sight. He removed his glove and slid his fingers down the face of it, appreciating the subtle curves in the plane. At first glance, it did not look like a work of expert craftsmanship, but Buddy's trained eye knew just how deceptive that simplicity was. A dilapidated log cabin high in the wilds of the Appalachian Mountains had no business possessing a door like this.

It meant he was in the right place.

Buddy took a deep breath and knocked. Even without his gloves, his knuckles made little more than a quiet tap on the thick wood.

There was a murmur from inside the cabin with the cadence of, "Come in." Buddy stretched a hand out to the door's handle but stopped short. It wasn't his place to presume upon old friendships. He could not screw this up. This meeting had to go perfectly. Lives depended on it.

The next sound from behind the door was that of a shotgun being cocked. No mistake there. Buddy resisted reaching for his service weapon.

He could not screw this up.

The door opened, and the warmth from the stove inside enveloped Buddy's body from head to toe. The old man stared at him. There was a glimmer of something in his eyes, but it passed too quickly for Buddy to count on it. There had definitely been a clenching of teeth beneath the stubble on his jaw — a tic he'd been able to hide back when he'd had a full beard, but one Buddy recognized all the same.

"Elmore," said the old man.

"Sir."

"I said 'Come in,' for goodness sake." He stepped back, motioning to the room behind him with the hand that held the shotgun.

Buddy stamped what snow he could off his boots and entered. "Thanks, boss."

"Don't call me that, kid. I'm not your boss anymore. 'Nick' will do just fine."

"Yes, boss. I mean, Nick." He removed his other glove and hat and set his snow-covered backpack on the small rug just inside the door. The room was stifling, but then, the old man had always preferred it that way. Beyond that, everything else seemed out of place. There were no pictures on the wall, no plants on the bare windowsill. There were no tables scattered about for the sole purpose of displaying lovingly crafted doilies and bric-a-brac. There was a stack of books beside the large chair in the center of the room and a hurricane lamp, but no pipe.

"You need a haircut," Nick said as he pushed the thick door closed.

Buddy raised his hand to his hair, pulled back into a short ponytail. He liked wearing it long now, so that it covered his enormous ears. Especially in weather like this. He noted Nick's almost military-shaved scalp. "You're one to talk."

The grunt Nick gave in response might have almost been a laugh. He placed a tea kettle on the stove, then moved to the kitchen area. He stoked the fire in the oven before sliding in a metal sheet covered in drops of what could only be cookie dough. The faint odor of sugar they added to the room was a wistful reminder of a time gone by.

"Please don't bake on my account," said Buddy. Judging by the old man's wiry frame, it was obvious he hadn't touched a cookie in a very long time.

"They're not for you," said Nick. He broke the shotgun in half, pocketed the shells, and leaned the empty gun against the wall. "So what brings you here, Officer Alvin? Business or pleasure?"

"It's Agent Alvin now, actually. Special Agent." He felt stupid the moment the words crossed his lips. Nick already knew that. Nick knew just about everything. Besides, a congenial visit wasn't an option. The last thing Nick had instructed Buddy to do was never to contact him again.

"We need your help."

Nick's bushy eyebrows lifted. "We?"

This wasn't playing out the way Buddy had hoped. He unzipped his parka and removed the plastic bag with the letters. He'd let the children speak for him instead.

"My pal Oki Johnson is a postal employee at the office in Anchorage. Around this time every year, he leads the team that receives and answers all the Santa Mail."

Nick grimaced and reluctantly took the package in his large hands. This sort of thing was a sore spot with the old man: Postal Services answering Santa Mail. Parents bearing the responsibility of gift giving. Imposters parading about in red suits. Marketing firms using his likeness willy-nilly until he was nothing but a colorful, two-dimensional cartoon. The population of the world had exploded and no one needed Santa Claus anymore, so Nick had retired. Disappeared. Vanished to where no one could ever find him ... except the senior elves who had once directly reported to him. By design, theirs was a magical bond that could be left behind, ignored, shoved under the rug of the self-conscious, but never forgotten.

"Those letters were directed to his home office sometime over the last few weeks. They have a whole system for Santa Mail up there, but once Oki came across two of these, he asked everyone to stay overtime and open the rest of the mailbox. They found twelve in all."

"There are only eleven here."

"I got the call from Oki about the twelfth on my way up here. Before I lost cell service." The kettle on the stove began to whistle. Nick settled his glasses on his nose and opened the first envelope. Buddy moved to shift the kettle off the heat. He didn't need to read them again. The words on that first tearstained page had been burned into his brain for all time, and the rest were all the same.

DEAR SANTA,

PLEASE SAVE ME FROM THE BAD MAN.

PLEASE SANTA. IVE BEN A VERY GOOD GIRL. I PROMIS.

SANTA PLEASE COM SOON. I MISS MY MOMMY.

I WANT TO BE HOME FOR CHRISTMAS.

SINCERLY,

YOUR GOOD GIRL BETHANY

Buddy ran through each one in his mind as Nick read them. Every name. Every teardrop. Every "please" scrawled in round-handed crayon. Every misspelled word. The angle of the stamp in the corner of every envelope. He waited to speak until Nick had finished reading them all.

When he was done, the old man removed his glasses and pinched the bridge of his nose. He laid his other hand over the small pile of envelopes in his lap, as if the gesture might somehow protect the children inside them.

"The lab found no fingerprints," said Buddy. "I have my team cross referencing the names against reports of missing children filed in the area. The postmarks on the envelopes are mostly from Wyoming, but there are a few from Montana and one from Idaho, which leads me to believe that this 'Bad Man' is holding the children somewhere in Yellowstone National Park. But that's thousands of square miles. And it's the only lead I have."

"Have you tried Bavaria?" Nick said in a low voice.

Coming from anyone else, the suggestion would have come across as ridiculous. "By all accounts, Krampus is still chained up in the bowels of Kinizsi's church in Nagyvázsony. Not an easy answer to get, by the way. It took me three days just to find someone who would take me seriously."

"Are they still worshipping him?" He didn't mean the Hungarian priests.

"Yes." Buddy wished he had a different answer. Krampus had been incarcerated immediately following the murder of Nick's wife. Despite that, the devil's popularity seemed to be having a resurgence. The most recent generation seemed to love the pagan heathenness of his story, embracing the cards and legends as if they were things to be celebrated. Krampus became a hip, kitschy historical figure ... while Santa Claus was reduced to little more than a seasonal lie told to entitled children.

Three smart raps on the door made Buddy jump. The odds of him finding Nick's cabin in the first place had been slim to none. The odds of two people happening upon it were nonexistent.

Slowly, resignedly, Nick lifted his tall frame out of the great chair. "I'll get the cookies. You get the door."

Buddy might not have expected the company, but Nick clearly had. The tea, the cookies: they were all for this new visitor. Buddy left his weapon holstered and answered the door as instructed.

Night had fallen quickly behind them, so the visitor was illuminated only by the soft, flickering lamplight. She was tall and trim, even in her fur-lined coat and headscarf layered beneath it. It covered her nose and mouth, revealing nothing but two eyes like coal. But live coal, black that burned with an ember glow. Buddy half expected her to remove the wine colored scarf and reveal a body made of fire.

And then he realized it was no mere scarf at all. "As-salamu alaykum."

"Wa-Alaikum-as-Salaam," she said in return. Buddy was honored to receive the full response typically reserved for other Muslims. But if she was here, on this doorstep, the woman undoubtedly had some idea of who — or what — he was.

She pulled down the lower half of her hijab and yanked a glove off with her teeth. Her dark skin was flawless. Her full lips were painted a color as red as blood. She was beautiful ... for a human.

Buddy blinked when he realized he was staring. He tried to mask it by pretending to compare her face with the image on the credentials she was holding up for examination.

"Agent Zhara Munin. NSA." Her voice was as rich as he'd imagined it would be, with a thick Spanish accent.

"Agent Buddy Alvin, ISB," he responded automatically. She did not move a muscle until he had removed his own credentials and revealed them in turn.

"Park Service?" Her mouth turned up at the corner as she said it. "Nice."

Buddy scowled defensively. "And you wouldn't be here without me."

"True. May I come in?"

Buddy was tempted to say no, but Nick had already emerged from the kitchen with a plate of hot cookies. He stepped aside and motioned for Agent

Munin to enter.

"Take off your coat," Nick said without a care in the world, as if Federal agents stopped by every day.

"We can't stay long," she said. "There's a storm front moving in, and the chopper needs to take off before that happens."

She had a helicopter? Buddy scolded himself. She was NSA. Of course she had a helicopter. And probably eight flying reindeer, and a partridge in a pear tree, and anything else her little heart desired. He'd had to fill out a mountain of paperwork just to cross state lines, and then personally purchase all the equipment he'd required to make the climb.

"We have time," said Nick. "Elmore hasn't even officially asked me what he's come here to ask yet. Please. Make yourself comfortable. Have a cookie. They're snickerdoodles. Your favorite."

Agent Munin stared at Nick and then at the rest of the room, just as Buddy had. She eyed the plate of cookies skeptically, and then unzipped. Buddy guessed the tailored suit beneath her long coat had cost at least a month of his salary. Easy. He tried not to be self-conscious of his earthier wardrobe, but then, *he'd actually had to climb the mountain.*

Agent Munin took a cookie from the proffered plate. Buddy took one as well, just to be polite.

"How did you know?" she asked. Nick's eyes twinkled in answer.

"He always knows," Buddy translated.

Agent Munin turned to Buddy. "If he knows so much, why must you still ask your question?"

Nick shrugged. "Call me old fashioned."

"Boss." Buddy caught himself. "*Nick*. These kids all appealed to you. You already know their identities. You probably already know who the Bad Man is as well. At the very least, you know where they're being held."

Nick leisurely poured a cup of tea and offered it to Agent Munin. Then he poured one for himself and took a sip. "Not off the top of my head," he said finally.

"You know what I mean." Buddy tried his best not to let his frustration show. "Nick, I'm asking you to check the list. One last time. Please."

Agent Munin lowered her teacup at the mention of the list. It rattled ever so slightly in its saucer as she set it down on the table. She said nothing, only folded her hands in her lap and waited for the men to continue.

Nick studied her intently. "The NSA has been trying to get their hands on that list for years, Elmore. What makes you think I'm going to use it for you?"

Buddy had about had enough of tea and cookies and intrigue. "Because it's not for me," he said. "It's for the children."

This time, it was Nick who set his teacup down. He closed his eyes. His brow furrowed between them.

"The list. It's real?" Agent Munin said calmly.

Her comment made no sense to Buddy. "You came here tonight in search of something you didn't know existed?"

"It hasn't just been years that the NSA's been hunting this list," she said to Buddy. "It's been *generations*. So long that it's become a legend of a legend, an afterthought written up in one agent's job description that no one has ever had to act on. Until now."

Buddy folded his arms across his chest. "Exactly how long have you been following me?"

Agent Munin sighed. "The mail is always monitored, as is the chatter. When I was notified of the red flags, I didn't even know why at first. Even then, I certainly didn't believe ..." Her voice trailed away and she turned back to Nick. "Well, I didn't."

Nick put a large hand over the delicate ones still clasped upon her knees. "It's all right," he said. "I'm glad it was you." He stood and turned to Buddy, defeated. "I'll get you the list," he said. "And may God help us all."

He disappeared behind the only door that remained closed in the house — the bedroom? — and rummaged about a bit. He returned shortly with a small wooden box. In the box were some tools, a few paintbrushes, a couple of polishing cloths, and a ghost of Christmas past.

Buddy gazed down at the articulated minstrel puppet, still dressed in his motley attire. "Hello there, Jeff."

Jeff did not answer.

This wasn't strange, as Buddy couldn't recall Jeff speaking more than a time or two. The strangeness was that there was no list present in the box, no paper of any sort to be found. Perhaps Jeff knew where the list was?

Nick handed the teacups to Agent Munin before pushing the books off the table between them and setting up shop. He gave Jeff a thorough sanding and dusting before attacking his eyes and ears with the detailing tool. It was amazing to watch him work again, those large hands deftly manipulating the tools with the skill of a master.

When Nick was satisfied with the shape of Jeff's head, hands, and feet, he brushed the puppet again and then began to paint. The arches of his eyebrows were both comical and sinister. His cheeks became rosy and his eyes were bright, and as soon as his mouth was painted, it opened up into a large yawn.

"It's been too long, old friend," Jeff said to Nick.

Buddy and Agent Munin both sucked in a breath. Buddy remembered Jeff speaking before, but he didn't remember these deep, resonant tones. This was not the voice from Christmases past, it was the voice of Christmas Future.

Despite the warmth of the room, a shiver went down Buddy's spine.

"Azrael," Agent Munin said quietly as she came to the same conclusion.

Death, be he angel or ghost or god, had even more names than Nick. But here, in this place that smelled of sugar and tea and wood smoke, he was simply … Jeff.

"I need to access the list," Nick said to the puppet.

"Are you sure?" Jeff replied. "You know how difficult it was to step away the last time. You might not be able to do it again."

Nick's eyes met Buddy's. The twinkle had gone, leaving behind sadness and exhaustion. "It's for the children."

The spirit within Jeff did not seem to have full control of the puppet, but he did manage to tilt his head up slightly. His face was still half red and half blue, a worn tint that Nick had not taken the time to repaint. "I spy an elf and a daughter of Piet, but neither look like children to me." He winked at Buddy in recognition. Buddy gave Jeff a small wave in return.

"There are children in trouble," Nick clarified.

"There have always been children in trouble," Jeff countered. "And there always will be. You retired and left them to fend for themselves, to live their own lives on their own terms, as you intended to live yours. This is what you decided all those years ago. This is what you told me to remind you of if the day ever came when you took it upon yourself to ask me what you're asking me now."

Nick hung his head. "I know."

"So I will ask you again and you must answer me truly. Are you *sure*?"

"Yes."

There was no boom in Nick's voice, no joyous chuckling undertone. The word fell from his lips like a wet snowball. Buddy could imagine invisible chains shackling themselves to Nick, the familiar burden settling itself into place. Buddy felt terrible. But if anything happened to those children, he'd feel even worse.

Agent Munin bowed her head as if in silent prayer, and then lifted a hand to her ear. "The storm is almost upon us," she said, at which point Buddy realized she was relaying the information she'd just received in her earpiece. "Just give us a direction and we can get the rest of the details on the way."

"Just so we're clear," said Buddy, "I'm still the lead on this case."

"Absolutely," Agent Munin replied without hesitation. "The NSA has no interest in your investigation. But we are happy to be of service."

Just as long as they got their grubby little hands on Nick and his list when all was said and done, of course. Buddy nodded, affirming both the spoken and unspoken words between them.

Meanwhile, Nick was grilling Jeff. "It would be a name on the Naughty side."

Jeff managed to throw a hand wildly up in the air. "You're going to have to be a little more specific."

"Male," said Buddy. "Between the ages of twenty and fifty. Has kidnapped twelve or more children and is holding them somewhere in Yellowstone."

"That qualifies as a direction," Agent Munin said through her teeth. "We could have been in the air already."

"Sorry," said Buddy.

"Bank the fires," Nick said to Buddy. "I'll throw some things in a sack and we can be on our way." He grabbed an empty tin off a shelf and tossed it to Agent Munin as he started back toward the closed door. "Pack the cookies."

She rolled her eyes, but obeyed. "Yellowstone. We're on our way." Buddy could tell she was speaking to the person in her ear and not to him, so he dumped the remainder of the teapot into the stove. Agent Munin stopped him on his way to the kitchen.

"You are aware of the statistics of kidnapping," she said quietly.

"I know." The majority of kidnapping cases ended in death.

"Even if your friend managed to intercept the letters as soon as they were mailed ... we've far exceeded the twenty-four-hour window."

"I considered that. But the kidnapper wants Nick's attention. He'll keep the children alive if only for that reason."

"I hope you're right."

Nick emerged wearing a thick fur coat as white as the driven snow. Buddy thought it odd to see him without the traditional crimson jacket. His trousers were a dun camouflage and the hiking boots were tan instead of black. At least the sack was familiar. It hung limply against Nick's back as if it held naught but a can of beans, but Buddy knew better. The entire house could have fit in there, and then some.

Nick tucked Jeff inside his belt and blew out the lamp. When he closed the door, he placed a bare hand on it, almost as if saying good-bye.

The helicopter was already spinning and humming when they exited the cabin — the wind had picked up to such a point that Buddy couldn't tell if what was being blown into his face was natural or manufactured. Either way, his cheeks were rosy when he reached the vehicle, and his clothes were damp from head to toe. He hoped the NSA could afford a *heated* chopper.

"Hiya!" A tiny woman with dark ponytails who looked barely out of her teens handed Buddy three headsets. "Put these on!" she screamed over the whine of the main rotor. "We need to be out of here like yesterday!"

She wasn't kidding. Almost immediately after Buddy pulled Nick into the cabin after him, a gust lifted the helicopter and blew it off the mountain. At least, that's how it felt to Buddy. Agent Munin yelled some curse as she slammed the door shut after herself — it was lost beneath the wind and the hooting of the young pilot as she rode the storm like a bucking bronco.

Buddy felt himself turning green. The sheer effort it took not to toss those recently-consumed cookies made him break a sweat. He glanced at Nick. The NSA might take custody of him when this was over, but in the meantime, Nick was Buddy's responsibility. Not that he needed to worry — the old man simply held onto the bar above his head and smiled nostalgically.

When they'd escaped the maelstrom and Buddy's heart returned to a far more manageable beat, he remembered the headsets and passed them around. He had to remove his jacket's hood so that the muffs fit properly over his ears. He heard nothing beyond the dull beat of the motor above them. Agent Munin tapped the side of her own headset and mimicked turning a switch. The fumbling fingers of his shaking hand eventually found it.

"... you hear me now?" Agent Munin was asking.

Buddy nodded, and then remembered the headset had a microphone. "Yes," he responded.

"Sir?"

Nick nodded as well. "Yes, I can hear you."

"Ma'am," the pilot said to Agent Munin, "if our destination is Yellowstone, I'm going to need to plot out refuel points along the route."

"No, you won't," said Nick.

"This helo only gets about 345 miles to a tank, sir," said the pilot. "Four hundred if I push it, but these winds aren't exactly working in our favor."

"Trust me," said Nick. "You won't need to refuel."

The pilot looked to Agent Munin, who nodded. "Yes, sir," she replied with a grin.

"I'm afraid we don't have a headset small enough for Jeff," Agent Munin said into her mic. Buddy wasn't sure if she was making a joke, but he spotted a dimple in her cheek that he hadn't noticed before.

"Who is Jeff?" asked the pilot.

Nick removed Jeff from his belt and held the puppet out for inspection. As the pilot turned to look at him, he raised his arm limply in a salute.

"Hello there," he said.

That terrible voice echoed as clearly and loudly through their headsets as if he'd spoken from directly inside their skulls. Instinctively, Buddy reached for the switch on his earmuff again, as if he could turn down the volume.

"*Santa Muerte.*" The pilot crossed herself and kissed her fingertips. "Lo siento, señor. Me llamo Lupita Flores."

"Yo se," said Jeff. "Encantado. The man we're after is Dwight Griswold."

"The governor of Nebraska?" asked Buddy. "Isn't he dead?"

"Yes," Jeff said confidently.

"The Dwight Griswold we're looking for is very much alive," said Nick. "And very angry at me."

"I'll say. What happened?" Judging by the way Nick clenched his hands into fists by his sides, Buddy guessed it wasn't good.

"He wrote me a letter," said Nick. "I didn't answer."

"But you retired long before Griswold would have been old enough to write you," said Agent Munin. "Wouldn't the post office have intercepted it and answered for you?"

"They can't answer the ones burned in the fireplace," Nick said flatly. "Those still find me." Buddy couldn't imagine how difficult it must have been to ignore all those childish pleas, fewer and farther between but still unceasing after all these years.

"What did the letter say?" Lupita's question was followed by silence in the cabin ... as silent as a helicopter in the rain could be.

"He can't tell you," said Buddy. "It's like doctor-patient confidentiality."

"Child-saint privilege," said Agent Munin.

"I'm no saint," Nick growled. "Not anymore."

"Are the children dead?" Agent Munin blurted out the words quickly. "Forgive me," she added. "I had to ask."

"Their souls have not entered my purview," Jeff said magnanimously.

"Thank you," said Agent Munin.

"Would you like to know their names?" Nick asked softly.

Normally, discovery of the children's names would have been a high priority. Victimology was essential when profiling such a kidnapper. Now that they had a name and a location, it didn't matter ... to the case. It still mattered to Buddy. "Yes, please."

"Bethany Finch. Jae Saito. Lynette Boulet. Robin Keyser. Kaitlin Oh. Paravi Patel. Tien Nguyen. Diana Cabrera. Namid St. Marie. Faris Hussein. Baird Langstrom. Kwame Bello." Nick said the names slowly, pausing reverently after each one.

"And a partridge in a pear tree," said Lupita. "Madre de dios. All those poor children."

"Hold on. Dwight Griswold is a white male, right?" Buddy caught Agent Munin's eye and knew she was thinking along the same lines. Children these days had all sorts of crazy names, but to hear them paired with their proper surnames gave Buddy a whole new perspective.

"Yes," said Nick. "Why should that matter?"

"Because it's odd for a kidnapper to choose victims outside his own race, never mind multiple races like the list you just mentioned," said Agent Munin.

"Do they have anything in common?" Buddy asked Nick.

"Not sure," said Nick. "As Zahra pointed out, they are all from varying races and socio-economic backgrounds. Let me think on it some more."

"A few of them are named after birds," said Lupita. "Does that make a difference?"

"Similarities are usually all or nothing," said Agent Munin.

"So he's a collector," Buddy surmised.

"Or he's covering all his bases trying to get Nick's attention," Agent Munin countered.

"Well, he's accomplished that," said Nick. "I just hope we get there before another child goes missing."

By Buddy's estimation, they made it to the far side of Yellowstone in a little over an hour. Their arrival was accompanied by much muttering in Spanish on behalf of Lupita — she eventually cut power to her mic, but Buddy could still see her lips moving. She turned it back on when Nick tapped her on the shoulder, guiding her in for the landing.

Buddy took a deep breath as he stepped gratefully back down on terra firma. There was snow here as well, and the air was as crisp as it had been on the mountain, but he could sense the change in altitude, the subtle rise in temperature. The trees here spoke to him as they did on the mountain, but up there it was a harsher, more solitary song. Here, it was calmer, more harmonious, embracing every living element as a part of the whole. Buddy had felt small and anxious on the mountain. Here, he felt ... wider, as if his lungs were somehow big enough to breathe in the sky.

Lupita cut power to the chopper so that they could talk, but she did not disembark.

"He's holed up in a cave," said Nick. "I can feel it. The entrance is down that way."

"Only one entrance?" asked Agent Munin.

Nick nodded.

"One way in, one way out," said Buddy. "There's a possibility that this won't end well."

"Can you sense the children?" Agent Munin asked Nick.

Nick paused a moment, and then shook his head. "It's all a bit fuzzy. It might be because the children are frightened. It might be because Dwight's overwhelming nastiness is blocking everything else."

"That's happened before," Jeff said from his spot in Nick's belt.

"Either way, let's proceed with caution," said Buddy. He began to walk in the direction Nick had pointed, but Nick grabbed his arm.

"I'll go first."

"Sir," said Agent Munin, "I'm not sure that's the best idea."

"I go first, or you don't find the cave entrance," said Nick. "Take it or leave it."

Agent Munin's lips formed a tight line. "Fine. But you're not going in unarmed." She offered her service weapon to Nick, but he declined. He opened the sack and pulled out the shotgun he'd met Buddy with at the cabin. He loaded the gun, but placed no extra shells in his pockets. Satisfied, he tossed the sack back into the helicopter. "I'll be back for that," he called to Lupita.

"We'll be waiting for you," said Lupita.

Nick was right: the cave's entrance was deceptively difficult to find. It was all but a mirage in the rocky landscape, accompanied by sparse meadow grass and little else that would have tripped Buddy's elf-sense. He allowed Nick to lead, as promised. Nick's brilliant white coat glowed in the darkness.

Buddy left his weapon in the holster, choosing instead to concentrate on making as little noise as possible on their approach. Behind him, Agent Munin managed to do credibly well in her own stealthy efforts. Of course, if she really was a descendent of Zwarte Piet, as Jeff had mentioned, stealth was more than likely in her blood.

Buddy's mind raced as they moved further and further down the winding tunnel. How had Dwight Griswold found this spot in the first place? He had kidnapped these children from three different states — where was his vehicle? Assuming they found the children alive, how were they going to transport them all home? He supposed Nick could stuff them all in his sack, but that didn't exactly seem the most comfortable way to travel. And if they managed to take Griswold alive, they'd have to see to his arrest as well …

While in the middle of thinking through that last idea, the tunnel opened up into a larger room lit by an old oil lamp. Buddy and Agent Munin moved to either side of Nick, flanking him, guns drawn but held low at their sides. They wanted to avoid confrontation if at all possible. There was no telling where a bullet set loose in this chamber would ricochet.

A man sat on a pillar in the middle of the room with a knife in his hands, his head bowed as if asleep. His hair was in disarray, his clothes were in tatters, and his beard looked as if it hadn't been shaved in weeks. He smelled like he hadn't showered in that long either. The fetid smell that reached Buddy was rank with body odor and sweat and feces. He wrinkled his nose, resisting the urge to cover it. He didn't want to let go of his gun.

There were no children in sight.

Good, thought Buddy. He didn't want them to see what was about to happen here.

"Dwight."

The man's eyes opened at the sound of Nick's voice. It took him a moment to register who exactly was standing before him. "You came," the man breathed.

"Yes, Dwight. I came."

Now that Griswold had found his voice, the words all tumbled out in an avalanche. "I didn't think you'd come. I believed you wouldn't. You didn't come before. You weren't going to come now. How are you here? You don't come. That's not what happens. Not really. YOU DON'T COME."

"Dwight," Nick said again, more calmly. "I'm here. Everything's going to be okay."

"I stopped believing," Griswold was crying now. "I didn't believe. Because you didn't come."

"I'm here," Nick repeated. "Put down the knife and we can all go have some cookies and a glass of milk and talk about it."

Griswold looked down in his lap, as if he'd forgotten he'd been holding a knife in the first place. He looked back up and blinked, realizing now that Nick had not come alone. Griswold lifted the knife and began to laugh. "You came, but you didn't come for me. You came for *them*."

He did not name the children, but he didn't have to. Buddy scanned the alcove. There were three possible archways beyond which the children might lie, all of them on the opposite side of Griswold's perch.

"I came for all of you," said Nick. "I'm sorry it took so long. But here I am! You got what you wanted. Please, Dwight. Let them go."

Griswold's face screwed up and the knuckles of the hand around the knife went white. "What I wanted? What I *wanted*? I wanted you to come *then*. I wanted you to come instead of him, punishing me when I was naughty." Griswold's face went slack, his crazy, bloodshot eyes staring at a faraway memory. "Punishing me worse when I was nice."

Griswold's voice trailed off. A moment later he raised the knife again, focusing on Nick. Remembering he was there. "I stopped believing in you. I stopped believing in everything. Because no one came for me."

Whatever the trigger, it was clear Dwight had suffered some sort of psychotic break. His repetitive ramblings were immature and irrational. Buddy counted this as an asset. It was possible that Nick might be able to use Griswold's own logic to disarm him before he hurt anyone.

Buddy turned to check Agent Munin's status. She tapped her ear and furrowed her brow. Something about Lupita? She scanned the room, and then looked back at Buddy. No ... she hadn't been indicating a voice in her earpiece, she was pointing out the silence. Buddy listened to the stillness of the cave. If there were twelve children somewhere close by, they were asleep or ... subdued. All of them.

"No one came. No one came. No one came." Griswold was rocking back and forth now.

Buddy stepped forward slowly. They were losing him.

Nick took a step closer as well. "Dwight, I'm here ..."

"I STOPPED BELIEVING BECAUSE NO ONE CAME. NO ONE CAME. NO ONE CAME."

Nick stretched a hand out to the knife, one of those large, beautiful, skilled hands that could chop wood, bake cookies, drive a team of magical beasts, and etch a portrait so detailed that it came to life. "Dwight ..."

Griswold focused on Nick again. He seemed surprised to find Nick so close, right before his entire body went perfectly still. "And then he came."

"Gun!" screamed Agent Munin.

No one had been watching Griswold's other hand, the one that had reached for the pistol tucked into his pants at the small of his back. Nick saw it only in time to lunge forward and knock it aside, resulting in Buddy being shot in the arm instead of something more vital.

But the concentration on the gun meant that everyone had forgotten about the knife, which Dwight promptly used to slit his own throat.

"NO!" Nick screamed, catching Griswold's body before it pitched backwards off the pillar. Nick silently cradled the man in his arms, his stern face expressing remorse and guilt in every wrinkle. It was natural for Nick to blame himself. If he had found a way to answer Griswold's letter, he would have had to answer them all.

Agent Munin rolled Buddy onto his back, forcing his eyes away from the scene. "Are you all right?" she asked.

"Through and through?" She examined the bullet wound and nodded. Buddy took a moment to mentally assess the damage. He needed to be strong. What he *wanted* to do was faint. "Happen to have an extra scarf?"

"I do, actually." She reached beneath her thick coat and expensive suit and pulled out a length of ivory silk. She wrapped it around his arm efficiently, tying knots over both the entry and exit wounds. Buddy's vision swam from the pain. Elves might live much longer lives, but their constitutions left a lot to be desired.

"Buddy," Agent Munin whispered his name. Even in the silence of the cave, it sounded very far away. "*Elmore*," she said sternly. Buddy winced again and opened his eyes.

"Zahra," he managed to croak. He wanted to scold her, but he simply didn't have the energy.

Thankfully, she only seemed to want his attention. "It's still too quiet in here."

Buddy grunted affirmatively. If they could have, the children would have reacted to the gunshot. He leaned his head back against the floor of the cave, desperately trying to turn defeat into anger.

"Can you stand?" She posed it as a question, but didn't wait for his answer before pulling him to his feet. Buddy cradled his wounded arm close to his body. He let her holster his weapon for him.

"Nick," she called out. She crossed to him and placed a hand on his shoulder. "Nick, we have to find the children."

Nick looked up at Agent Munin with that ravaged face and it broke Buddy's heart.

"Dwight Griswold was a child once. And I let him down."

"Well, here's your chance to make up for it," said Agent Munin. "Come on. Let's go."

"He must be keeping the children somewhere else," said Buddy, "or they would have cried out when they heard the gunshot." Nick shifted his eyes from Agent Munin's face and stared at Buddy.

Yeah. Buddy didn't believe himself either.

"Dwight's soul is here with me." Jeff's booming voice ricocheted against the cave walls, louder and longer than the gunshot. Buddy tried not to worry about the walls collapsing. He didn't relish the idea of being shot *and* buried alive in the same day. "I still cannot sense the children."

It was a small glimmer of hope, but Buddy took it. Nick must have, too, for he kissed Griswold on the top of the head, laid him down on the cave floor, and stood. All but the collar of his white fur coat was now ruined with bright red blood. *Like the old times*, Buddy thought to himself. *But not like the old times.*

Nick took up the lamp and led the way. The middle of the three archways behind Griswold opened up into a chamber, then a tunnel, and then several more tunnels. Eventually, they found them.

Nick lifted his lamp inside the chamber. The calcite sparkled in the light like new fallen snow. Stalactites hung like giant icicles above them. In the middle of the room was a white-topped dais, its fluid edges dripping as if with candle wax. And upon the dais was a pile of bones, each one picked completely clean.

Nick froze with the lamp lifted high. A single tear fell from his eye. From behind him, Buddy could hear Agent Munin quietly chanting a prayer.

"This can't be them," Buddy said aloud. "Jeff couldn't sense them."

The puppet shrugged from inside Nick's belt. "I still can't."

Buddy walked to the dais, still refusing to believe his eyes. Separate from the pile of bones on the table-like formation were two birch branches, lying across each other in an X. One was silver. One was gold.

Gold for good children. Silver for the naughty ones. Buddy knew this legend. He knew it as well as he knew his own. "No."

Nick lowered the light, casting the sight back into darkness. "And then he came," he said into the shadows, quoting Griswold's last words.

Buddy thought back to that moment, right before Griswold had pulled the gun. Remembered his body language. In the moment, Griswold hadn't been ranting. He hadn't been lost in a memory, terrified of whoever the monster had been in his childhood.

When Dwight Griswold had said that last "And then he came," he'd been referring to the monster *now*.

Oh, he'd gotten attention all right. Twelve children, like the twelve days of Christmas, descended from bloodlines all over the world, crying their hearts out and praying to every god they knew. Nothing else would have had the power to break those sacred chains. It was the perfect sacrifice.

Krampus had returned to the world of men.

"Devoured souls are beyond my purview," Jeff said as quietly as his booming voice could manage.

Nick shook his head. "This is all my fault."

"No, it's not," Buddy said reflexively.

"It was my *job*," Nick growled through his teeth. "I may have been reduced to nothing, but this was still my job."

"It still can be."

Buddy and Nick slowly turned back to where Agent Munin stood framed in the archway.

"I've been authorized by the Director to offer you your own team."

"Wait. What about me?" asked Buddy.

"And me?" boomed Jeff.

"Ask him." Agent Munin pointed at Nick. "It's his team."

Nick raised his hands. "Hold on, hold on. What exactly are you saying?"

Agent Munin crossed her arms. "I'm saying, let the Anchorage post — and all the other offices all over the world — handle the letters. Let the people handle the presents. Let the department stores and the corporations manufacture good will and pay for the advertising. Don't retire. *Evolve.* Use all those magical abilities and resources at your disposal to handle the cases like these that fall through the cracks." She dropped her hands and her eyes went soft. "Let's save the lost ones."

Those bushy brows knitted together as Nick scowled at her. "Can I have some time to think about it?"

"Yes," she said quickly. "Of course."

Nick looked back to the dais full of bones and stared at them a long time. Then his eyes met Buddy's. For the first time since he'd arrived at the cabin, Buddy thought he saw the faintest glimmer of a twinkle there.

"Someone has to stop Krampus," said Nick. "It may as well be us."

Dear Santa.

I have been very good this year. I would like a unicorn bicycle with tassels on the handles please. But not a pink one. Pink is for girls.

Dear Santa —

My baby brother is a brat. Please bring me a sister instead. Please and thank you.

Dear Santa,

Are you fat because you eat too many cookies? You should not eat too many cookies. Mom says sugar makes you fat. Except for me. I get hyper. If you give the cookies to your reindeer and eat the carrots instead, I promise I won't tell.

I would like Legos please. A huge pile of Legos. All the Legos you can carry. Do you like Legos? How many Legos do you think would fit in your sack?

Dear Santa-
HELP ME.

KATY HARRAD AND GREG STOLZE

REQUIEM FOR A MANIC PIXIE DREAM

CHAD STARED AT HIS phone without really seeing it. He could stare out the window instead, he supposed, and not really see that either. He was on a train, hurtling along the tracks at … Chad didn't know how fast trains went. Chad didn't care.

The train was clipping along, but every time he turned to the scratched Plexiglas, he saw the same thing. Power poles. Leafless oaks. Maples cut into Y shapes so they wouldn't interfere with telephone lines. A flat, black, even strip of empty road.

"Rutabaga country," he whispered, realizing he was looking out again. He looked at his phone again instead.

'A' 'N' 'M' 'I' and 'C.' He kind of hated Alphabear. What sort of a word was he supposed to make from that mess? The M and A were blinking red. They were about to turn to stone. He knew how they felt.

He spelled out "MAN" and hit the green check mark beside it. Cartoon bears capered in synthetic joy. He glowered at the number that came up. Not enough for even a blue egg.

"Fuck you, Alphabear," he mumbled. The train rocked to a halt.

Chad almost had a moment of pleasure when he realized he'd made the whole trip without craving meth. But then as he was stepping down to the dirty yellow rubber warning strip, he saw an ad for men's cufflinks, and his mood crashed back down into misery. It wasn't actually even an ad for men's cufflinks, he saw, as he moved closer. It was for cologne, but the man in the ad was wearing cufflinks.

He walked through a very small train station, and then his head twitched up, alert.

The day was grey, the station was wood and scuffed tan linoleum, and outside the window, just for a moment, there was beauty. It was a heather-lavender something, a blend of faint purple next to orange. It should have looked awful, like action movies from 2011-2013, but somehow it worked. The tangerine-heather moment, which must have been clothing because it had moved out of view, was functional, counterintuitive, like a sunset that ought to be garish behind skyscrapers but instead somehow laughs lightly, devastatingly, at the labors of man. "Look upon my works," the purple-gold sunset that shouldn't be sublime seems to say. "Silly."

"Honey!"

Chad blinked hard and there was Mom. Ooh.

If the garments of the brief vision (woman? Probably a woman. Men didn't wear purple and orange in rutabaga country, not unless they were fans of the Denver Broncos, which they wouldn't be) had blended despite clashing, the clothes on his mother clashed despite blending. Flower prints. She hugged him and he remembered the time he'd gone to something that had been described as "a rave, if they'd had raves in Edwardian times." It had been held in a greenhouse in Fordham Heights, of all places, and he'd taken drugs that had something in them that did a number on his inner ear and left him sprawled in a bed of geraniums, unable to stand until two guys in matching pinstripe suits had stopped laughing and helped. At least, he assumed they were geraniums.

"Hey Mom," he said, smushed into her shoulder.

"Oh sweetie, let's take you home," she said. "Let's get some seven-layer bean dip into you. You still like seven-layer dip, right?"

"I still like it."

"They haven't invented an eighth layer in New York, have they?"

He chuckled.

As they got into the minivan, he turned his head around his hometown, noticing that everything looked exactly the same, except smaller and more worn and grubby, and the billboards advertised energy drinks instead of cigarettes. He wasn't consciously searching for an intoxicating melange of orange and violet. Not consciously.

That night he woke with the abruptness of a taut rubber band snapping apart. One second he was too asleep to dream, the next he was round-eyed, staring into the dark but seeing, in his mind, Scott standing over him. "You're gonna have to do better than that, cupcake." It was silent, but more real to him than the sound of owls hunting voles through the rutabaga fields.

He did say I might have flashbacks, Chad thought, and went down to find his mother drinking the biggest milkshake he'd ever seen. She'd made it in the orange juice pitcher, and as he came into the kitchen she wiped aside a white smear studded with Oreo flecks, eyes guilty.

"Hey Mom."

"Oh sugar pie, I hope the blender didn't wake you up. It's supposed to be whisper quiet but I think there's a hitch in its gitalong."

"No, I just … I didn't hear anything."

"I hope you don't want any," she said, raising it once more and gulping down a long, chunky sluice. "I've had my mouth on it and, you know …"

"Um, I think I'm more in the mood for savory." Next to the mixer he saw a honey bear with its head twisted all the way off, a banana peel, a small carton of whipping cream, the lidless peanut butter jar, and the cookie package. "You hungry?" He couldn't remember what they'd had for supper.

"I don't do this very often at all," she said. "It would send my figure into a tailspin."

"Yeah, well, if you don't have your health …" He rummaged in the cabinet and pulled out a box of Chicken in a Biskit crackers.

"Oh honey no," she said. "You can't eat those, they're full of gluten."

"You can't get them in New York," he said, though he had no idea if that was true or not. "All the stores have imported Kobe beef and goat cheese, but you can't get these."

"Your father buys them," she said, before taking another long suck at the pitcher. "I suppose we all have our vices."

"I suppose."

Something in his tone made her look up. "Oh Chad! Chad sweetie, you don't think I'm passive-aggressive do you? That I'm passively aggressively commenting on your problem? Because I wouldn't do that."

"I know Mom."

"I wouldn't and I won't."

"I know."

"Was it because I was a bad mother?"

"What?"

"Was I a bad mom? Or, was your dad a bad father and that's why you started shooting the meth?"

"Smoking Mom. You smoke meth."

"How did you even learn that?"

"Look, everyone in New York goes through a drug phase," he said. "It's usually after some kind of blindsiding setback. Like my friend Kolos? The guy who did the enameled portraits of NAACP leaders on machete blades?"

"What sort of a name is 'Kolos'? Is that … Dutch?"

"Close, it's imaginary. When he had it legally changed, he couldn't decide between 'Carlos' and 'Koala.' Before that, he was named Vaughn."

"That's a nice name."

"Anyhow, Kolos married this woman who already had a kid, right? And the kid's father, he'd gotten the mom pregnant on, like, the second date and then just vanished? So there's trust issues; they were off and on for years with the daughter fighting Kolos and yelling at him, 'you don't get a say; you're not my dad. I don't even have a dad,' and all these tears, right?"

"Mm hm." Mom's expression was rapt as she finished her milkshake with a spatula.

"Well. They're married for five years, and the daughter is sixteen and finally calls him 'Dad' and all that. They go out for dinner and see a friend from long ago who mentions how he likes the mom's hair now that it's her natural color. 'Oh,' says Kolos, 'What color was it before?' and she says red and mentions how different she looked and he says, 'That must have been when I had the beard.' Kolos can't grow a beard at all now, he got a skin graft on his face after a motorcycle accident. So she can't imagine him bearded and they go digging for old photos. It turns out that the guy who got her pregnant and ran off? It was him."

"What?"

"Yeah, he was pretty shook too."

"No, I mean … I don't think I understood the course of that story, dearheart."

"I mean that after all the years of Kolos trying to be a father to this girl, whom he loved and whose mom he'd married, it turned out that Kolos literally was her dad after all. In, like, the strictest biological sense."

"I don't …" Chad's mom frowned, thinking it over. "She didn't notice her new husband had the same last name?"

"He got rid of his last name, and anyhow, it was 'Smith.'"

"But … but he never thought anything about how the bad dad who left them had his old first name? 'Vaughn' is hardly as common as 'Smith.'"

"Yeah, no, that's so, but she'd always called the first guy 'Don', and he'd never corrected her. His hearing's not great."

For a moment, Chad's mom just stared, the spatula ruminatively stirring in her mouth.

"And after that he started sh … smoking meth?"

"Yep."

"And after your cufflink thing, you …?"

"Well, actually, it was more like I'd been at Kolos's place once and he had some. But it was after … you know, the business …"

"That's when you started doing a lot."

"Yeah."

They were both quiet for a moment. The crackers didn't taste as good as he remembered, and he wondered if they'd replaced the onion with an artificial onion flavonoid.

"Chad? You remember the Christokuloses?"

"Your canasta homeys? I remember."

"They're having a dinner tomorrow. There's someone there you might want to meet."

"Is this a thing where you try and fix your son up with some eligible bachelorette?"

"Well honestly Chad, I just thought you might find Cassandra interesting."

He ate one last cracker. "Okay."

Cassandra was not interesting. Cassandra wore a calf-length plaid dress with no sleeves, just frilly ruffles that framed fearsomely-toned arms. Chad didn't care for plaid. Kolos had once said, "The only place for plaid is on Catholic high school girls who don't understand consequences," and Chad hadn't even laughed politely. He disliked plaid that much.

"So!" Cassandra said brightly. "Your mother tells me you're back from New York?"

"Mm hm." He sipped a mainstream-but-not-big-label beer. It wasn't even interestingly bad.

"What did you do there?"

"I made bespoke cufflinks."

"Excuse me?"

"Cufflinks. I hand-crafted them. Usually out of fordite, which is an agate-like accidental material they dig out of old car factories. The paint, it got layered and layered and baked and baked."

"I ... see." She frowned. "Did you sell a lot of them?"

"Not at first, but I got a lucky break. A Lehman Brothers executive was wearing a pair when he got exonerated and demand just surged. I had art school paid off in seven months."

"Wow!"

"Yeah," he said bitterly. "Wow. But then they turned on me. Harry Styles showed up wearing cocktail cuffs at the Golden Globes red carpet, and everything was over. I'd become a dinosaur, overnight, without anyone even telling me I was extinct. So. Now I'm back here." He took a deep drink. "I'm going to have to sell shit on Etsy."

"... huh."

"Yeah."

There was a pause and then she said, "I do CrossFit!"

"Can you excuse me for a minute?" Chad said, and walked away with no intention of ever going back.

Then he rounded a corner and there she was. The woman in orange and purple. It had to be, and not just because she was wearing fuchsia with a sort of off-chartreuse and making it work, it was because of the way she moved, the way she walked, unselfconscious without being self-absorbed, loose and free. Her red hair looked windswept.

"Were you at the train station the other day?" he asked, and she turned around to face him. Her face wasn't beautiful exactly, but it was quirkily narrow and wide-eyed, like a doll's, and her skin was so pale that for a moment Chad thought he could see right through her.

She raised an eyebrow. "Perhaps I was. I couldn't say." She had an accent. An English accent.

"I saw you in heather and orange," he said. "Well, more of a burnt sienna."

"Heather grey or heather purple?"

"The purple, obviously. I'm Chad, by the way."

"Oh, you're Chad. Right." Her eyebrow quirked. "So have you given up the meth?"

For the first time in years, Chad blushed.

"Um … here, come out where it's quieter and I'll tell you."

When they were outside the wind caught her hair and its scent flowed over to him. It was like fresh air and static.

"How'd you know I had … you know, that, um, issue?"

"Oh, everyone knows."

"Ah."

"It's all they talk about."

"I see."

"But you got out with your teeth intact! That's something. An accomplishment, really."

"… true." Chad was not usually tongue-tied around women. "What do you do?" he asked.

"Chimerical taxidermy. Well, I don't make it, though I've dabbled, but I'm writing my thesis on it and the intersection of fantasy-prone psychology with American hunting culture."

"Oh, so the jackalopes."

"Exactly. Fascinating stuff!"

"… sure."

She was looking at him expectantly.

"So …" he prompted.

"The meth!" Her eyes were bright and curious.

"Oh. Well, I went on a, um, non-traditional treatment program. This guy named Scott runs it out of his gym."

"How was it 'non-traditional'?"

"It was pretty physical. I mean, the first thing? He punched me right in the face."

"What?"

"Yeah, that's ... boxing is a big element of his therapeutic modality."

"It sounds like he just enjoys beating up drug abusers. Are you sure his name wasn't Batman?"

"Look, I know it seems weird," Chad said, defensive, "but it worked. He said sk ... um, clients like me, we needed to move past self-pity and understand how enviable our lives were, pre-meth."

"Clients like you?"

"Yeah."

"You were going to say something else." She brought a lacquered fingernail to her highly polished lips, which were a deep cerise. "Something that started with 'sk'?"

When her mouth parted over her teeth to say 'sk,' Chad lost his train of thought entirely. Her teeth were a flawless, toothpaste-ad white, but the front left incisor was slightly crooked outward.

"Skinny white boys," Chad said. "Scott said skinny white boys needed to learn there were worse things than meth withdrawal. Then he'd put up his thumbs like Fonzie and point them at his nipples, which you could always see through his t-shirt. I think they may have been pierced."

"Wow."

"But I got clean, and I don't really miss it."

"What's a Fonzie?"

Chad spent the next twenty minutes explaining Arthur Fonzarelli to her, and that was how he met Ingénue Hermione Meredith. He didn't even see the glare Cassandra shot at him as she left at a sensible hour. He and Ingénue were still on the porch.

"... it would be like, if you took that bass you just caught? If you took that and put, I don't know, an iguana head on it, maybe some little horns or something. Making something completely new out of old parts. Kind of like how she makes me feel," Chad said, three days later, with a little self-deprecating chuckle.

"Huh," his father said. They were fishing.

"What was she even doing at the Christokuloses' party? I mean, no offense, but she's hardly a ... well, you know, a Cassandra."

"I don't know. She just shows up. I really don't know her at all."

"She's brilliant, Dad, you'll see. Really insightful, and funny, not in a mechanical way but a way that makes you really think, you know?"

"She's sure got you chattering away." He cast his line.

"Hope I don't scare the fish!"

"You're not ..." Chad's father frowned at the water, watching how the wind shifted its surface. "You're not 'getting high' again are you?"

"Dad, where would I even find meth out here?"

"The rural methamphetamine economy is widespread and booming," his father said in a funeral tone. (He was a funeral director.)

"I'll have to take your word for it. Ingénue doesn't even like it when I drink!"

Chad was a changed man. Dating in New York had been foreign movies and ethnic molecular gastronomy bistros. Nights out in his hometown had typically involved tallboys in the tall grass behind the bleachers. But Ingénue had him walking through the woods and hand-crafting art supplies for sculptures. They photographed snowy egrets at dawn and pored over low-print-run volumes of local history at dusk.

Long-disused parts of his face were engaged to form smiles, and long-disused parts of his heart were forming feelings for her. He was, of course, eager to have sloppy filthy sex with her, but that had (to his great regret) so far failed to happen. But she'd promised him a special night at her place, which he had not yet seen. (He had no car, so she often picked him up from his parents' home in her charmingly dilapidated windowless panel van.)

Not only had he seen nothing of her home, he knew very little about her family, or her past, or her ambitions or experiences. He knew how her ankles curved in kitten heels and how her cool smooth hand felt in his, and that was enough.

Chad laughed when he realized Ingénue's house was "the old Hellwright place," which, if the stories from junior high could be believed, was where Satanic natives had buried werewolf serial killers once aliens were finished probing their anuses. He'd walked the whole way, legs strengthened by seasons in a studio walkup, and pulled up the flashlight app on his phone to light his way as the sun went down. It wasn't a sunset like Ingénue's wardrobe. It was clear, cold, a dry-baked yellow shading down to gray.

Then the door opened and she was waiting for him, lustrous in a robe of heliotrope and citrine. (Or maybe jonquil. It was hard to tell in the dim lighting.) She was smiling like a goddess. Chad had a brief impression of intricate black curling tattoos covering her arms — but wouldn't he have noticed them before? — and then forgot everything else as she leant in to kiss him.

Everything went black in an instant of flawless bliss, her lips tasted like some kind of delicious wasp-sting and time stood still, he felt dizzy and flushed and entirely head over heels until he realized that, no, he actually was hanging by his feet. He had passed out and was now trussed up and suspended, head swaying, artfully moussed hair brushing a crumbly concrete floor.

"Ingénue, I'm down for whatever, but I have to insist on a degree more consent for this kind of power-exchange."

(He was pretty calm, considering. He trusted Ingénue, and this was not the first time he'd woken up somewhere with no recollection of falling asleep.)

Ingénue was standing nearby, bending over a large black hole and muttering. He smiled to see that the robe was gone and the tattoos he'd noticed were now all over her body. But how were they moving? They didn't even have moving tattoos yet in the Village!

She turned round. Her face was just the same as ever, he thought, except for something about her eyes. Had they always been so large and glittering?

"You're awake," she said. "Good. You probably have questions."

He shrugged and gave her a smirk he hoped was sexy and knowing. Her head dipped forward a notch and her mouth opened just a bit. Incredulity looked smashing on those full lips, giving a glimpse of that crooked tooth. With a small head-shake, she walked over and sliced the rope above him. He thumped to the floor, breath thoroughly knocked out of him. It hurt a lot.

"I like you considerably, Chad," she said. "So sweet. So naïve. Your cynicism's especially naïve. I doubt that's any consolation, though."

"Hey," he said, "I'm sure you didn't mean to hurt me, but that really did. I think my back is seriously out of alignment." He squirmed against the ropes. "Mom would say I have a 'hitch in my gitalong.' "

"It won't last long," she assured him. "I mean … come on. Surely on some level you know what's going on here." She nodded towards the big black hole. Beside it lay a very sharp knife. In the silence, Chad could hear some kind of sound issuing from the hole. A kind of echoey hissing.

"Knife. Basement. Ceremonial designs?" The snake-like marks on her arms slid around her elbows. "Does the concept of sacrifice mean nothing these days?"

"It was all a lie?" Chad whispered. "Is … is the accent even real?"

She reached out affectionately to stroke his hair. "Shhh," she whispered. "Once you see the Serpentine Goddess, you won't even want to struggle any more. You live for beauty. This is a beautiful thing we're doing. Have you ever felt so alive?"

The deep hissing was getting louder.

"Don't tell me how to feel!" choked Chad, unsuccessfully trying to crawl backward away from the hole and the sound.

"Silly Chad," she chided, as the tip of a gigantic forked tongue licked its way over the edge of the chasm. "We both know that without me you'd feel nothing."

Ingénue, aka Dreamchild, aka Glowflower, aka Joy, aka so many pseudonyms she'd forgotten half of them, paused to appreciate the moment. Although it was familiar, she tried to never take it for granted, always to take it all in: the bound man understanding life and its fragility for the first time, the Goddess in her massive devouring glory emerging to feed, and she, the virgin priestess, ministering to both of them. On the nights when she lay awake wondering if she'd ever really done anything with her life, it was this recurring image that reassured her. Not only had she kept the Goddess replete and content, she'd also brought meaning to the lives of dozens of callow, disaffected men. True, when it turned out that they were meant to be fed to a giant divine snake, the revelation didn't always go down well. But meaning was meaning, even when it wasn't what you wanted to hear.

She gazed at Chad with unfeigned love. She always loved her boys. They poured themselves out to her like water from a jug, giving her their dreams and their ideas and their entire life stories, never asking for hers. She'd never lied to any of them. She'd never needed to. If any of them had ever asked about her ambitions or her beliefs, she would have told them the exact truth about the Goddess and the swallowing. It was a matter of personal pride. But the occasion had never arisen — not even with Chad, who had been one of her favorites — and now it was too late. This was her final sacrifice.

A snake's head the size of a car began to appear, intelligent lidless eyes bright in the darkness of the cellar. Chad began to scream, a breathless choking sound. "Mother Serpentine," prayed Ingénue, facing her deity, "I bring you a new soul as I have brought you many before." She raised her voice to be heard over Chad's incoherent shouts. "Accept this empty vessel in honor of your glory, and be at peace. This is the fiftieth and last."

"Fiftieth?" spluttered Chad behind her. "You've killed forty-nine people before me? You're only 25!"

"I look only 25," she corrected him. "And I've never killed anyone."

"Then what's the bigass knife for, huh?"

She rolled her eyes. "It's a symbolic penis, *obviously*. Look darling, I don't want your last moments to be wasted on a comparative anthropology lesson. I bring gentlemen to the Mother and they do her honor in the way she will accept."

"By eating them."

"Well, yes." The Mother's jaws were visible now. The sight of them opening was always awe-inspiring to Ingénue. It struck Chad silent, too. Together they watched the mouth open and open and open.

"You're the last," said Ingénue quietly.

"I know," Chad grunted, starting to thrash against his bonds with renewed vigor. "You said. Why am I the last?"

"Fifty was the agreement. I don't know ... nice round number? Forty wasn't enough, sixty too many? Let's chalk it up to mysterious ways." The Mother's head waved from side to side, closer and closer. Ingénue stepped into a corner to allow Her access. Chad stopped struggling. He just gazed up at the monster — Ingénue corrected herself — the divinity. "So I will be free now," she breathed, mostly to herself. "I can call myself Ruth or Sandra, I can date people who live longer than a few weeks. Maybe I could be a pharmacist. File taxes, lease that Nissan Sentra ..."

Chad's head snapped around. "I'm sorry ... I'm dying so you can have a mid-range sedan?"

Ingénue reached out and smoothed his hair absently. "Come on, don't be a baby about it. Don't you want me to be able to live my life to the fullest? Not be bound to the worship of a giant snake? Not that it wasn't an amazing experience I'll always treasure," she added hastily as the Serpentine Goddess's eyes flickered in her direction.

"I made you a necklace!" he shouted. He flipped from side to side like a beached fish, making one last effort to get loose. "My best piece of fordite! It'll look great on you!"

"That's a lovely gesture but ... I always thought your work looked just a *little bit* garish."

That ended his resistance. He crumpled.

"I don't want to die ..." Chad whimpered, his eyes fixed on the impossibly long, forked tongue. It seemed almost shy, tentative, as it caressingly explored his ankle.

"But I want to live," Ingénue replied. She turned away, ignoring the sounds behind her — she'd heard them all before — and began to climb the ladder to the trapdoor leading to the outside world, to her freedom. She left the embroidered robe behind, happy to abandon it. Upstairs, a powder blue tracksuit and Crocs awaited her.

If Chad had somehow survived to see her walk away, he would not have even recognized her.

ADAM-TROY CASTRO

THE GIRL IN THE REFRIGERATOR

MY GIRLFRIEND AMANDA SURPRISED me by installing a personal refrigerator in her abdomen. I didn't even know such a thing was possible. Amanda said, oh, sure, lots of people are getting them. It's the latest thing. Don't you remember Verna? I didn't remember meeting Verna. Amanda reminded me of a party we had been to. I remembered the party. She reminded me of a woman who had made a mortifying spectacle of herself there. I remembered that, too. But the girl who had made the mortifying spectacle of herself was not Verna, just somebody who had been standing next to Verna.

I never ever succeeded in remembering Verna, whom I know nothing about except that she had her own belly fridge before Amanda decided to get one for herself.

By that point Amanda and I had been a couple for nine months, living together for seven in a cramped little apartment we'd chosen only because it was acceptably close to the part of town worth being in. Beyond that, the place was classic micro-living. Its bathroom, a toilet and a sink and a tiny stall shower, was set off by a translucent sliding curtain instead of a proper wall. The clothes closet was not a closet but a rod stretching the length of one wall, that when laden with her hanging clothes and mine, filled up half of what we laughingly called our living room. The shelf above it, stretching the same length, was our pantry and our library and our storage space and our TV stand. On the opposite wall, our bed occupied a loft hanging low over her drafting table, but not low enough below the ceiling, and while acceptable for sleeping, was way too cramped for any but the most cautious sex, meaning that we had to cover the narrow patch of floor between clothes and loft with our comforter whenever we wanted to get frisky, which was pretty often. Even our kitchenette was barely large enough to qualify for the -ette suffix, to the point where we sometimes called it a kitchenette-ette, and made a habit of draping plastic over the pull-down ironing board in order to have a sufficient food preparation surface on those rare occasions when we did any but the simplest cooking at home.

To do anything in the space we had, we had to shift objects around to create empty space in whatever part of the apartment we wanted to occupy, an exercise in determined organization that would have descended into chaos if either of us ever operated out of synch with the other. We used to joke that every new couple should live this way, that if we hadn't killed each other yet, like rats in some crowding experiment, we were probably meant to be together for life; but the truth was that we were young and the glorified closet we lived in was much of the time not much more to us than a place to store our bodies while unconscious, in-between forays into a world that offered us more room to breathe. But there were tensions, in that there was never enough space to put anything, and bringing anything new into the house became a cause of serious protracted negotiation.

In that context, the belly fridge had major symbolic value, as far as commitment was concerned. Whoever she got to do it had done a superlative job, making room for the soft-sided, collapsible chamber inside her without any obvious physical deformation of her anatomy. Whenever the fridge door was closed, you couldn't even see a seam, let alone feel it (and I must admit I tried because there were plenty of reasons other than mechanical curiosity to run my hands over that flat, tanned midriff of hers). But a little depression of the switch hidden in her navel and that door swung open, revealing a sterile insulated space capable of maintaining a constant internal temperature of 37 degrees.

The space was unfortunately not large enough to accommodate a true abdominal six-pack that would have made the device a fervent exercise in the literal realization of a pun. There just wasn't enough room in Amanda, a svelte and elfin girl, for that to be possible without doing serious physiological damage. Her fridge was, however, large enough to store about half that much, in practice three aluminum cans or the equivalent in mini water bottles or sandwiches and snacks if we were up and about and didn't want to stop somewhere for provisions. And then it sealed up, becoming a secret compartment every bit as invisible as it had been when its existence was still unsuspected: a little additional personal space, inside her personal space.

I was appalled at first. I demanded to know the medical realities. She assured me that everything she'd had beneath the skin before was still there, if a little shifted about; and the side effects would be few, among them increased farting as the only possible way to get rid of the heat buildup. Someday, she said, when we moved to a bigger place, it could be removed without leaving a scar. But until then the extra storage space would come in handy. And until then it would serve as reminder that for us there would always be enough space.

I remained skeptical until later that night, after we'd gone out and walked the streets and listened to the music coming out of the clubs and stopped by the river and watched the lights across the water for a while and went back to where things were happening and run into some friends and talked with them for a while and come back to the space that belonged only to us. She hauled the comforter down from the loft and covered the floor with it and we made love in that tiny place between her work space and our closet space, her on top, warm as always, soft as always, the constant hum of her belly fridge somehow not at all distracting between the sounds I made and the sounds she made, even as the slyest possible look came over her face and she opened her belly long enough to touch the back of her coldest place and emerge with fingers that felt like ice against my chest. She closed the door and warmed what she had just cooled with her lips, and teased me with sly questions: do I feel cold to you, hmmm? What else do you want to keep in me, hmmm? Do you think you can keep me hot? Hmmm?

I had honestly never known myself to be the kind of man who makes love to a woman with a fridge in her belly. Up until this night I had never suspected that this was even one of my possible categories. But the climax, when it came, was historic, and as we lay together afterward I found myself aware that it was no small part to that extra added vibration inside her, that revved up to another speed as we neared the moment and the fan had to labor harder to keep the environment in the refrigerator at the same constant temperature. It was Amanda plus. And that night as we slept spooned, something we pretty much always had to do because of the tiny loft we shared, I lay awake aware of that constant whir inside her, the motor that was now as much a part of her as her heartbeat, or her breath, or the way she laughed.

I went crazy about Amanda within about five minutes of meeting her. She was funny, funky, unpredictable in most of the good ways and fortunately not in many of the bad ones. I was always a harder sell, not a turnoff but not an immediate starter either, and so her crazy trailed after my crazy by about two weeks, after which the two crazies sped up like comets and spiraled around one another like bi-planes. For a little while, until we realized we were doing serious damage to our respective wardrobes, we ripped the clothes off one another like lunatics. Then we calmed down, moved into this place, and buried ourselves in domesticity. Passion didn't ebb but it did become a harnessed force.

The addition of a fridge changed her in small endearing ways. She became a belly-shirt kind of girl, for one; long partial for black tops and distressed clothes worn in layers, even when it was so hot outside that it was impossible to understand how she remained cool under all of that, she now favored skimpier outfits that exposed skin and made access to the fridge convenient for both of us. Always outspoken, always uninhibited, she had also always nurtured a paradoxical shame over passing wind, blushing and stammering and apologizing over those occasions when she could not manage to flee somewhere out of earshot before letting fly; now that it happened about ten times as frequently as before she became almost arrogant about it, calling it the price for living with modern conveniences and explaining to total strangers that she had a fridge in her belly; see? She became less a girl who took care of snacks and soft drinks when she got to a place and more one who seized the opportunity to pull out a can of soda, raise an eyebrow, and say, with a little odorless poot, nothing like a good pop on a hot day. Once upon a time, she'd delivered hilarious riffs about the kind of people whose tattoos or piercings were the most interesting things about them. But she loved her fridge. She loved being the girl with the fridge in the girl.

We had access to a car we could borrow from time to time, and on balmy weekends liked to head out of the city to places where there were trails to hike and waterfalls to see. She packed her fridge in secret, and from time to time opened up to reveal whatever treats she had stored for us: grapes, wine, sometimes a little cake. When we didn't have the car we went to the park instead and she brought the treats that were many times more expensive if purchased on site; even more so when we went to the movies, and her belly proved the perfect way to avoid refreshment-stand prices (but only as long as we unscrewed the interior light bulb first because if we didn't the sudden glow had a way of alerting management). Other times, when we had to travel in sketchy neighborhoods, it proved useful in ways that had nothing to do with the storage of food and drink; it was a personal safe, keeping our valuables secure even as we pretended that we really did have nothing of value on us.

A few times we found ourselves in dark places without a flashlight and she opened up her door, revealing the light that always came on, to reveal what was now, by default, her most private place.

"I've always been bright," she said.

"You've always been cool," I replied.

We joked about the little man who lived inside her refrigerator, making sure the light turned on and off, and I affected great jealousy over his literally moving in on my girl, threatening to wring the little fucker's neck if he ever tried anything funny. We made up stories about him. I made Amanda laugh a good long time by bringing home a little fashion model doll and offering it to Amanda as a blind date for the refrigerator man. She slipped it into the fridge and much, much later, when I'd completely forgotten about it, produced the doll, its clothes ripped, its hair mussed, its feet missing one of its two detachable high-heel shoes. Amanda told me, "Look. The poor dear's been ravished."

For a long time we hauled down the comforter even more often than we had before, driven by the new ritual Amanda had come up with: the secret post-coital snack surprise, unveiled without the need of any special exodus to the more conventional mini-fridge only a few feet away. Sometimes she made me close my eyes so I didn't know what to expect, before feeding me whatever she'd been storing inside her: cherries, grapes, jello, a gooey éclair. A couple of times it turned out to be champagne or soda so agitated by our lovemaking that it erupted on opening: a mock orgasm in and of itself, that somehow seemed a crucial part of the joke.

Then, one night about four months into her life with a belly fridge, Amanda asked me when I was going to get one.

We were streaming some zombie film on the tube when she popped the question with the too-casual air of someone who'd been hoarding it for far too long. I didn't have enough context to understand what she was asking and for several seconds wondered why she was asking me if I'd be willing to get a zombie.

"No," she said, punching me in the arm. "A fridge. Or something. Make your own contribution."

I confessed that I hadn't even thought about it, not even a little bit. I had never wanted to carry a little fridge around in my belly.

She said, "Well, something else, then."

I asked her, "Like what?"

She said, "Forget it."

It was the kind of "forget it" that women utter only in arguments like this one, where the man has given some kind of irredeemable offense and the only offense even worse than that is his failure to understand what it was.

"No," I said, "tell me, seriously."

She said, "You haven't even thought about it at all up until now?"

I had to admit I hadn't. The fridge had struck me as a weird, sweet, little eccentric gesture, something that added a little welcome strangeness to lives that could always use a little welcomed strangeness, but it had never occurred to me, even for a moment, to consider it the kind of romantic gesture that needed to be reciprocated. It certainly hadn't struck me as the kind of thing that she might have been waiting for: something that had turned my silence on the subject into an exercise in unmet expectations. But the look on her face revealed that this had also been the wrong thing to say, and so I backpedaled and said, "But we can go to wherever you went, tomorrow, and see what else they have available, okay?"

She sniffed. "Don't do me any favors."

I said, "Come on, Amanda. I'm trying here."

She looked away, but by now I could tell she was in the phase of the argument where she was actively trying to remain mad. She'd already gotten the concession. It was victory.

The zombie movie ended. It was a warm night so we opened the window and went out to the fire escape, and from there to the rooftop opposite our narrow alley, where we sometimes went if we didn't want to go anywhere else, but where we didn't go too often because we could reach it only if we braced ourselves on the railing and then took a giant step over a gap that promised a truly fucked future if we ever slipped and fell. It was just a roof and it was better than our own, where we went rarely, only because it had one side that offered an almost unobstructed view of a neighborhood we liked; not much of a reason to court crippling injury. But tonight we bridged the abyss and crossed the pigeon-crap minefield to the overlook, and stood there for long minutes enjoying the breeze and the lights and the quiet that comes after a tiff.

She asked me if I was thirsty.

I said I was.

She opened her belly and pulled out a bottle of my favorite hard cider, so hard to find locally that we greeted the discovery of any store that carried it an occasion for genuine celebration.

I took it and said, "What about you?"

She said she wasn't thirsty.

"Are you sure? Because I can go back downstairs and get you something."

She said, "If you had a belly fridge, you wouldn't have to."

I tried to think of an acceptable reply.

She said, "I'll take a slug of yours," and guzzled a third of the bottle. At my momentarily aghast expression, she grinned and bumped her hip against mine. We drew close and watched the lights for a while, saying nothing, the silence between us growing relaxed as the blowup was rescheduled.

Life did what life does and intruded. I had two double shifts at the steak house and she had to hit her drafting table to complete an illustration by deadline. The argument faded into the background and we talked about other things, heading downtown on the third night to be with friends, including the friend of a friend who had had a church key imbedded on one palm and a can opener imbedded on the other. Everybody complimented him. I said it must make jerking off difficult. He said, yeah, I get that a lot. The conversational possibilities of this were now exhausted, but then some latecomers joined us and the guy ended up showing off his church key and can opener a second time. Then an hour later some new folks came around and he brought them up to date with iteration number three. I noted out loud that the chief drawback of imbedded equipment like that seemed to be the necessity of explaining it. Folks who just carried a church key on their key ring didn't have to point it out to everybody who passed within earshot. The guy grinned and said, really.

Later, as we made our way home, Amanda said, "Why do you have to be like that?"

I said, "Be like what?"

"The way you were with whatshisname."

"He didn't seem to mind it."

"He said he gets that a lot. Which isn't the same thing."

"What do you expect me to say? That I'm impressed? Because I wasn't. It was one of the fucking lamest things I've ever seen."

She said, "Like my fridge."

"That's different."

"How?"

"Well, in the first place, it's different because I love you. I loved you before you had your fridge, and I had a lot of things to love about you before you had your fridge. I want to be with you because I already see you as a lot more than a fridge with legs. This schmuck, whose name I notice you can't remember either, I know absolutely nothing about except that he once thought it vitally important that for as long as he lived he'd never again have any trouble opening cans of baked beans. It's one stupid trick and it's lame. Why would I be impressed?"

We walked in silence for a while, and I was just foolish enough to think I'd won the argument. She had time to pass wind twice.

Then she asked me, "Do you think my fridge is lame?"

I said, "I think your fridge is great, but it's not the part of you I care about most, no."

"I got it for us."

"I know, I appreciate that. I thought it was sweet as hell. But even so, we don't live in the goddamned Taj Mahal. I'm never more than three steps from the mini-fridge the place came with. I can walk those three steps. It's not something our entire relationship needs to rest on, you know? Seriously, what are we even talking about?"

We walked a little further. It was a clear night in the middle of summer, but a cold front had rolled in and in just a few minutes the temperature had lowered from cool and comfortable to cool and not quite warm enough for the way we were dressed; a blast of air we didn't expect hit us as we emerged from the wind-break of some storefronts to the open space of the busiest intersection between us and home. It wasn't freezing or anything, but it made home and bed someplace I wanted to get sooner rather than later. The lights were with us but turning, so we had to hurry across the street in order to make it before traffic cut us off, and what with one thing or another we were halfway to the next intersection before Amanda said, "You don't really want to get one for yourself, do you?"

I wanted to snap no. Instead I told her I would go with her to whoever did hers as soon as we could make our way there and see the possibilities. Just no can openers. They were stupid.

She said okay.

We got home. It wasn't all that late but we were tired and stressed out and not in the mood for anything more than going to bed. The comforter didn't get hauled down. I got undressed and climbed up into the loft, scooting all the way against the wall so she'd have room to join me when she got around to following. She said she wasn't quite ready for bed yet and would work a little at her table before coming in after me. The lamp came on, and the glow spilled upward from around the edges of the loft, like the first rays of a sunrise making itself known before it gets around to rising in the east. I wanted to call her up and say all the important things, among them that I didn't like the way our grip on one another seemed to be loosening, all of a sudden. But I didn't. Instead I just curled up in the shadow of her light and listened to the scratching of her pencil against the cardstock. I closed my eyes, fell asleep, dreamed, and much later, woke again, to that same occluded light and the same sound of Amanda, still working, near me but not anywhere I could see.

We went to the same guy who installed her fridge, whose establishment was two flights of stairs above a night club we'd visited once and despised, for more reasons than I need to get into because we hadn't been there since. The stairs began at the vestibule to the club and rose past the ambience we'd hated to another floor I found not much of an improvement: a narrow hallway illuminated by one wedge of light at the far end.

The first thing we saw when we entered the parlor was a woman with raccoon eyes lying naked on a bench while a man fried link sausages on her bare belly. The heated portion of her anatomy was marked by a glowing red circle and the flashing letters WARNING: STOVE IS HOT. Her boyfriend or product tester or whatever the hell he was turned the links with a spatula, to ensure even cooking. Her hot spot was so shiny from the sausages that I couldn't help wondering why her boyfriend or whatever didn't use a frying pan, but that would have been too stupid a question to ask out loud. Nothing stopped him from using a frying pan. Cooking on her bare skin was the whole point.

Amanda asked her if it hurt.

The woman said, "Naaah, it's all insulated."

I said, "Yeah, but what about grease spatter? I get spot burns all the time just standing at a hot stove."

She gave me the kind of look reserved for people who crap their pants on purpose. "Naaah," she said, "we thought of that." She pressed the lit end of her cigarette against her right nipple, to no ill effect, and explained: "See? I'm insulated all over." Then she went back to studying the ceiling with the bored patience of a home inspector looking for roof leaks.

The curtains in the back of the room parted and the proprietor came out, looking about what I'd expected him to look like, best described as a guy once caught in a shrapnel explosion who had decided he liked his face with all the little metal bits still stuck in his skin wherever they hit. He would have been bald, I guess, but he'd also implanted silver fiber optic hair glowing pink at the tips. He said yo to Amanda and she said yo to him and he asked her how her fridge was working and she said it was great and he looked at me and said, "So what are you in the market for?"

I said I wasn't in the market for anything in particular but was willing to hear suggestions. So we went into the back to talk about the possibilities and I got my education in just how far the tech had come. Nothing really grabbed me. I didn't want to turn my butt cheeks into a microwave or my dick into a power-vac or my kidney into a blender because none of that had ever intersected with my fantasies in any way. But this had become some kind of weird relationship power struggle I didn't understand and I knew that if I backed down now the sudden strange friction between Amanda and me would certainly escalate. So I gave an unenthusiastic yes to the toaster oven. Amanda interjected that a pop-up toaster would be even cooler, but I thought a couple of parallel slit orifices in my abdomen would be a bit much. A toaster oven that could be hidden under flesh like Amanda's fridge, something that I could pretend wasn't there most of the time, that would be fine. So I said, naaah, make it the toaster oven. We can do a lot more than just make toast with a toaster oven.

He said, "That takes a few hours to install. We'll have to make an appointment for that one." Consulting his ledger, he said, "Noon Saturday okay?"

I said fine. Any number of things could happen between now and Saturday.

But I wasn't going to get out of there that easily. Amanda grew petulant and asked him if there was something small I could do today so I didn't go away empty-handed.

"Oh, sure," said the guy.

And so, over the next twenty minutes, he put in my reading lamp.

The procedure wasn't very invasive, nothing compared to what Amanda had put herself through. It was just a thin light-emitting strip imbedded in my chin, just beneath the skin. You couldn't see it when it was off. But if I needed the lamp, I could click the activator with my tongue and the light would come on. The light was faint with the same reddish tint you get when you try to cover a flashlight through your hand, but it was bright enough to read by, and a likely life-saver in situations where it was dark and I was having trouble fitting a key into a lock. I supposed it was not a bad thing to have. Amanda told me it was beautiful and asked me if I liked it. I didn't tell her that when I went to the bathroom, turned off the lights, and flicked my chin light on to see what it looked like in the mirror, I was a little disturbed by the spooky effect the blood-tinged lighting from below had on my face, what with the streaks of scarlet along my jaw and cheekbones making me look like I'd just been face-down in viscera. It would be useful on Halloween, I supposed. But I left the bathroom with a smile on my face and told Amanda it was great.

We stayed out late and returned home to a dark apartment, where we had some of the best sex in our shared history. Amanda pulled down the comforter and said, let's fuck with the light on. I said why not. So we turned off all other ambient sources of light, even pulling down the blackout shade so we couldn't get any neon or moonlight or light sources opposing apartment windows filtering in on us from the alley. I turned on my chin and she said oooh, look at him, and I said whatever stupid rejoinder came to mind and we got into it, missionary style, our proximity caging the red brilliance between us and making tiny scarlet flames dance in her eyes. We finished up, I rolled off and she immediately climbed on, insatiable, saying that this time she wanted the spotlight. With her energetic help I recovered faster than I ever had and we went a second time, slower, her riding me, lit from below, my chin casting a distorted but still recognizable silhouette of her on the ceiling.

Afterward, she rolled off and we lay side by side, facing the pink tint of the ceiling. The spotlight may have been dimmer, at that remove, than it had been within coital range, but I saw no reason to turn my chin off. It wasn't a bad afterglow to have.

I said, "Whoo."

"Yeah," she said. "Whoo."

"Got a snack?"

"You're gonna have to go to the kitchen. I'm not stocked."

"Really?"

"Of course really. It's not automatic, you know. There's not always going to be something there. I have to put something in, in order to have something to take out."

"I'm just saying. You usually."

"Well today, I forgot. It's no big deal."

"Okay, okay."

I got up and went to the kitchenette-ette, popping open the fridge and finding only one half-consumed bottle of water there. It was that or crap from the tap. Our building had tinny crap from the tap. So I took the water bottle and brought it back to the comforter and took a sip, handing the rest of the bottle to Amanda.

I said, "Did you like it with the light?"

She drained the bottle. "What do you think?"

"I think it was great."

"Me too. Never better."

"I love you."

"Me, too."

But hers sounded no better than polite.

It had been as good as we ever got but as soon as it was over everything that had been bothering her had bubbled back to the surface, as if to prove that we hadn't been able to drown it. "What's wrong?"

"Nothing."

Again, daring me to figure it out.

This was not the best time for me to say one of those stupid boyfriend things that comes out of a man's mouth already feeling like a mistake and enters the room with all the grace of a three-year-old running naked into a fancy dinner party and shouting, "doodie!" Even as I heard myself speak my next words, I wanted to reach after them with both hands, yank them out of the air, and stuff them back down my throat.

I said, "I seriously don't think it would have been all that better if I'd been able to make you some toast now."

The way her eyes turned toward me, right then, should have provided me with sufficient warning to shut up.

She said, "What?"

"I'm just saying. I know you're disappointed I didn't get my toaster oven today. But it wouldn't have made that much of a difference, right? I mean, you can't tell me that the number one thing on your mind right now is toast."

"You never know. Maybe I used up so many carbs getting you off twice I want to pound down half a loaf of cinnamon raisin right now."

"I'm just saying."

"You sure expected your stupid snack."

I blew up. "Damn straight I expected the snack. I don't need the snack, I don't require the snack, I don't get mad at you when you don't have the snack, but for God's sake I saw nothing wrong in asking for the snack because every time we've made love since you got that damned fridge you've always offered me a snack. You trained me to expect it, so I asked. It's Pavlovian."

"You're right. You're absolutely right. I shouldn't ever offer you a beer unless I intend to always have a beer ready. In fact, while I'm at it I'll have to flatten the top of my head so you'll always have a place to put it down."

Having this hoary chestnut of arrogant prick humor shoved in my face didn't do anything but piss me off. "You'd make a terrible coffee table."

"Why?

"You're too goddamned tall."

It would have been hard to say, in the next four seconds, whether it was her eyes or her mouth that described the best circles. Either way, I knew that I had taken it one step too far. She got up and drew aside the hanging curtain that separated the bathroom from the rest of the room, pulling it back into place behind her. In our apartment this was the equivalent of a slammed door, sealing her behind what the unspoken rules of etiquette in our relationship dictated that I respect as solid walls. It was stupid, but it wasn't a fiction I felt like shattering right now, so I grumbled and muttered to myself and gathered up the comforter to return it to its non-coital location on the loft. Meanwhile, she started running the shower: another layer of separation.

I turned on the apartment lights so I could switch off my chin.

We cancelled the Saturday appointment. I volunteered for extra shifts so I wouldn't have to go home. When I did get home she was either absent or already asleep. When she was home she was so sullen I made no overtures. We spoke only to negotiate the minutiae of apartment living, confirming whether or not the garbage had indeed been taken out, the front door indeed locked. I ate out or brought food in from outside to spare myself the uncomfortable prospect of taking anything from the fridge in the kitchenette-ette, a wholly innocent use of an appliance that, in context, suddenly seemed like further provocation. When I found her awake and working, I climbed to the loft first and put her in the position of deciding whether or not to climb in after me. When I found her already up there, I hauled out our extra comforter and slept on the floor instead.

For at least four nights the question seemed not if we were going to break up but when.

That surprisingly didn't happen. The chill thawed, but not because of any grudging apologies, rather because maintaining a fight on that scale requires a lot of conscious effort and neither one of us was up to it. Sooner or later, one of us forgot we were supposed to be fighting and said something civil. The other forgot to reject it. Then the other one said something affable and again received no angry retaliation. From there it moved on to friendly and from there to affectionate. We exchanged smiles. We did little favors for one another. Eventually, we kissed again; not long after that, we made love again, me not using my reading lamp, her not offering me another treat from her fridge, our respective modifications becoming attributes unused and un-remarked, baggage that neither one of us wanted to bring up. The big question was now not whether we'd always have the remaining tension between us but how and when it would manifest again.

Then one night we went to a party to catch up with friends, and found that a large number of them had new appliances to show off. One guy had turned his arm into a scrolling message board and for the better part of an hour took suggestions over what text to program into it, an exercise that inevitably grew dull as it devolved into a competition over who could come up with the most offensive suggestions. One woman dispensed frozen daiquiris from her nipples, strawberry from the left and coconut from the right. Somebody we didn't know, who might have been kidding, offered to cook waffles on his butt. It came around to Amanda and me, and requests for her to show off her fridge and me to show off my reading lamp. Amanda said she wasn't dressed for it, and I noticed for the first time that she hadn't dressed in one of her midriff-baring outfits for easy access. I said that my lamp was on the fritz and that I wouldn't be able to turn it on again until I went in for repairs.

Then another couple we knew said that they had the best modifications ever. He rolled up his shirt and pulled out a baby bottle, kept warm by body heat. She rolled up hers and revealed something she'd gotten to go along with the beginnings of a baby bump: a belly pouch, to carry the little one around after in infancy. "I'm a marsupial," she beamed. The crowd showered them with congratulations.

Not long afterward Amanda whispered in my ear that she had to get the hell out of there before she exploded. We made our excuses and left.

It was a cool but comfortable weekend night and so we drifted in the direction of the river. The sidewalks teemed with happy and laughing people. We walked in silence among them, pausing here and there to look in a shop window or to make way for larger groups. We stopped for a long time at a bridge overlooking the water, watching the party boats go by and saying nothing of any real consequence until Amanda said, "It's really all pretty much ridiculously beside the point, isn't it?"

I exhaled in relief. "Yeah. It is. It really, really is."

We kissed, earning a light cheer from tourists in a sightseeing boat, just before they disappeared under the bridge. I told her I loved her and she said she loved me and we kissed again, this time not earning a cheer because the boat had passed and there were no others in range.

She rested her forehead on mine. "I almost had it removed the other day. The fridge, I mean."

"I never wanted you to do that."

"I know. But I almost did. I passed by the shop and considered dropping in to make arrangements. But then I thought, why should I? It's not hurting anything where it is. I can still make good use of it, sometimes. It just doesn't have to be the center of anything. That makes sense, right?"

"Perfect sense. But while we're on the subject, I passed by the shop, too."

"Oh, no. Don't tell me you got the toaster oven!"

"I've got to admit, it was a near thing. I wanted to do something, to get past whatever the hell's been going on with us. But the more I thought about it, the stupider it seemed. Nobody needs that much goddamned toast in his life. And I knew I didn't want to carry around the same thing we were fighting about. But while I was there I did stop in and confirm that there was something else I could get installed, something a lot simpler and more important than a toaster, that I could save for a rainy day."

"What?"

"I don't have it yet. Like I said, it was just something I considered. But I think I'll surprise you with it someday soon."

"You're such a tease."

"The worst," I confirmed.

We kissed again and went downstairs to the river level site of a gourmet coffee shoppe we frequented a lot less than we would have liked. She saved one of the waterfront tables and I went to the counter, returning a few minutes later with lattes and a pair of the establishment's jumbo cupcakes, the kind of snack that could make a starving person fat just by looking at it.

Amanda had never been a calorie-counter. She'd never needed to be. But the party we'd left had already included a buffet with a selection of comfort foods and desserts that neither one of us had denied ourselves. So she regarded the unexpected treat, a pink monstrosity that all by itself probably met a full week's minimum required carb count, with a palpable mixture of longing and dismay, her mind racing through the hundred and one mental negotiations that would permit her to allow the additional indulgence. After a minute or so, the inner treaty with her conscience was both signed and notarized. "We can split one. I'll store the other away for another night."

I shook my head and took her by the wrist before she could pull up her shirt.

To her round and startled eyes I said, "Please, not the fridge. This one I'd like to be for right now."

Her smile was blinding. "Okay."

So she inhaled half of it in one bite, getting the required amount of pink cream on her nose.

DELILAH S. DAWSON

THE FIRST BLOOD OF POPPY DUPREE

ON THE MORNING THAT Poppy Dupree crawls out of bed covered in blood, her mother makes pancakes to celebrate. The real kind — not the usual microwave crap. Poppy can smell them before she walks into the kitchen, her socks silent on the faded linoleum. Her mother's cigarette-yellow smile is both knowing and pitying.

"So how was it, honey?"

With a groan, Poppy sits, pushing just-washed hair out of her face with fingernails still mooned with the deep, black soil of the forest. Three places are set at the table, although only two people live in the house. On the plate reserved for the dead father she's never met sits the decapitated head of a red fox, the tongue lolling out onto the cracked porcelain.

Poppy thinks for a moment, flicks the fox's ear. "Hurts more than I thought it would."

Her mother slides a lopsided pancake onto Poppy's plate and fetches a chipped mug full of hot syrup mixed with melted butter. When Poppy pours it over her pancake, it spreads out in perfect imitation of the wet, red puddle by last night's bonfire.

"I still remember my first time." Her mother carries over two jelly jars of milk, pulls her own chair back with a squeak, and sits. They look so alike, with the same bear-brown eyes and dark curls, but Poppy is still all elbows and legs while her mother looks like a bunch of old couch cushions strapped together, cushy and sunken in at the same time.

"What was it like?"

"It was a hell of a surprise."

They both laugh and look down quickly, as if the fox might disapprove.

"Your grandmother never told me what to expect. I'd heard the other girls whisper, but nice girls didn't talk about that sort of thing, back then. That's why I told you, way ahead of time." Poppy's mother chews, swallows, and keeps on talking, a ring of cheap red lipstick sliding around her mouth. "I felt normal when I went to sleep that night. A little bitchy maybe." She raises an eyebrow at Poppy, and since Poppy can't raise one eyebrow, she shrugs and rolls her eyes. "And then I had weird dreams and woke up covered in blood." She rubs Poppy's shoulder, and Poppy flinches. "Just like you, honey."

Poppy doesn't stop chewing as she nudges the fox head with an elbow. "What was your first ... you know?"

"Don't laugh."

Another shrug from Poppy.

"A goat. Guess I stopped at a neighbor's farm for some fast food. Woke up with a horn in my armpit."

"What was Grandma's first one?"

Her mother shakes her head, stabs her pancake like she wishes it was the old bat's kidney.

"Your uppity, know-it-all grandma says she brought home a big-ass stag. Oodles of antlers."

"Figures."

They eat in companionable silence, and Poppy's pancake is gone too soon. She's ravenously hungry despite the fact that her stomach's clinched hard enough to make her teeth grind. It's a different kind of pain than she's experienced before — cramps. Her mom left the supplies she needed on the bathroom counter this morning: a pink box of pads and a bottle of ibuprofen. She must've noticed the rusty footprints and twigs trailing from the back door to Poppy's room. It's a weird, messy feeling — constantly leaking blood. Poppy squirms in her chair, waiting for the pain and squishiness to go away as she watches her mother spear another floppy pancake and flip it onto her plate.

"Why weren't you there? Jessie's mom was there."

Her mom smirks. "Jessie's mama ain't Jessie's mama." When Poppy just stares, her mother sighs and sets down her fork. "Jessie's adopted, and her mama can't make babies. It starts when it starts, but it ends when you get pregnant or quit your cycles. When you're done being a maiden, as they say."

"Not when you ..."

"Give it up?" Her mother laughs, a shockingly bawdy sound that makes Poppy even more uncomfortable. "Sugarfoot, this is small town South Carolina, and it don't change much. There's nothing to do here on Saturday night but get drunk and find a quiet spot to make out in your boyfriend's truck. If losing your virginity was what ended it, this whole county would go to hell."

Poppy tries to resettle her bottom on the hard chair, but she can't get comfortable. The pain, the physical discomfort, the creepiness of discussing her newly arrived womanhood with her mother, and the dead black eyes of the fox all combine to make her breakfast feel like less of a celebration and more like a case of the flu. She's been waiting for this to happen, but she thought she would wake up with some sort of magical knowledge, that she would feel and look different, maybe suddenly be a few inches taller or have bigger boobs. But she's the same old country girl in the same old Walmart jeans with the same old dark brown eyes and the same old quiet sullenness. And there are things her mother still hasn't told her.

"There was a boy there," Poppy says to her pancake.

Her mother perks up, the fork dropping from her hand with a clank.

"Who was it?"

Poppy closes her eyes and tries to remember, sinking back into the dream.

She sees firelight and starglow and dark green and moonbeams and wet red and foxes screaming and girls laughing and old clay bottles of sweet red wine and bare feet dancing through the smoke. On the other side of the fire, always on the other side no matter how much they dance, there's a shadow man sitting in a throne that sometimes looks like a camp chair and sometimes like a majestic sculpture of antlers and leg bones twined with vines. The skin of a fawn flaps around her thighs, the inside wet and sticky from when the other girls ripped it off the still-warm creature, welcoming her with hugs and bloody hands. She feels sorry for the deer for just a second, but when the shadow man begins playing the pipes, the regrets curl away like smoke.

There are dozens of women gathered around the fire, from a few other girls in Poppy's grade to older girls to Jessie's adopted mom to the mousy lady who works at the post office. It's not a big town, and Poppy knows everyone. They're all dressed in fawn skins, barefoot, with hair down, digging their hands into the dirt as if looking for buried treasure. Jessie herself isn't there, which tells Poppy something she's been dying to ask about her friend's weird, week-long case of the stomach flu last year. That trip to the specialist must have been to the free clinic. It would have been good, to hold hands with Jessie and dance, but the women there feel like family, like sisters, and she's happy enough to be among them.

Unfamiliar, unnatural shadows burst into the clearing, and the women stop dancing around the flames. It's an older girl in a sundress and sandals, dragging behind her a good-looking boy in a letterman's jacket. He's slightly out of breath and reluctant to approach the fire, probably because it's surrounded by half-naked, mad-giggling women wearing garlands of ivy and necklaces of garter snakes over moonlit skin splattered with fawn spots and gore.

"Becky, come on. I'm not into this. Let's go back," the boy says.

The senior girl with the long blonde hair and perfect dress is popular and beautiful, and Poppy has never spoken to her, never dreamed of being near her. Becky isn't one of them — the wild women in the fawn skins — but Poppy can feel that she was once, that she knew exactly what she was doing, bringing this boy to their circle.

"Too late, Wade." Becky flashes her trademark smile, which is so sweet they made up a yearbook category for it. Her lips go just a little too wide, betraying the still-sharp teeth within.

The night goes still, ice-cold. Puffs of breath rise as they wait.

"He is a rapist. He enjoys hurting women." The voice from across the fire is ancient, old, deep, and brooks no refusal. "Destroy him."

The boy tries to pull away, but Becky's hand on his wrist might as well be carved of wood. The other girls surround him, and Poppy presses close enough to smell with faraway longing his drugstore cologne mixed with the iron tang of fear. As one, the girls tear their nails into him, rending flesh from bone. Becky backs away slowly and disappears into the night as Jessie's mom pops the boy's head off like it's a beer cap. Poppy bares her teeth as her fingernails dig deep; it's like deboning a raw chicken. His jacket flies into the fire to snap and crackle with the scent of burned flesh. He didn't even have time to scream.

Poppy gently lays the fork across her plate and meets her mom's eyes. "It was Wade Castleberry."

Her mother nods, thinking.

"Football team?"

"Linebacker." She says it too fast and immediately knows she's been caught out. She blushes. "Or something. I don't know. Doesn't matter now."

"Doesn't happen often, but it happens enough." Her mother's face is sympathetic and yet hard as stone, the same face she wore when their cat had to be put to sleep for drinking antifreeze. "It *has* to happen."

"But won't the police ... I don't know. Investigate?"

A chuckle. "You go back up the mountain today. Ride Maisy, if your feet are too sore to walk it again. See if you can find a single shred of evidence. Look for the fire. Look for the wine bottles. Look for the bones and the blood-soaked dirt." Mama nods knowingly. "You won't find nothing."

"But how do I know it's true? That Wade really did ... what they said?"

Her mother's dark eyes go far away as her voice goes soft and loses its country twang. "Gods don't lie. They don't need to. The ones who are brought to the fire are a danger to society, to women especially. The rapists. The wife beaters. The baby shakers. It doesn't happen every month. But when it does, it makes the world a better place. It makes our town a safer place. The police can't help until the crime's committed, until it's too late, and even then, they'll cover it up if they can. They won't believe a beat woman until she's dead. But the old gods know. They remember."

Poppy doubles over as another cramp rips across her stomach like claws sunk in her innards. She feels too hot, and she thinks she might be hung over for the first time, and she knows she's in too much pain to saddle the old mare and take her mother up on her dare. The pancakes threaten to come back up, and she drinks the rest of her now-warm milk, tasting honey and dirt from last night. There's this deep down certainty in her chest, an understanding that this is how things are, and this is how they've always been. She's just another tool fit to a masculine hand, to be held and discarded by gods and men, as women are doomed to be. Just another weapon. She can't get away from it, and she can't get out from under it, and no matter what she does or how much she wishes things were different, that invisible fist has her guts in its grip and is going to crush her from the inside out until there's nothing left.

All Poppy has ever wanted is to get the hell out of Cadmus, South Carolina, for good.

"Why, Mama? Why us?"

Her mother sits back, one hand unconsciously on her now-soft belly.

"A long time ago in Greece, the god Dionysus came down to Earth. He went to the city of Thebes, where he was born, and nobody knew who he was, even though he was the god of wine. The people wouldn't worship him, and that made him angry, so he drove their women crazy. They started ripping everything apart, including the king. All because he wouldn't say boo to a goat for Dionysus."

"This ain't Greece. And nobody worships Dionysus."

Leaning close, her mother lifts a long, wet black curl from Poppy's shoulder. "You ever seen a real Greek? You'd fit right in. This whole damn town's descended from the Greeks. Straight from Thebes. I know most of our neighbors act like your usual redneck assholes, but when our ancestors came, they brought their gods with 'em. Old Dionysus likes being worshipped, and about all this town knows how to do is drink and screw, which suits him fine. Lucky for us, he stopped tearing people up just for being ignorant. Now he's a god of vengeance."

"So?"

"So we got our curse, just like every small town. Some places have a ghost or a famous Civil War general or a pedophile mayor. But here in Cadmus, we got low crime rates and the safest, happiest, prettiest little city you ever seen. Only difference is that our girls get real bad PMS."

"And kill people?"

Poppy waits, watching her mom carefully, feeling judged by the fox head for asking what she knows is an obvious question.

"Only if they deserve it. Real justice is hard to come by. One day, you'll be grateful."

Poppy stands so violently that her chair clatters to the ground behind her. She feels a rush of blood and clinches her knees together. Her fingers are splayed on the kitchen table, and she wishes like hell she had scrubbed under her damned nails instead of leaving the dirt and blood there to mock her like smug smiles.

"Grateful? For this?" She points at the fox head, accidentally knocking it over with a sick thump. "I'm a vegetarian. I never drank before. I don't want to be like you and the other dumbass, go-nowhere, didn't-get-a-GED girls in this shithole town. I want to get out. I don't want to be a ..."

"Maenad?"

"A goddamn murderer!"

"You're not a murderer, honey. You're a hero."

"Heroes don't kill people!"

"You're doing a god's business. A public service. Did you feel like you had any choice?"

Poppy remembers again the shadow across the fire, the voice commanding her. The glee she felt, giving herself up to the madness.

"No one in this town ever has any choices, Mama."

She rights her chair and sits back down, mainly so she'll quit gushing blood.

"We stay here because it's home, Poppy. Because we're tied to the god and the god is tied to the land. Because he takes care of us, and we take care of the bad guys. You go somewhere else, you don't know where you'll end up on that day of the month. But I guarantee you'll miss it. They call it ecstasy, that feeling, when you give yourself up to Dionysus, and he uses you."

Ecstasy. Yes, Poppy remembers it. It's like flying, like dreaming, like having a fever but loving it. Maybe she was drunk on the wine, or maybe it was the god. She hates loving it, but she loved it still.

"Is it always this messy?" She's practically begging now, and she hates that, too.

"Only on the first day. After that, it's easier. Less blood, less pain. But if you need to skip school, Nurse Betty will understand."

"Her, too?"

"All of us. Every girl born here."

For just a moment, her blowsy mama doesn't look like a middle-aged single mother who works at the Dollar General and eats too many Little Debbies. She looks like a statue, like some timeless maternal goddess with dark eyes full of starlight and destiny and knowledge. For just a moment, Poppy sees the wild woman she once was, the girl dancing in the fawn skin one night a month as the god behind the fire played his pipes. And then the moment ends, and she gets up for another pancake and spills syrup on her Snoopy sweatshirt, and she's just a mother again.

While her mama's back is turned, Poppy finds the strength to ask the question that's been on her mind ever since she woke up with Wade Castleberry's blood in her eyelashes.

"Did Dad know?"

Her mother turns around, leans back against the counter.

"Only at the last moment," she says softly, one hand to her cheek. "When I pulled him toward the fire."

Sara M. Harvey

RED LIGHT

IT'S AN OCCUPATION AS old as time, lingering in the dark corners of all of human history.

For me, it is more than a job, it fills a need, it satisfies my hunger. Hunger is the nearest analogy that a creature like me can make. I am far past physical hunger, mortal hunger, but I require sustenance. And so, I hunt.

I am very good at what I do, both the hunting and the fulfilling. Too good, usually. I have to be careful, I have to move around. Someone always catches on that there's something different about me. And it scares them.

Lots of times it's the other girls, they get jealous, they get paranoid that I'm taking their customers. So they call raids on me, or get their pimps to do it. The pimps don't like me, either. I make it clear that I've got no need for them or what they do. They don't like that, they think I'm going to upset their precious system, make the girls uppity so they won't do as they're told, won't pay them their due. They think that I'll set a bad example and they will lose control.

And I do.

So they come after me, but they regret it. Each and every time.

And no one cries when a pimp goes missing, I'm just saying.

But that's not why I'm there. And after a while, too much attention, of any sort, good or bad, makes it difficult for me. It makes it hard to work. Because once the other pros know I'm different, it isn't long before the johns do, too. And that disrupts everything. I can't have them knowing what I am. At least, not ahead of time. It changes the dynamic, taints the experience.

And for what I am and what I do the experience is *everything*.

So, I move around a lot.

I used to work in a brothel. I've worked in a few, over the length of years that I have been at this. Most recently, it was a nice one, near Vegas. It's a decent living, really. But I only saw the same type of men, night after night. I have very specific requirements that they rarely ever met. I have come to realize that I work best on my own, faring much better being the active hunter rather than lying in wait. Setting the perfect trap is its own kind of gratification, but I rarely snared the quarry I needed.

I like to slink between upper class neighborhoods and poor ones. I thrive on variety. I go where I will find what I need, what satisfies me and fills, however briefly, the great emptiness within. It might take me weeks to find just the right person, or sometimes I'll encounter two or three in a single night. It can be unpredictable at times, although I try to stick to territories with plenty of game. Cities are the best, they have vast networks of business operations on the downlow and offer me ample ways to blend in, to hide. They are busy places, always changing, making it easier to snag my marks from those ever-churning currents and not draw a lot of attention to myself. There is a time and place for drawing attention and before I have what I want in my grip is not it.

My appetite is keen, nearly desperate, by the time I step out tonight. The numbers are dwindling here. I can't take the same provender more than once. But there's one I've been waiting for, saving for the very last. Like dessert.

I've been trailing him discreetly, carefully, since I first arrived; keeping him in the back of my mind even as I took others. It's difficult to put my finger on exactly why I fixate on him like I do, but deep within, I know he's perfect; the cues are subtle, even subconscious. Hunters always know. He seems the type to scare easy. He's proven elusive and difficult to catch. Those always give me the greatest thrill, whetting my appetite with anticipation, desire drawn out and longing.

I have to get myself under control. If I'm too piqued, I'm going to ruin this carefully crafted game of cat-and-mouse I'm playing. It's tempting to say "we," the carefully crafted game of cat-and-mouse *we're* playing, but he doesn't know it yet. He will, and soon, but not yet.

I'm trawling the edge of downtown, waiting for the stayed-too-late-at-the-office types to finally decide to leave work. It helps to look nice. These are executives, they don't want fishnets and trashy cheap lipstick.

No, tonight I have to look legit enough to tell the cops that I'm on my way somewhere — home from work, meeting up for a girls' night out, bachelorette party, whatever — in case I get hassled. And really, the cops always know. But they don't want to deal with the paperwork and no one likes to have that particular crime statistic attached to their beat, so as long as I'm not causing any trouble, they leave me alone.

I've been at this a long time.

I am very good at what I do.

I wait in the deep shadow of the building's edge; with high-rises all around, the street exists in an eternal twilight, day or night. Just the way I like it. I do love big cities, very much.

I see the guy and my excitement surges. That still catches me by surprise, after all this time, how sharp is my response. Especially for one that I've been watching and following. The moment before I pounce never gets old, never gets any less titillating. I am practically drooling in anticipation. But delayed gratification is always the best, so I won't rush this.

He steps out of the building and I know he's looking for me. He thinks he's just looking for someone *like* me, but really, he is looking for me, personally. My subtle clues, casual contact, intercepting his life at seemingly random intervals have caught him as surely as if I had baited a hook. A little shudder of delight erupts between my shoulder blades but I immediately calm it, now is not yet the time for celebration.

Now is the time to reel him in and reap my reward.

This is going to have been well worth the wait.

He's got swagger, the nervous kind, as he heads up the block. He thinks he's chosen a direction at random, but he's got a lock on me, unconsciously responding to my inescapable draw. He looks around a lot, checking for witnesses. He makes sure he knows where his wallet is, his keys, his phone. He moves away from his building, because he knows better than to shit where he eats. No one wants to be caught with a whore on the block where they work. But he knows he doesn't have to go far. I'm just three blocks away, watching him the whole time.

He sees me. I smile.

I went for the red shoes tonight because I love red shoes and bright, blood red is a universal symbol for sex. Red is the color of lust, the color of desire, the color of flushed skin, and throbbing lips.

He stumbles on the curb, just enough to throw off his stride, and he hesitates. He doesn't stop looking at me, though, and I can see the wheels turning in his head. I can see him fast forwarding to the minutes from now and checking in with himself to see if his fear is greater than the demand within him that begs to be slaked.

He decides against fear.

I smile wider.

As he nears, I can almost taste the terrible weight he carries. His emotions are raw, gaping like wounds. There is an aura of desperation about him, as tempting as ripe fruit. I know I have chosen wisely to come to him tonight. He is, at last, perfect for the plucking.

I stroll down the sidewalk towards him, like we've known each other for years.

"Oh, darling, you look like you've had a rough day," I say. "Would you like to make it a great night?"

He falters, thinking for a minute that we may actually already be acquainted, then nods. "How much?" he asks quietly.

There are several ways I handle this question, depending on the client. Sometimes I play the naïve newbie and lowball the number, letting the john up the ante with a lot of bravado. Mostly, what works best is that I give them a price I know to be too high and then tell him, "But just for you ..." and come down to the market rate. That strokes the ego quite nicely. But tonight, I just tell this guy the going rate around town. He has enough to worry about without my little head-games designed to make him feel better about himself.

He nods again. "I've got fifty up front, if we stop at the ATM, I can give you the rest."

"Sure. Shall we grab a drink on the way?"

He surprises me by agreeing. Some guys like to cut to the chase, others like to pretend it's a date. I suppress the victorious outburst that threatens to make things really awkward. I am really going to enjoy this. He is absolutely perfect.

We sit at a little table by the window of an upscale bar. Neither of us look out of place. There's some smalltalk, very one-sided, as I ask him what he does and whatnot but he feels compelled to not return the questions. But the chitchat and the alcohol serve their purpose, he becomes more at ease with me. After we finish the single round of drinks, he stops at the ATM and takes out the rest he owes me, plus a little extra. He's already paid for the drinks, and he's smart enough to realize he's going to pay for the cab and the room.

The cabbie we flag down recognizes me and doesn't make a fuss. Right between the frayed edges of downtown and the recently-gentrified formerly-seedy trendy zone, is a band of well-kept little motels that service the likes of me. I'm sure some travelers use them for their intended purpose, but they generally rent their rooms by the hour. It even says so on the sign.

My john looks vastly disappointed in the old-fashioned motor-court style motel. I give him a kiss on the cheek and tell him that he won't be paying any attention to his surroundings in just a few minutes.

He pays for the cab, but I slip the cabbie an extra tip and tell him to return in two hours. He agrees and leaves the parking lot.

I have a room I like. They let me keep the key. I tap on the motel office window as we pass and hold the key up for the manager to see. The lights in the office flick on and off twice and I know the manager has seen me and will check on me when my client leaves. It's good for business, for both of us, that he's the conscientious sort.

Inside, the room is dark. I leave it that way. With the lights on, it looks like any motel room that has seen better days. I leave the client in the doorway. Next to the room key is a smaller one that opens a little cabinet under the desk.

I light the candles that I keep there, one for the desk and one for each night-stand. The room looks very different in their glow.

I approach the man in the doorway, savoring the look on his face, his eyes staring into a world he cannot comprehend. It dawns on him that I am not exactly what I seem.

"Tell me your name," I say to him.

"Alden," he tells me.

"Why are you here?"

He hesitates and scowls at me. "Isn't it obvious?"

"Some of it, yes." I teasingly run my hand down his chest, caressing the front of his pants and hooking a finger behind his belt. I pull him towards me and shut the door. "But the rest …?"

He lets out a long breath.

"It's all right if you aren't ready to tell me yet. We have plenty of time."

"You told the cabbie two hours."

I laugh. "That's how long it will be." I tilt my head towards the door. "Out there. In here, is an entirely different story."

"Are you going to hurt me?"

"Do you like that sort of thing?"

I am moving too fast for him, I can tell. If I am not careful, he might bolt, so I lead him to the bed, teasing out the knot of his tie and working my way down his shirt buttons. His aftershave smells like leather and vetiver and I inhale it deeply; it reminds me of incense.

As I pull his shirt off, he begins to warm up to the situation. He puts his hands on my upper arms, squeezing them with trembling fingers.

"I … I don't know what's going on."

"Are you afraid, Alden?"

"Yes," his voice comes out as a crackle.

"Don't be." I press him down onto the bed, deftly unbuckling his belt and releasing the button in a quick series of movements. I push his pants down over his hips as I lean into a deep kiss that lowers him into the waiting pillows. His shoes hit the floor, muffled in the tangle of his pants. "You can call me by her name, if you wish, I won't mind."

That brings him out of his building lust. But only for the moment.

"Wait … what? How do you …?"

"Some people come to me simply for the gratification of their bodily hungers, some for a different kind of solace. It has always been that way. You want more than a solid fucking, that much I can tell you. Although, a solid fucking you shall have, regardless."

He laughs at that. "Well, I hope so. I have paid good money for that."

"You'll get every penny's worth and then some. Now, tell me what's bothering you?"

"Are you a hooker or a therapist?"

Now, it is my turn to laugh. "Neither. Both. By the time we're through, I think you'll understand a little better. Let's start with something simple: tell me what you see."

"You. But different, different than you looked outside." He runs his hands over my body, stroking the loose, diaphanous gown that barely covers me. "Different. Impossible." He gently touches my hair, not a simple ponytail any longer but elaborately braided now. Then he turns his head. "This room, seems so much bigger than is possible, all this marble, and these pillows, everything looks like it's made of gold." He frowns. "Did you slip me something? Am I having a hallucination?"

"Do you really care?"

He seems to seriously ponder this before shaking his head. "Nope."

I climb atop him, straddling him teasingly close. "What have you prayed for?"

"Prayed?"

"When you despair, when things are at their darkest, what do you seek?"

"Answers," he says after a moment's hesitation. "An end to pain."

"You loved her a great deal."

He nods.

"And you fear you will never love again."

Slowly, as if it embarrasses him to admit it, he nods again.

I reach out and touch his cheek. "You will, I promise. And tonight, you will start with me."

"I don't even know you."

"You know me," I assure him. "And by the end of our time here together, you will love me."

I move onto him now, sliding up the silken gown and showing him that I am fully naked underneath, starting a slow and easy rhythm. Whatever he had intended to say, it is gone. There is nothing but the sound of our breathing growing deeper, coming faster, punctuated by a moan or a gasp.

His soul is laid open before me and gently I kiss the places where it is harmed. The wounds are layered, new upon old, a latticework of emotional scars. I am moved to great tenderness. I see that he wants, more than anything, an experience to take away the sting, to take the place of her. He had tried before but had failed — his only thoughts were of her. She had been good for him, in their time together, but that time was done now. I take her image in my hands and wrap it carefully and gently, blunting and blurring the sharp edges, the harsh spikes, softening the memories of her into nostalgia as faded as photographs. And I put it back, square in the center of his life, where she merited being, but no longer at the forefront, no longer within easy reach.

He moans loudly, arching his back, grabbing my hips.

"Give me …" I whisper.

He relinquishes the pain first, the darling lad. I knew I chose well. It lifts from him like a fog, darkly bruised. I take it from him and lay it upon the altar.

He breathes more easily at once, freed from this burden dragged upon him. The rest will release easily now, he has done the hardest work first.

I indulge in wriggling gleefully, he responds with a delighted groan.

"Give me more."

The fear is next, uncoiling like a snake. Anxiety wraps around my arms, as if it could harm me, clutching and clinging, but it, too, goes onto the altar.

His hips are thrusting up to meet me now, his desire suffusing him, surging to fill in the spaces left by the fear and worry. He does not offer that up so much as opens it to me, showing me the pleasure within it. I accept my share, drawing it around me, portioning some for the altar.

"Good," I tell him. "Yes, so good. Give me more."

A patchwork of emotions, unrelated to one another, filter through: pride, bitterness, anger, frustration, joy, all in a stream of barely consciously formed thoughts.

Our movements are wilder now, bordering on violent, teetering toward ecstatic. He grunts and sighs, striving for the ultimate pleasure that eludes him.

I cover his mouth with a kiss, enjoying the feel of his lips and tongue so cold from all of his lustful panting.

"You cannot have it until I do, and I cannot until I have your love."

The sound he makes is at first one of defeat, then he opens his eyes and looks up at me and it becomes one of surrender. His eyes have dilated so widely that I wouldn't know what color they were. His motions lose the edge of desperation to them, they become more focused. He seeks to move with me, meeting me at the peak of each wave so we ride it together.

I let go of all my illusions.

And he sees.

His fingertips clench deeply into my flesh and the love emerges, golden and shining like the light of the rising sun. It fills me, spilling into every curve and crevice. I let it fall from my fingertips, onto the altar, among the other things there. Each place it touches, it burns, cleansing everything else away like holy fire. And when it is done, it returns to me.

I throw my head back as the pleasure consumes me from within. It is as powerful, as beautiful, as delightful as it has ever been.

In a hoarse voice he shouts, half a gasp and half the name he associates with me. His orgasm annihilates every thought in his head, replacing it with a momentary crack of lightning followed by the quietest, most fulfilling darkness he has ever known.

I rest my head on his shoulder and we lie together as the tremors pass through us.

My skin shimmers with golden light, it drifts lazily through the air like a slow motion shower of glitter.

He makes a heartbreaking sound of disappointment as I disengage from him.

He starts to speak but I put my finger on his lips.

"There is nothing you need to say."

He nods, relieved.

"How do you feel, now, Alden?"

He can only grin.

"Good." I lay down beside him and hold him close, my fingers dancing across his chest and throat, stroking the bridge of his nose, teasing his nipples. He lounges, utterly relaxed, and lets me. We spend what feels like indolent hours this way. "It's time to go," I say at last. "The cabbie will be returning for you, shortly."

We languidly disentangle our limbs between stretches and kisses. He fumbles with his buttons and his socks. He banters with me a little, awkward and adorable in his after-sex giddiness.

I recline against the pillows and watch with a smile.

Where there was darkness, he now glows. Where the chains of despair once pulled him down, his steps are now easy. Like a bloodletting, he has been purged of what ailed him.

He is gone too soon. He's one of the few I wouldn't mind seeing again, but I never will. It's bad for them, they withdraw from the world of realities and dote upon me alone to the point of obsession. And as much as I love the worship, once I have cleansed them of their self-inflicted poison, they have nothing left that will truly sustain me. But there are always more clients, always more heartache, always more opportunities for healing. And love.

I sometimes miss them, though. Especially the ones like Alden, earnest and longing for the salvation only I can bestow.

Once there were temples, but they are all gone now. I only have this little motel room, and soon enough another one almost exactly like it.

MICHAEL MATHESON

UNTIL THERE IS ONLY HUNGER

BONES COME UNDONE AT the Magician's touch. Wind themselves up like silver and dance into the air. Strung like copper wire. Their fire a shimmering, living thing.

She's all smiles for the crowd.

And, of course, they are never *her* bones. That's not the trick.

The trick is to keep the audience from noticing how much lighter they all feel. They'll notice a twinge, an emptiness later, deep in the night, when the carnival is done and home and the softness of white-sheeted beds have called. When sweet-souled revenants beckon, and the witching hour is but a memory.

Everyone gives something for the magic. That's how it works. You are not spectator. You are participant. Always.

The Magician in the too-tall top hat has no assistant. Her great-tailed coat keeps time with her spidery limbs as she sways: limbs and torso too long, wild hair a knotted, tangled halo. Her shadow spans double her height, twelve feet easy. It swallows the stage around it, outstretched arms like wings unfolding up to the star-flecked sky. Hungry. But patient. Always patient.

The bones pinwheel before her. The audience applauds, eyes transfixed on light and colour and fire.

Later, when the last show is done and the carnival an hour from closing, only stragglers wandering the midway, she smokes behind the three-ring tent. Her shadow curled back inside her greatcoat. Drawn tight like the warm arms of a lover, stroking her chest, its chin resting on her shoulder. The Magician draws the cigarette from her lips and lets the smoke billow up to the night sky to coil. She stands outlined in castoff light from the dusky glow of carnival lamps, brown skin glowing gold with the fire. Takes another drag before examining the night's take.

Rib bones, tiny finger bones, cochlear bones. Always the bones whose loss sneaks up on you. The ones whose lack you doubt, until the absence of them is a pit in you, gnawing. Fingers finding the hole and probing, curious, at new-made rawness.

They are so easily missed. At first.

The Magician examines each carefully. Polishes their slicked surfaces, and stuffs them in the bag at her belt that is not a bag. The Tattooed Lady and the Lizard Woman, hand in hand, nod at her as they pass. She returns a salute and a smile after the couple, the cigarette making a tiny, smoldering arc.

"You look cold," says the Ringmaster from behind her, slipping through the fabric of the tent as if it weren't there to lay a lazy arm over her shoulder.

"I'm always cold," whispers the Magician over her shoulder.

The Ringmaster presses in against the Magician's back and angles her head up to breathe into the Magician's ear: "We could go somewhere warmer."

The Magician's smile is a mirror of the moon's sliver.

She pins down the Ringmaster's legs to bury her tongue deep in her lover as the Ringmaster moans. The taste of the Ringmaster salty-sweet, like the sea. *The ever-present sea. The endless weight of it crushing down on her. The nudge and graze of deep-diving sharks. The caress of deep-dweller squid, tentacles curious as they shoot past.*

And hunger. So much hunger.

The Ringmaster throws back her head as she comes, and the Magician drinks down her bucking and her heat. Drinks it down deep. Lets the heat and weight of it fill the emptiness in her. Lets it fill the hole where her heart should be.

Wrapped in a tangle of limbs, the Ringmaster's head on her chest, the Magician dreams.

Bones wash out of the sea to deposit on the sandy shore – white contours oil-slicked, up-ended. Way markers leading in from the swell and crash. Great sleek bodies drag themselves out of the sea after the charnel – sharks blackened from fire where there should be no fire, oil coating the surface of the sea, lit and burning. They beach and falter in swift measure, gasping for air, gills flapping. Hundreds of them, until the beach is a scour of bloodied foam and effluvia.

Out in the water, the behemoth wades closer to shore. Powerful strokes take her in. Her long arms slicing through the water, legs kicking up long waves. She draws in a lungful of air and dives deep again.

Rises, sluicing water, silent at the beach's edge. One long hand after the other gripping mud and propelling her up the long, slow incline, every line a perfect angle, every edge scalpel-cut. Kinked black hair drips down her dark chest as she wades through the sharks, cartilage crushing unheeded beneath massive feet.

In her wake there is only thrashing and moon-kissed sharkskin, razor-sharp like teeth.

She turns. Features contorted in sleep. Fingers clasping for something impossibly far.

In her dreaming, the Magician remembers walking the face of the world as cloud and ash cover the sun. Cities burning. Her body a towering monolith, impervious. Or it might be what's coming.

Time out of joint. Cracked and broken. Always.

The Magician wakes with no memory of her dreams. Just fleeting images. And a pain behind her eyes. The same one that's always there on waking. Too much of her for this skin to contain. Her shadow beats against the cage of her bones. Unheeded.

The Ringmaster stirs beside her. Throws a long-fingered, ebony hand across the Magician's stomach. For a moment she can't tell which limbs belong to whom. Takes comfort in it. "Whass wrong?" the Ringmaster slurs, still half-asleep.

"Nothing," says the Magician. Kisses the Ringmaster's lips. Morning breath mingling. Leans in to breathe the shea butter scent of her lover's plaited hair, and slips from the bed. Dresses and rises while the Ringmaster wraps herself deeper under the covers against the morning chill.

The Magician glances back at her lover, tent flap raised, before slipping quietly out into the midway.

Pale sky shadows her steps. The roar of nightfires slowly extinguished. Ghostly memories of children, unfleshed, testing the borders of their guard fires by the dark of the moon. They get closer every night.

Come a few more nights even the Ringmaster's magic may not be enough to keep them at bay.

They need to move on. Soon.

The smell of baking bread and a soup pot pulls her to the makeshift cookhouse, open to the air. White-bellied sand much-scuffled under the pale sun at the centre of the tiny tent city hidden behind colourful tents and concession stands.

The Twins are the first to greet her, bending at their shared hip. She returns their bow with a flourish, setting the young girls giggling. Her shadow lingers a moment too long after them, and she snaps it taut again with a crook of her finger. She's learned not to feed on her fellows. It never goes well.

And this isn't the first carnival that's hidden her.

She finds her usual place with the Lizard Woman and the Tattooed Lady. Drinks in the scent of their breakfast, but takes none for herself. Just draws her coat tighter around her shoulders.

"Aren't you going to at least pretend to eat something?" asks the Lizard Woman, her scales glittering like black lotus petals in the sun. The Tattooed Lady nudges her, and shakes her head at her lover. Laughter dancing at the edges of their lips.

They don't know her secret. But the Magician's sure they'll guess it eventually. Some of it, perhaps.

"They're getting closer," says the Magician. Gaze drifting to the banked fires.

"A day, two days, we'll be ready to move on," shrugs the Tattooed Lady. "Ringmaster's not done here yet."

"This one should know," says the Lizard Woman into her bowl. Licks her grinning lips with her forked tongue. The motion lascivious. Slow.

The Magician smiles. Ignores their play. Other things on her mind this morning. "I've never seen this many at once. It doesn't take many to overrun a city. Or us."

The Tattooed Lady shrugs. "They're shadows. Disorganized. The fires will hold."

"Will they?"

"You afraid of them?" asks the Lizard Woman, putting down her bowl.

The Magician shakes her head. Stands up and stretches. Filling more space than her slender body should. Turns to leave and stops. "I'll probably be missing breakfast tomorrow."

There are ages. There are days. There are tides. All burning down from an empty sky. All beating like the thing in place of her heart. The weight there. The one that doesn't go away.

She coils her hand around it. Hand buried deep in her ribcage, slipped like twine between her bones. Squeezes and lets the liquid darkness there seep between her crushing fingers.

"Excuse me," calls a young woman, a townie, from the edge of her tent. It pulls her from her reverie.

The Magician pinches the bridge of her nose against the pain. "Can I help you?"

"You're the Magician?"

She nods. Waiting. The townie hesitates, and the woman with her lays a hand on her shoulder, matching rings on their hands. Wives then.

"The barkers told me you find things?"

The Magician draws up to her full height. Lets her raised eyebrow answer for her.

"My daughter ..."

The Magician shakes her head. Turns away. "No."

"*Please.* I can feel her. Every night. Little hands beating at the walls of our house. Begging to be let in." Her wife takes her hand. Clasps it tight.

The Magician doesn't fail to notice. Sighs and crumples in. Her shadow tries to warn her. Reminds her what happens when she helps. But they both know she will anyway. She always does.

"How old is she?"

Both women look up. So much hope in their eyes. The Magician steels herself against it. "Eight. So little when we lost her."

"You live in town?"

Both women nod.

"How deep do your roots go?"

"Back to the founding, and further still," says the other woman, breaking her silence. Squeezes her wife's hand. "Our foremothers came across the sea. Built the boats that brought us here. They fled the burning and the end of the world."

The Magician stares at their hands. Intertwined like unbroken roots, rich and brown as watered earth. She aches, remembering. Longs for the touch of the Ringmaster's skin to quiet memory. Her shadow shakes its head at the Magician's weakness. Whispers words she doesn't listen to.

"How long ago did your daughter disappear?"

"A year. We thought her gone. Until the noises started — the scratching at our door; the tiny beating at the walls. Please. Can you bring her back to us?"

"You're sure you want her back?"

"Of course."

"You know what she's become." It's not a question. The Magician sure they know. And they don't disappoint.

"It doesn't matter. She's our *daughter.*"

The Magician swallows. Doesn't even bother trying to dissuade them. A conversation she's had so many times before. No one ever listens. "Yes. I can bring her back."

Both women draw in sharp breaths. The townie who first made their request buries her face in her wife's chest, tears streaming down her face. Her wife holding back her own.

When the townies have paid her — a meagre collection of coins; not that she needs them, but there are proprieties to be maintained; and the tiny bones they don't yet know they're missing — and plans have been made, the women leave. The Magician watches them go from the edge of her tent, shadow coiling around her arms and slipping home into the hole where her heart should be.

"You won't want what comes back," the Magician whispers after them. They don't hear her. No one ever does.

The Ringmaster finds her while she's packing her bags. "Are you leaving us?"

"No."

The Ringmaster lays a hand on her arm. "Another request?" The Magician doesn't look at her. Just keeps stuffing what she'll need into the weathered bags. "You can't make them whole again."

"No, I can't." The Magician's smile doesn't reach her eyes. She kisses her lover, hand on the back of The Ringmaster's neck to draw her in. Rests her forehead against her lover's. "That's not what they want."

"You'll be back tomorrow?"

"Yes. Keep the fires banked high after sundown. There are more of them every night."

"We'll be fine. Just another day or two and we can move on. I need to finish laying the groundwork or it won't hold when we leave."

The Magician nods. Thinking. "Don't let the others exorcise any of them. It'll set the rest of them off."

"You'd think I was new to this the way you worry." The Ringmaster cups the Magician's cheek. "Don't make me leave without you."

The Magician hoists her bags over her shoulder. "Not yet, no."

The Geek, the Twins, and the other carnies lingering at the edge of the makeshift midway cleaning up the damage done to their defences in the night watch her go. Watch her head past the banked train, coal-stained engine cool and quiet in the early morning sun, iron tracks gleaming off into the distance.

Out across the sea of waving grass, trampled by hundreds of tiny feet. Across the path made smooth by larger feet, booted and shod carnival customers coming to see the attractions: the freak show, the thrill acts, and the ten-in-ones. Or to watch the concession women conjure food from thin air. The kind that leaves a customer emptier than before; the lie of it the need. And the thrill of the big top and the high wire acts. The iron jaw their greatest draw, her dagger teeth necessitating a new bar every night.

It's not a long walk to the town. They've set up as close as the town council will allow. The Magician doesn't know the exact deal the Ringmaster made with the councilwomen, but she can feel their welcome wearing thin. It's in the eyes of the guardswomen at the edge of town. In the looks of the women coming off shift at the foundries, black skin coated grey from the ash and coal dust powering the furnaces. It's in the wide berth the merchants give her as she makes her way through narrow, cobbled lanes. The black stone of the town, its high towers and sloped, gabling roofs and crooked sprawl at odds with the soft, waving grass just beyond their borders. The rail station rising dug out of the earth beyond the town's edge a concession to both worlds, the stockyards at its edge straddling the wall half-in, half-out. The smell of the abattoirs drowned out by the soot from the foundry district. The town a small city, walled off from the world falling apart around it.

The Magician doesn't know its name. Doesn't care to know. They're all alike to her. And she never lingers long.

The only reason she can see that this town hasn't been overrun yet is the height of its walls, and the stone of it heavy gates. But it's just a matter of time.

She shares a midday meal with the wives who've contracted her services. Eats though it does her no good. The weight of it settles in her stomach like iron.

They ask her so many questions. Her answers are short. Easy lies, rolling off her tongue with the weight of long practice.

The Magician tells them she needs the entire day to prepare. The only truth she's spoken since she crossed their threshold. And they leave her to it. Trying so hard not to let their excitement, their hope, show.

They leave her in the daughter's room. Untouched since the night she disappeared. Her mothers cleaning it, keeping it woodshine bright, but it's a shrine. As if they expect her to return with the break of every dawn.

The Magician sits down on the floor in the middle of the girl's room and closes her eyes, getting the scent of her. She lays out her tools. Empties her bags. And begins arranging the bones she's scattered before her. All the things she'll need to call their daughter back from spirit to flesh.

When the circles are arranged around her, sanctified with her own blood, she closes her eyes and seeks the emptiness where her heart should be. And waits, asleep in the arms of her cradling shadow as it rocks her softly.

It comes in the long, slow hours after midnight. When the night is deepest, and the moon hidden by passing cloud.

The thing that was once the girl.

The Magician can hear it long before the scratching at the door begins. Long before a small child's hand knocks against wood. Plaintive. Quiet. So soft you'd swear it wasn't there if you weren't already listening for it.

She opens her eyes at the sound. Drawn up from dreams of depth, and water, and hunger. From dreams of stalking through fire and blood.

The wives linger at the edge of their daughter's bedroom. Waiting for the Magician to guide them.

"Answer it," says the Magician.

She's not sure which woman answers the door, her back to them as she rises to her feet. The latch unlocks and the Magician draws her coat tighter around her against the sudden cold that fills the house.

"Child, is that you?" asks the mother further from the door, her voice choked with need. Tiny feet enter, and the door shuts behind them. The Magician closes her ears to what follows. The sound of bones breaking. Of bodies flung against wood and rent open by tiny hands. The screaming. It takes forever for the screaming to stop.

When the Magician turns, the thing that was their daughter is there, at the threshold of what was once her room. It stares at the designs the Magician has drawn on the floor. Its body an absence of light in the shape of a small girl, about eight. More presence than body there. Blood and gore trailing from little fingers. Its eyes points of white light in negative space, its features lines traced in charcoal across a mostly hollow frame.

It mimics breathing, remembering.

The Magician watches it. Coat held tight around her, her own features drawn tight, straining against the bonds of her flesh.

The revenant crosses the threshold, one tentative foot laid into her old world. Into the space she left behind, the room oppressively full with the memory of her.

The Magician's hands unclench, and her features soften. "I'm sorry." The ghost locks eyes with her, no understanding there.

She opens herself wide, lets her shadow unfurl. Shapeless. Dark. Hungry. It floods back against the walls of the room, blots out what moonlight comes through the room's lone window, and sloshes across the length of the wood. A flood of oil and motion and teeth.

It falls on the revenant. Tears the embodied ghost limb from limb to get at precious bone. Splattering second-hand gore across shadowed walls and windowpane.

When it's done, the Magician rises from the floor where she's fallen. Body shaking, the hole in her so full she can barely stand, she gathers up her things and erases any trace of her presence.

She waits until the cool breezes of dawn are blowing before she leaves town. She passes through the black gates as the rising sun lights their edges in pale fire. Different guardswomen than the day before eyeing her back as she makes for the carnival grounds, distant pennants crowning big top tent poles waving in the wind.

When she gets back to her tent the Ringmaster's waiting for her. "Did you give them what they wanted?"

"Yes," says the Magician, and drops her bags on the only table in the room.

"They came in the night?"

"They came. The fires held them at bay. But they won't for another night. You're right: their numbers are higher every time. What happened in this place that so many linger?"

"Same thing that happens everywhere. Children die." The Ringmaster casts down her eyes. "Are we ready to leave?"

"Yes, I've laid down the cage. All the revenants are forever bound to this place; to the city. You know, the city council wanted them bound to the tracks — wanted them scattered along the rails as we left. As if secrets can be kept from coming home."

"It'll be a slaughter," says the Magician.

The Ringmaster shrugs. "They brought it on themselves. Whatever they did to have so many dead children to shift. We need to move on anyway, the numbers were down while you were away; this town's had its fill of freaks and magic. The advance sent back word of a contract down the line. Another binding. I've closed the show for the day to tear down. We'll be gone before we're missed."

"Always a binding," says the Magician. Throws off her coat and tosses it across the table.

"Better than nothing. Can you imagine trying to support this place with ticket sales alone?"

The Magician's reply is slow to come. "I'm so tired."

"I know," says the Ringmaster, and strokes her lover's face. "But the moving on is all there is."

It's twilight by the time the carnival train gets up a full head of steam and pulls away from the former midway. The sun riding low along the horizon, aching to kiss the ground, as the Magician watches the town whose name she couldn't be bothered to learn fall into long shadow.

The ghosts of the town's dead children glimmer along the edges of the fields. In gulleys and long stretches of waving grass, bent low in soft wind.

The Magician watches them mass. Watches an army of them drawn toward the town by the Ringmaster's binding. Watches it call them home.

The first alarm bells sounding from behind the walls as the guardswomen catch sight of the revenants on their doorstep. The sound faint and already growing fainter.

The Magician's alone on the caboose as the town grows smaller in the distance. Just her and the cold of the rail under her fingers, the wind carrying the scent of dry creekbeds and the stink of the abattoir. And even that fades as they start their curve south along the rail lines, steam dispersing into the sky. The engine's lonely, whistling scream their only goodbye.

When the town is out of sight and dusk has almost given way to night, the Magician heads inside.

Her shadow rumbles from deep inside her chest. Still sated from their last meal. It's sleepy. Contented, nestled in her breast, in the hole where her heart should be. Its warmth the stroking of a lover's hand along the inside of her ribcage.

She catches her reflection in the edge of a silvered windowpane. Kinked, hopelessly tangled hair wild and windblown, threatening to come free of the tie she's used to bind it. Every line of her face as flawless as cut stone. Her body a carved statue, cast in flesh. No sign of her age, even if she knew how old she is.

The Magician studies her reflection. Runs a too-smooth hand along the edge of her jaw. Along the line of her neck. Takes up her top hat, tamps it down smartly, and completes her costume.

Another name. Another role. Another mantle to wander the world with, in a body too small to hold all of her forever.

But she's fed. And she has the Ringmaster. And there's always somewhere else down the line.

It's not enough. But it'll do.

She smiles at her reflection, and goes to find the Ringmaster. The rumble of the train under her feet, and the roar of the engine in her ears.

The whole world waiting for them to bring a little magic into their lives.

MAURICE BROADDUS

SUPER DUPER FLY

TOPHER BLANDERSON STARED AT his computer screen, knowing something wasn't quite right but unable to put his finger on it. The account numbers scrolled past, a series of figures moving so quickly, they were almost hypnotic. His head ached. It hadn't pained him this much since his accident at the ski lodge so many years before. Topher felt his mind drift, not quite going to sleep, but relaxing. Expanding. Touching something deep and otherly. Suddenly everything seemed perfectly clear.

Topher touched the computer screen. His fingers danced across the monitor, the data spinning past a blur of ones and zeroes, fragments of information coalescing into folders. He pressed his hand flat against the surface, the warmth sinking into him. He shut his eyes for a moment and briefly there was darkness as ...

... *his manager, Ana Pedestal, waited at a restaurant at the hotel of the conference she attended. With him. Not him. He was there, but it was in someone else's body. The CEO. Her shoe dangled from the tip of her foot. She touched his arm ... they were in his (not his) hotel room. She poured champagne into a flute which had Gummi Bears in it. Ana threw her head back in laughter. They kissed. She...wore dark sunglasses. She was lost, a stranger walking about the corridors of the Cayman Islands National Bank, not wanting to be seen. Not wanting to be noticed. More numbers. Account names. Money transferred to ... sand. So much sand at the beach, with its ocean view. So blue. So blue. Cobalt blue. Cobalt Coast. Her body brown in the sun. She held her empty glass out. A young man quickly refilled it for her. She allowed her gaze to linger on him for a heartbeat longer as she ... broke off her kiss with him and dismissed him from her room. A knock came a minute later. She opened it expecting the attendant, but the CEO barged through. His (not his) face a sneer of anger. Ana pulled away from him. His desperate fingers searched for any purchase. He tore the thin cloth of her sundress. He slammed his hand over her mouth. She bit into the fleshy side of his palm. He pulled away then backhanded her. She licked the warm trickle of blood from her lip. She grabbed the phone from the nightstand and swung it in a large arc connecting with his head with a loud thunk. Her eyes bulged. Her face went pink to red as she slammed the base of the phone into his head again and again. He tried to scream ...*

"... don't put the Gummi Bears in the champagne glass," Topher yelled.

"What did you say?" Ana said from his doorway. And then he was back. He wiped the thin sheen of sweat from his forehead. She squinted at his computer monitor. "Is everything all right, Mr. Blanderson? I hope you aren't using company resources for anything ... inappropriate."

"Yes, yes. Everything's fine. I just ... dozed off."

"Might as well go home then. You're the last one here. We aren't paying you to sleep on the job."

"I'm fine. I just wanted to check a few things."

"That's the thing, Mr. Blanderson, you're not fine. I've been keeping my eye on your call metrics. They've dipped precipitously in the last weeks. Yet even as your work began to slide, you're staying later and later, running through files and reports that are out of your purview."

"I just wanted to go over a few reports. I thought I found a few anomalies."

"We don't pay you to ferret out anomalies. We pay you to balance the accounts in front of you."

"Yes, but in order to reconcile ..."

"... the only thing you need to reconcile is your job and your place in this company. Do you like your job, Mr. Blanderson?"

"I'm grateful for the opportunity."

"Good. We've had our eye on you for a long time. We want you to be a part of our family for a long time."

"Me, too. Didn't you just get back from a conference?"

"Yes, with the entire management team."

"Including the CEO?"

"We're getting off-track. The path you're on can go two ways, but only one involves having a future at this company. Do I make myself clear?"

"Yes, ma'am."

Ana turned and walked out of his area, leaving him alone on the sales floor. Topher leaned back in his chair. He didn't know what his vision meant. Only that it wasn't just a dream.

The sales floor took on a whole different aspect when he was the only one there. The cubicle farm had more of an echo, like the vast belly of a corporate beast which had long ago swallowed him but hadn't finished its digestion of him. The vent sighed the way old buildings did. The tell-tale click of a door opening sent a shiver of apprehension through him. He hated knowing he was alone. The realization that should anything go wrong, no one would be around to help him slowly crept up on him. The same sense of dread filled him when he walked through the garage, all shadows and silence. A low squeak neared, increasing his vague panic. A figure appeared down the hall. All that registered with him was that the man was black and they had no black people working at their firm. They tried that once. Ruling out the idea of attempting to defend himself with his cell phone, Topher reached for his stapler.

"That you, Mr. Blanderson?" the man asked.

The familiar strains of Bagger Hallorann filled Topher with relief. He relaxed his grip on his stapler. Bagger was just so safe. He even wore glasses. Black people with glasses always seemed less threatening.

"Yeah, it's me, Bags." Topher called him Bags. He gave the man the nickname because it made him feel more connected to the janitor. Obviously Topher cared. He'd wager no one else in the company even bothered to learn his name. "Another late one."

"It's never too late to be what you were meant to be."

"Excuse me?"

"When was the last time you made time for your family?" Bags nodded toward the framed picture on Topher's desk. "You have to be careful not to neglect them."

"It's just that I have all this money and opportunity and education, but I can't seem to figure out life."

"The love of family is much more important that wealth and privilege."

"You always know the right thing to say," Topher said. "How come you're always there when I need you even though I barely know you?"

"I'm the wise janitor. I come to impart wisdom and assuage fears." Bags emptied the trashcan. "It looked like you needed some friendly, black, optimistic advice."

"You ever have that feeling where you're not sure if you're awake or still sleeping?"

"The hardest thing to do is wake up and not sleep through your life. You're looking for the answer to a question you haven't yet thought to ask."

"What's that?"

"You tell me. Has anything unusual happened lately? Anything at all?"

"You wouldn't believe me."

"Try me." Bags leaned against his trash bin. "You'd be surprised."

"I had a dream. Not a dream exactly, more like a vision. I think it was both of the past and of the future."

"Go on."

"I think there's something terribly wrong with the company."

"It's like the world doesn't quite make sense anymore but you're the only one who has noticed."

"Exactly."

"Maybe you're ready after all." Bags straightened.

"Ready for what?"

"First tell me, were you ever hit in the head? As a child? In an accident?"

"Yes. When we were skiing a few years back. How did you know?"

"I think your employers have underestimated just how important you are."

"I am?" Topher rested his chin on his hand and leaned forward.

"I have plenty of things to show you, but I don't know if we have enough time."

"What kind of things?"

"You have potential. A power within you. You may be one of ... the Chosen."

"I ..."

"Sh! We don't have much time."

Bags fished around in his pocket. "In my right hand is a red Skittle. In my left hand there's a green Skittle."

"Skittles?"

"Who doesn't like Skittles? You eat the red and life goes on as normal. You eat the green one and life as you know it changes."

"But they were in your pocket."

"They'll be coming for you soon. I can guide you or you can worry about pocket lint. You need to choose."

Topher eyed each piece of candy carefully. He reached for the red one and almost took it before pulling back. Then he snatched the green one. He glanced at it then at Bags. The janitor watched him with a cool, level gaze. Topher popped the green one in his mouth.

"Good, good. Now you just sit here for a minute while I prepare a few things."

"All right," Topher said. "What do I do in the mean time?"

"Finish your Skittle." Bags wheeled his trash bin back down the hallway. When he rounded the corner, he swung by Ana Pedestal's office. She was about to switch off her light when she caught sight of him. She jumped with a start before recognition filled her eyes.

"Getting a late start?" she said.

"As long as you're breathing, it's never too late."

"What?"

"Sorry. Wisdom reflex," Bags said. "I don't know if this is any of my business, but Mr. Blanderson's down at his desk going on and on about affairs and embezzlement."

"Really?"

"Sounded mighty peculiar. Thought you ought to know."

"Thanks for telling me." Ana punched in the extension for security.

"If you can't trust a white woman, who's left to trust?"

Bags wheeled his trash bin down the long hallway as security came around the corner. The hallway stretched on and on. The lights flickered until they finally gave out. Bags kept walking even though the trash bin he held onto faded into the shadows. In the distance, light outlined a door. He took the handle and pushed it in.

"Welcome to your judgment, Bagger Hallorann," a voice said.

Five columns of light broke the chamber of shadows. Within each beam stood a figure. An old man stepped awkwardly forward as if peeling himself from a box of rice. He shuffled toward Bagger with an easy grace. Two large hummingbirds, their colors too bright to be natural, materialized out of nowhere and flitted about the man.

"The Tom. It's been … not long enough." Though Bagger met him with his gaze, the old man's eyes remained downcast.

"Bagger Hallorann? Seriously? Boy, you don't think that name's a little too on point for The Magical Negro?"

"It is a little dated. I figured no one would notice."

"The Magical Negro is not bound by the rules of space and time. It is a sacred responsibility." Another man stepped from his light. Over six and a half feet tall, weighing over two bills, he strutted toward the two, all swagger without consequence. He held his arms out, either for an embrace or waiting for a white woman to swoon and fall into them. "You had one job. One."

"What was that, The Buck?" The Magical Negro asked.

"You help the white hero on his journey."

"The Chosen?" I can barely say that with a straight face. "I wasn't even the point of view character in that scene."

"That's not your job, child." A large, buxom woman sashayed toward them. She wore a checkered apron and a handkerchief around her hair. "Your job is to get them out of trouble. Help them recognize their own faults and help them overcome. Transform them into competent, successful, and content people."

"The Mammy? Is that you?" The Magical Negro asked. "I thought you got a perm?"

"In their hearts, I'll always have a handkerchief."

"What was he 'chosen' to do?"

"We'll never know now. He may have gone on to become a super hero,"

The Tom said.

"Or he may have saved a whole village of us. You know how they love to rescue us from the mess of their own making," The Buck said.

"Careful now. That almost had the bite of critique," The Magical Negro said.

"Well, it's just us here now. We can speak plain."

"Your job, your one job, was to help him finish his story," The Tom said.

"I don't get a backstory?"

"No one cares about your backstory!"

"I ... I think you may be right about that. If I had a story, they wouldn't read it. But if they have a story and I can help them through it or Lawd Jesus," The Magical Negro turned toward The Mammy, "they can save not just me but my whole people, then now we have something they want to see."

"The story served The Market," The Mammy said.

"The Market," The Tom and The Buck whispered in unison.

"They want us around to remind them of how diverse a life they have but not in an inconvenient way. You know, having to get to know us. We're here strictly to keep them safe, tuck them in at night."

"You cannot thwart the journey." A light-skinned woman glided toward him. She stared at him with her tragedy-filled eyes. With her high cheekbones, thin nose, and straight black hair — she had some good hair; probably had some Indian in her — she could've passed for Greek or Italian. Something exotic.

"Even you, The Mulatto? You are nothing but backstory."

"You'd have probably told the boy with the ring to just stay on his giant bird and fly his ass to the mountain to drop the ring in it," The Tom said.

"Hand me a tall glass of white man's tears. With two ice cubes." The Magical Negro looked around the room. "So say you all? Even you, The Coon?"

A minstrel in an ill-fitting tuxedo, grinned broadly. Clutching his plate of fried chicken and watermelon, he bugged his eyes out in alarm as if busted by his white boss.

"You know we don't let him say much," The Mammy said.

"For all the good it did us. He's got another sitcom deal on BET," The Buck said.

"Now things could've been worse: you could've let the dog die," The Mammy said.

"Yeah, you definitely don't want to be the black guy who let dogs die," The Buck said.

"We may have to downgrade you to helping out a black guy," The Tom said.

"Can a black guy have a Magical Negro?" The Buck asked.

"I don't right know. I guess," The Mammy said. "First he'd have to go on the hero's journey."

"We're going to give you one more chance. Know your place," The Tom said. "Fulfill your role. If we listen and are polite, we can succeed."

"That's what we've always been told. It's our hope. Our legacy," The Mulatto agreed.

With that, The Tom, The Mammy, and The Mulatto retreated to their places, preserved like relics in a museum. The Buck glanced over his shoulder at them, then turned back to The Magical Negro.

"Hold on, Negro godmother. Let me holler at you for a second."

"Now what?" The Magical Negro asked.

"You should know, they're afraid."

"Afraid of what?"

"Of you."

"Me? What did I do?"

"The Tom is going to resent you no matter what you do. The Magical Negro already works his side of the street, if you know what I'm saying. But there's a legend we all speak about. Well, not them. The Council of Negro Stereotypes don't exist for our benefit. But among us, the true us, there's this hope that one day we'll be able to tell our own stories. Fulfill the role of griots the way our most ancient story keepers once did. That maybe there will come one with a sense of agency. One of us who has a complex interior life. Who has real desires, real history, and a real journey."

"You think that might be me?"

"I don't know. They fear it. It might mean the end for them if someone like that comes around."

"But not you?"

"Not as long as a white man needs a sidekick or a white woman has a fantasy. You don't know how close I came to making it to hero status. Perhaps one day. But for now, you have a job to do."

The two men rattled back and forth in the cab of the old Farmall truck. The engine grumbled all along the winding dirt road, sputtering and coughing with every turn and incline. J.C. tilted his head back, lost in his thoughts. He no longer cared. He took in the scenery with a blank resignation which worried the prison guard.

"We're almost there, Joe," the prison guard said.

"Okay, boss," J.C. said the words as if they left a bad taste in his mouth. He shifted in his seat, his large frame taking up most of the space as it was.

"We've come a long way, you and I."

"What do you mean?"

"I was terrified of you when I first saw you. Never met a colored like you before. You were the size of three grown men and the cuffs and chains barely seemed to hold you. It was like you wore them as a courtesy. I think that was what first fascinated me about you. When we get back to the prison, I hope you'll do me that same courtesy when I have to put you back in chains. But for now ..."

"... for now I'm free." J.C. smiled his unassuming, sweet smile. But something was different about him. Just a little off. It was a big night for him. One last adventure to heal the prison guard's daughter with his gift. Then after that, he had a date with Old Sparky. Gentle and self-sacrificing or not, he had been found guilty of the crime everyone knew the son of the governor committed. But someone had to die for those sins and J.C. fit the bill as good as any.

"Can I tell you something, Joe?" the prison guard said.

"What's that?"

"I never had any colored friends before."

"A good ol' bullgoose like yourself? All them years as a block superintendent, all those cells occupied by so many black candidates, powerless against your authority and privilege, and you chose me. Because of my gift. Now we're out breathing this here fine country air. I'd say that this certainly beats getting to know one."

"What privilege? I'm struggling to get by same as the next man. And for all my power, I'm here, pinning my hopes on you."

"Yes, yes. I have all sorts of power, while you're not even living up to your potential. Yet I'm still here to serve you." J.C. turned toward him, his tone almost unreadable.

"This is so ... touching." The prison guard wiped away some tears. "That's so ... what you're doing is so beautiful. It's teaching me so much. I'm all choked up."

"Yeah, someone should be choked."

The trees whirred past, dark, sharp shadows against the darker, moonless night sky. Nothing felt familiar and all the usual landmarks seemed strange. The prison guard kept his eyes on the road when he wasn't checking the rearview mirror to make sure no one followed them. Innocent or not, J.C. was technically an escaped felon. If they were caught before the guard could return him, he'd be in nearly as much trouble as his prisoner.

They swung into the guard's gravel driveway and parked the ratty truck. The guard closed his eyes as if reflecting on whether he'd made the right choice and if it were too late to turn the vehicle around and get J.C. back to his cell without anyone being the wiser.

"We have to go if we're going to do this, boss." J.C. wrapped one of his massive hands around the guard's entire wrist.

"Yeah, might as well see this through."

The guard led them up to his porch. He turned the key in the lock and slowly opened the door. When he flicked on the light, a little girl stirred on the couch. She rubbed her eyes. A blue-eyed little moppet of a girl with long pigtails. She ran to hug her dad.

"I knew you'd come," she said.

"I promised you, didn't I?"

"Is he the one with the gift? The Whining?"

The guard turned with embarrassment to J.C. before returning to his little girl. "Not every black person has The Whining. You know how some people get," the prison guard says. "Complaining that they aren't in enough things then when they do show up, in an important role at that, they complain."

"No, honey. I'm here to heal you," J.C. said.

"You're saving my life," she said to him with a grateful smile to her voice. "The spring formal is next week."

"And you want to live long enough to have your first dance?" J.C. dropped town to one knee to meet her almost eye-to-eye

"I'd say. If I go right now, I'd just die."

"What do you have?"

"Can't you see it? It's huge." The little girl stepped closer. She turned her face to the side. That was when J.C. saw it.

"It's a zit." He wobbled, suddenly off balance. The girl covered her face at his reaction.

"You let me out of jail so that I could take her sickness upon myself right before you string me up for a crime I didn't commit."

"Do you know how long a wait we have to find a good dermatologist?" the prison guard asked. "Besides, my deductible is huge."

"I need to go to the bathroom."

"Why?"

"If you want me to touch a little white girl, I'd think you'd be expected to wash up first."

"Good point."

J.C. pushed past the guard and strode down the hallway toward the living room and beyond the kitchen to the last door on the left. The light buzzed to life above him. He ran the cold water and splashed some on his face. He looked into the mirror. His face was wet as if from a day's labor sweating in a field; his arms exhausted and heavy. Turning to his left, he spied a small window. The thought leapt to his mind by the time he was halfway through it. With a bit of contortion, he twisted his bulky frame through the opening. He scrabbled along the roof and hopped onto their landing before running off into the night.

A disembodied head faded into view alongside him as he ran.

"Where are you going?" The Tom asked.

"Home," J.C. said. "If I can heal people, I'm going to open up a free clinic."

"What about the girl?" The Mammy appeared beside them.

"They got good health insurance."

"I think he's gone insane," The Tom said to The Mammy.

"No, he may be … The One," The Buck materialized beside them.

"The One?" The Tom turned to him. "Surely not."

"Who's The One?" The Mammy asked.

"If he's really arrived, maybe now, he'll have his own story to tell. The One who actually saves the day himself. He's the hero."

DRAFTY AS A CHAIN MAIL BIKINI

A TWIG PRODDED KES in her upper left thigh — right where the tasset should have been and wasn't. "Plague take it!" she spat and all the woods around went silent. "Whosoever designed this so-called-mail should be forced to wear it himself. With pattens and one of those ridiculous hats!" She slashed at the offending shrubbery with her sword.

The falling-stones sound of Angeli's laughter came from behind her. "Oh, but I think your outfit is quite cheeky," the little dragon said with a giggle that set a small bush on fire.

Kes patted her free hand against her buttock and found a considerably greater degree of flesh exposed at the bottom of the brief ... umm ... brief than she had realized. She whipped around, glaring, and pointed her sword at her draconic companion. "I'll thank you to stop sizing up my backside, wyrm, or *you* can walk in front and clear the way."

It was an outrageous outfit: mail it may have been, but the hauberk was little more than a bandeau that shaped to her breasts with the familiarity of a drunken lord's groping hands — and not much larger than the same — while the lower business was neither leggings, nor even a chausses, but something far more akin to the tiniest of smallclothes that covered her derrière like peach fuzz. Steel peach fuzz that tended to pinch, chafe, and yank out any strand of pubic hair that happened to curl round the leather-bound edges. In addition, she had nothing like a proper gambeson and the rings pinched her skin —especially any bits which happened to be somewhat upstanding by dint of the irritation of cold steel nipping like a thousand insects. And it had a draft like a blacksmith's forge in full roar. It rubbed Kes quite the wrong way, but it was all the covering she currently had, aside from inadequate boots and a hair ribbon. She'd donned the ridiculous ensemble that morning and used the ribbon to secure her hair in a plait, which she now twitched over her shoulder.

Angeli ducked its head and attempted an abashed expression — which resolved poorly on a face so scaled and inhuman. "It's a nice backside ... for a squishy-two-legs."

Kes clonked the dragon on its snout with the flat of her blade. "It is not an ornament for the delectation of spark-wits. And extinguish that shrub before the whole copse is afire, if you please."

Angeli grumbled a bit before it said, "Oh, all right ... Grumpy." It turned aside to pat out the flames with one partially-unfurled wing.

"I am not grumpy," Kes said, kicking some dirt over the nearest smoldering plant life. Though, certainly she had a right to be.

"Are too."

"Am not! Ow!" she added as an ember burned through her thin leather soles. "Blasted things!" They weren't even proper sabatons — just soft boots. Fine for hunting, but not up to a real battle — or dragon fire. "I shall definitely kill the blackguard —"

"When we catch up to him," Angeli said.

"Oh, we'll catch him up. I've a good idea just where the toad's got off to. Is all flora and fauna extinguished now, Angeli?"

The dragonet looked around, spotted a small smoldering weed, and sat on it. "All clear, My Lady Kes. Not even particularly singed, I'd say."

"What *you* would say, my dear Angeli, is quite likely to get us both thrown out of even the lowest bawdyhouse. You have the tact of a leprous pickpocket."

"Yes, but I'm charming about it! And I always leave a tip."

Kes snorted. She hadn't wanted the whelp, but it had arrived a few days before her twelfth birthday and nothing could make it go away. Six years on, whither went Kes, so went Angeli, and she was, by now, used to it, its bad jokes, worse timing, and fierce companionship. Truth to tell, she'd hardly know who she was without it — but she would never admit such a thing.

They left the scene of the minor conflagration with Kes in the lead and walked west. The sun was just behind them, but coming up quickly. The woody landscape was all very much the same and Angeli scuffed along in Kes's wake. The dragonet snaked its head back and forth on its long neck, looking for something interesting in the underbrush, and frightening small animals and birds with little puffs of steam. It was quickly bored with their skittering, chittering, and running, and went back to merely dragging along behind the woman in the measly mail.

After a while, Angeli asked, "Are we going to High Tower?"

"Where else?" Kes replied. "Now hush."

"But we don't like High Tower. Do we?"

"It is of no consequence whether we like the place. It's Assembly Day and therefore it is undoubtedly where our quarry has flown —"

Angeli chuckled. "Hah! Imagine that one flying! He hasn't any wings!

Silly squishy-two-legs."

Kes turned around and gave the young dragon a disapproving glare. "While you, ruler of the slop heap, have two perfectly good ones that you never use."

Angeli huddled to the ground in the dragonet version of a sulk that nearly hid it from view among the brush and tree trunks. "Are you implying that I'm too fat to fly?"

Kes looked the miserable creature over with a critical eye and started to reply.

There was a crashing from the brush behind her and a voice called out, "Hold, and hand over your purse, sweetheart."

Kes clamped her mouth closed and narrowed her eyes. Then one eyebrow rose, pulling her face into a singularly sinister expression. Angeli tucked its head under one wing, muttering, "Uh-oh," as she turned slowly around.

Three rough-looking men had arranged themselves across the path ahead, armed variously with a cudgel, a crossbow, and a plain but serviceable sword.

"Where do you imagine I might conceal a purse in such harness as this?" Kes demanded, spreading her arms. All three men goggled at her largely-undressed form. None seemed to notice she held a sword of her own in one hand, or that a small dragon cowered behind her barely-booted legs.

"Maybe you've tucked it under your bubbies," the one with the sword suggested. "We'll search you, eh?"

The one with the cudgel said, "And if your purse is truly empty, maybe we could lend you a yard or two to put in it." The others laughed as he started forward.

Kes flicked her sword upward with a chilly smile on her face. "Come closer, and I'll take your yard and serve you my own."

The advancing bandit stopped and swallowed, watching the gleam of sunlight off the edge of her blade. "What's a pretty thing like you need a nasty great sword for?"

"For skewering meat."

"Well, if you didn't want our attentions, why d'you go walking the woods in little more than your skin?" he asked.

"Perhaps I'd a mind to feel the sun on my hide. Or perhaps it's no business of yours what I choose to wear, any more than it's mine if *you* choose to go unclothed in the wildwood, yourselves."

The one with the sword cast a nervous glance down, possibly wondering if he was displaying anything that was better off hidden. "We're not undressed."

"You might as well be," said Kes. "Not a whit of armor among you all." She let the sunlight flash on her sword again.

"But ... there's three of us ..."

"And that should give you pause," she said.

The bandits looked at one another, confused. "Why ain't she afraid of us?" the one with the crossbow asked.

"Exactly," said Kes.

"Them mail smallclothes ... maybe they're magic ..." the bandit with the cudgel whispered. "Why else would she be walking around, brazen as that?"

"Maybe we should just —"

While the bandits were distracted, Kes dove sideways toward the one with the crossbow and shouted "Angeli! Storm up!"

Angeli may have been young, and small, and something of a coward, but it knew when to follow orders. The dragon leapt up, unfurling its wings with a mighty crack and a gust of air that sent two of the three bandits staggering and dropping their weapons. True, its wings weren't much for flying, yet, but they made an impressive display.

Kes knocked the crossbow upward as she rammed a shoulder into the bowman's gut. His bolt shot off into the trees and he fell backward with a grunt. She wrenched the crossbow from his hands and whirled to deal with the other two, but they'd already taken to their heels. Their companion scrambled to do the same. She smacked the flat of her blade across his backside to hurry him on his way.

Angeli bounded after them a way, snarling and blowing puffs of flame. "Yah! Run, cowards! Scared of a woman in mail smallclothes! Nyah!"

"Enough, Angeli," Kes said.

"Aren't you afraid they'll come back?"

"They may, but all the better reason to take our leave."

"Awww ... but then you could run them through — or I could eat them!"

"Curb your bloodlust, dragon. We've more important things to do than spit fools on their own swords. Withdrawal being the wiser course upon occasion — a strategy clearly unknown to the fathers of that lot."

Angeli did its best to rein in its enthusiasm, but was still bounding and puffing most of the way to High Tower.

The gate guards at High Tower were apparently cut from the same cloth as the bandits in the forest. They leered at Kes and one said, "What's this? Come for a bit of sport on Assembly Day?"

"Make mock at your own peril," Kes said and pointed at Angeli. "I've a restive dragon and a sword as keen as my temper."

"But dressed as you are —"

Angeli looked over her shoulder. "I wouldn't say that if I were you. She beat three bandits in the forest for such talk."

The guards gave way. Kes and Angeli continued into the courtyard and through a gathering crowd. At the bottom of the tower's wide stairs, another guard hailed them with a similar observation.

"What ho! A dainty that comes unwrapped and ready to be served!"

Kes rolled her eyes. "Turn a hand to such service, and your fist will never know another weapon."

"Oh, a spicy one! Surely such a clever tongue —"

Angeli poked its head around Kes's side and gave the guard a toothy smile. "Oh goody! She slew three bandits in the forest for better turns of phrase than yours. It was fun, but now I'm bored, and a little bloodshed is so entertaining!"

The guard retired swiftly.

Near the top of the tower yet another guard stopped them, as sure of his clever observation as all who'd come before him.

"Oh, a wench with her own chain!"

Kes leaned on her sword and sighed. "If you imagine yourself a wit, you're only right by half."

"That's bold for a woman in a —"

"Oo," Angeli said, looking over Kes's shoulder. "We skewered and ate three bandits in the forest for less. But maybe you should chatter on, morsel — I think I could manage a bite of dessert by now."

This one also discovered silence and a pressing need to step aside.

Kes and Angeli passed through the doors and onto the tower's roof. The westering sun gilded the stones. A man stood at the north parapet, looking down on the assembly of people below. Golden light reflected off his armor and fair hair. The armor could have been better burnished, but it still glinted in the sun and, from any distance, he was an impressive sight.

"Take it off," Kes said.

The man turned. "Why … Kes!" he said with a smile. "How delightful to see you! You look … perky." He was a handsome beast, but it cut no ice with Kes.

Kes raised her sword and narrowed her eyes. "Take off my armor."

"But you're wearing so little," the man objected and smirked.

Kes growled and took a step closer. "Speak neither of *your* wit, nor of this travesty you left behind when you absconded, Ormand. Remove *my* armor," she said, tapping the point of her sword against the breastplate. "The armor you *stole* from me."

It chimed at the touch, startling Ormand. He cleared his throat and said, "But it fits me so well, it couldn't possibly be *your* armor."

"Adaptability and perseverance are the nature of a woman's plate," Kes said. "And it's the nature of men like *you* to think someone else's pride always looks better on them."

"But you're a *girl*! You don't *need* armor! Men are the ones who go out and fight!" Ormand objected.

Kes scoffed. "Say rather, it's vainglorious men who go out and *pick* fights and women who are left to defend themselves with what weapon comes to hand." She shifted the point of her sword from his chest to the gap between the tassets that hung down from the breastplate to his thighs. "Now, off with it, or I'll *unmake* a man of you and let Angeli loose to finish off the rest — and you well know what a mess that will be."

Angeli spread its wings and stretched upward so the sun shone through their membranes, scarlet as blood. "Ah, a skirmish! I knew I'd come in handy, though you always say I'm so inconvenient. Inconvenient *this*!" it added, with a well-aimed puff of flame.

Ormand yelped as the blast warmed his hindparts. Then he scrambled to remove the stolen armor before the dragon — or the lady — could take further offense.

The crowd below muttered and gabbled. Ormand blushed, but kept his mouth shut until he stood in nothing but his smallclothes. The pile of Kes's armor lay between them on the stones.

"Well, there," Ormand spat. "You've made a mockery of me and left me bare besides."

"If *that* were mockery, it's you who've made it of yourself," said Kes. "While I've come all this way covered in naught but a wisp of mail and the aegis of my wits."

Ormand started to say something and Angeli snorted a stream of warning smoke in his direction. The man stepped back and glowered at Kes. "Fine for you. But what am *I* to wear, now?"

Kes took off the paltry mail, donned her armor, and tossed the tiny woven-chain garments to Ormand. "You may have these back. I'm certain they'll offer all the protection you need, as they have withstood so many barbs already."

Ormand slumped and sat down against the nearest crenellation, digging his naked toes into the cracks in the floor. His mouth turned down in chagrin and he cast his glance anywhere but at Kes and Angeli. "Small comfort," he muttered.

"It is what you make of it," said Kes. She sheathed her sword and started back toward the stairs with the dragon in her wake. The plate, now on its proper owner, shone bright and golden in the sun.

"Pretty," Angeli said. "It fits so well. But I think you were just as fearsome in the other stuff."

"Of a certainty," said Kes. "But this is warmer. Though I think the draft I felt before was as much from holes in wit and common courtesy as the gaps between the rings."

They went down the stairs and across the courtyard. A few of the crowd murmured or whispered, but not a single lascivious comment was foist their way. They stepped out the gate and onto the road again in peace.

Angeli looked around and grinned. "Can we go teach those bandits a lesson in manners, now?"

Kes tried a disapproving frown, but it broke into a laugh. "Perhaps next month."

MICHELLE LYONS-MCFARLAND

SWAN SONG

"A KING was once hunting in a great wood, and he hunted the game so eagerly that none of his courtiers could follow him. When evening came on he stood still and looked round him, and he saw that he had quite lost himself. He sought a way out, but could find none. Then he saw an old woman with a shaking head coming towards him; but she was a witch."
— The Brothers Grimm, "The Six Swans"

WITCH'S GET, THEY SAID. Demon spawn. I was made, not born, the progeny of my mother's congress with the Morning Star. A fair story, is it not? A tale to frighten away even the bravest woodsman. Well, whether or not you or I would believe such tales, they kept us quite to ourselves, my mother and I. As for myself, I cannot swear to the truth of my origins. I asked my mother about my sire from time to time during the days of my innocence, but she never would answer. I wondered who I might resemble among the villagers ... perhaps it was the cooper, or perhaps the baker. Or perhaps yet, the priest who reportedly said prayers for our souls at Mass, the one with dark eyes like a river under a silver moon. If there was such a resemblance, I could never discern it. I found it more comfortable, or at least more likely, to imagine my mother under the rough hands of the smith, sheathing his metal, or against the soft skin of the priest even as he swore his contrition, than I did to believe that my mother held the power to tame the rod of Satan himself. There are some thoughts even I dare not entertain.

We lived alone in our small cottage, my mother and I. She would go out gathering, buying what we needed from the village or foraging it from the woods, then bringing it home. Some of it was for food, some for our own care, and some was for my lessons. She took care to educate me in her ways: what were the best plants for bringing on (or stopping) a woman's courses, what will lower a fever of the body, what brings sleep to restless souls. I went with her when I could, but once my eighth summer had come and went, she forbade me to go any further than the edge of the clearing in front of our house. She said I would not be safe out there in a world filled with predators all hungry for little girls to consume. Whether she was right to keep me thus confined, I cannot say. My experience of the world since, however, tells me she may not have been wrong.

In any case, between my lessons and my chores, I had little time to mourn my fate. I learned to spin and weave and sew at an early age. Between my mother and myself, we kept not only ourselves clothed, but a good portion of the village as well. From stockings to shirts, we traded for wool and gathered flax ourselves. Baskets were made in the summer, along with enough food to keep us through the long winters.

Sometimes the villagers would come, in ones or twos, to ask my mother for charms or potions or cures. "An' will ye risk the damnation of your soul, then," she would ask them, "that you would go against the will of the priest's God?" A few blanched and shook their heads, leaving with silence or curses, depending on their nature. Most, though, merely swallowed and nodded as she gave them whatever they asked for. I was to stay silent and still through these sessions in our shared bedroom while they shared the main room, but no door is so solid that one cannot spy through its cracks. She smiled as she gave it to them, taking the gold and silver and copper from their hands.

It was thus we spent many years. So we might have lived until the end of our days, although my mother doubtless had other plans. "You're like unto a woman grown," she said to me one day, "with charms set to snare any man."

"I don't want to snare a man, Mother. I'm content to stay with you," I said.

She laughed at that. "Your mouth says so, but those dark eyes say something else entirely. No, a husband you must have and raise both our fortunes. I'll not see you wither here in the shadows. The price I paid for you was too dear."

I protested, but my words sounded weak even to me. She laughed and shook her head, refusing to say anything more.

A few days later, she set me to work making the finest cloth I had ever spun. A brew of honeysuckle and rose, henbane and hyacinth, milkweed and mint tinted the yarn. Words were said over the cloth as I wove it — I'll not bore you with them, save it was no Lord's Prayer. Bits of shroud, too, and nightshade, and poppies and passionflowers ... oh, it was a rare tea. I would not drink it, though, if I were you — not one drop.

When it was done, it was fine as silk and smooth as a petal. From that cloth I sewed a gown according to my mother's instruction. It was fitting for a peasant girl, but no priest would have let me enter chapel wearing it. It draped as though I'd nothing on beneath, and yet it showed nothing improper. It was a bewitching combination, a lure to trap an unwary lord. This was my mother's gift to me: my apprenticeship was complete.

Once I finished the dress, my mother began spending more time away from the cottage. I had learned from her the skills of simples and potions as well as charms for the gullible or hopeful, and so our income continued unabated. If the villagers were surprised to see me out from behind the bedroom door, no one said anything about it. Even the priest came once; he looked at me with his dark eyes and refused to drink the tea I offered him. He asked after my mother, offered to pray on our behalf, and then left before she returned. I never saw him again.

Summer curled in on itself, turning thoughtful, and changed into autumn. The gown stayed in a chest and waited for its time to come. Hunting horns sounded through the forest and wood smoke drifted on the breeze, full of promise and warning in one. My mother was gone even more, sometimes days at a time. When she returned, she would have brambles and burrs on her skirts and leaves in her hair, as though she had been rolling about on the ground. "He'll come, don't you worry," was all she would say.

The sun rose later and later, although chores never waited. It was a crisp, dark mid-autumn morning when I rose from bed and stoked the fire. Mother had only just returned a few hours before, stumbling in from the frost and cold in the middle of the night, heat steaming from her skin. When I came back inside from my chores with firewood and goat's milk, she was awake and pouring tea for us both. "Drink up," she said, "and let's see what the day will bring."

The cup was heavy and fragrant, with mint and angelica and rosemary. We both drank in silence, honoring the steam and the fire and the day at hand. Neither of us made a sound until Mother finished her cup. She looked down at the bits of leaf, turning it this way and that before frowning and setting it aside.

"Anything?" I asked.

"Not to speak of. Now read yours," she said.

I drank the last of the tea and turned the cup, looking for hints of the future. "A crown ... a ladder ... and an arch of stars above."

She took it from my hands before I knew what she'd done. "Speak ye truly?" She stared into the cup for some moments, as though she would stare through it into the hours to come. "An axe ... the arch is over an axe."

"Is it? Are you sure?"

She spared me only a glance, but that was answer enough. "A swan there is as well, with a shirt above."

"That ... that makes no sense."

"Read the bad with the good, aye? It'll not pass by just because you refuse to see it." She sat the cup aside by hers. "Still ..." She looked down at the cup again. "Take out your fine gown, girl. This is the day."

The morning passed with unaccustomed speed. I bathed myself with care and twined my hair with the last of the sweet William, arranging it with care. As I put on my gown, I heard the door open and close. When I came out, arrayed as finely as I had ever been, my mother was gone.

I spent the day almost as a fine lady would, doing little that would risk the enchantments on the gown. I spun yarn in the morning, made simples in the afternoon, and sewed finework on a shirt as the sun sank lower, throwing gold and violet across the sky. Supper was bubbling over the fire when the door opened — a gust of cold wind made the shadows dance against the wall.

I looked up, startled. A withered crone stood there in the doorway, wrapped in a threadbare cloak with the dark trailing in behind. I would have sworn this woman was a stranger to me, with her stark white hair and dried apple cheeks. She laid her finger across her lips, though, and then I knew: it was my mother transformed.

She stepped aside to reveal the man standing behind her. He was richly if plainly dressed, all fine wool and hunting leathers lined with thick fur. A heavy embroidered cloak hung from his shoulders and a plain circlet of gold glinted from amidst the dark waves of his hair. He blinked against the sudden light, raising his arm to shield his eyes against the fire. My mother moved to the side of the fireplace, her cloak deepening the shadows around her so that nothing stood between he and I.

I took a deep breath, willing my voice steady. "Welcome, my lord," I said.

He lowered his arm then and looked at me, and his eyes grew wide. He opened his mouth — a wide, pleasing mouth, it seemed — and said, "Well met, lady. I beg your hospitality. Your mother ..." He turned his head as if to look for her, but his eyes never left me. "I rode with the hunt today but lost my way in the chase. She offered me shelter for the night."

I inclined my head, careful not to let the blossoms fall. "Be welcome then, my lord, and warm yourself. These nights can bring a chill."

He nodded, pale despite the fire's ruddy glow, and sat at the table before the fire. I rose from my work and served dinner to all three of us. His cloak I laid by the fire to dry, then poured him a cup of ale to go with his supper.

I kept my own eyes lowered except for the occasional glance, but I felt his gaze constantly upon me. When I brought him his food, I saw a hunger in his gaze that had not been there before. It was no food that he hungered for, though; he watched my hips and breasts as I moved as a man who has not had water for days eyes a newly discovered spring. There was something in his expression, though ... some glimmer of knowledge whenever his eyes met mine of the trap in which he found himself. He shuddered when he looked upon me even as his body roused at even the barest brush of our hands. He would not hold my gaze, but his eyes were constantly drawn back to me, would he will it or no. There would be no escape.

My mother told me in whispers that he had promised to wed me in exchange for guidance. He had bargained for his life and found the exchange sweeter than he had dreamed possible. A king's hand for the witch's daughter; a goal not to be dreamt of, and yet my mother had done it. Perhaps she was Satan's whore after all.

That night, when I went to him with water and sweet wine, the blossoms fell as he loosened my plaits. He paid my bride price as he removed my gown and we both knew it — and if the dark hid my eyes and his, so much the better for both.

When morning came, I donned my gown and stepped out into the cool grey mist at his side. He put his cloak around me and lifted me up onto his horse, taking the reins and leading it through the enveloping fog. My mother walked ahead to unwind the path she had carefully obscured, the warp and weft of the spell falling like burnt threads in her wake. An hour later, we slowly emerged from the woods back onto the common path.

I looked at him, my king and my betrothed, as we entered lands he knew once more. A horn sounded in the growing light and he shook his head, blinking away the strange ensnarement. A pair of his courtiers shouted from across the clearing, calling his name.

"Your Highness," one of the men said, "where were you? We have searched these woods since last evening to no avail."

"Yes," said the other, his voice unsteady with fatigue. "There was no trace of you, my king. It was as though the forest had swallowed you whole."

The king looked at both of them, and then up to me. His courtiers acknowledged me only then, only when he had forced them to see the lowborn girl who sat on the king's horse. "This lady," he said, and then stopped, only to begin again with a faltering voice. "This lady and her mother sheltered me for the night, and I am indebted to her. Pay honor to my future bride."

The courtiers stood a moment, shocked into rude silence, before they gave me their best courtly bows. As they did, my lover's eyes met mine briefly. The knowledge of what he had done — what we had done — lurked darkly there. I held his gaze until he looked away, then calmly nodded to the courtiers. "You are most kind," I said. "I will be honored to be your lady queen."

I could tell you of our betrothal. You have perhaps heard of the fortunes spent on entertainments, of the gardens pillaged for their blooms, of the herds slaughtered for the bellies of the people. My mother lived in her cottage no longer but was moved into a grand home in the country, with servants to attend her as befits the mother of the queen. My best gown was replaced by finery I had never seen nor known of before, yet still I kept it in a chest in my apartments, out of sight of courtiers and maids. When we wed, nations across the land sent emissaries to drink to our union. Lords gave toasts to my beauty and virtue and ladies spoke of my lord's devotion to his new queen and sighed after their own beaus, whether they were wed to them or no.

More than these things, though, people whispered. Voices speaking ever so softly said the king wept still for his former queen at night, staring at the faces of his sleeping children to see an echo of hers. His new bride had bewitched him, or perhaps he wed her not for love but for a promise he had to keep. Louder voices, usually in their cups, said the new queen had an unnatural beauty that caused animals to shy from her presence, or that she never spoke with the priests who offered services and benedictions for her continued health, or that she was cold to those beloved children, those threats to her own happiness. Perhaps there was even talk of cruelty, of the maid who was whipped until blood ran for touching the wrong chest. I know the speed with which these words sped through the halls and into the villages. I know how cruel those people can be.

In the end, though, no one denies that once he left his children, it was to my chamber that he came. He dismissed the maidservants, blew out the candles, and there in the dark he gave in to his hunger. I let him maintain that small dignity. A king may go to his knees if there are none to witness it, not even himself, and whatever it was that drew him to my chamber would not allow him to stand before me.

Whether it was my mother's gifts to me or the echoes of that first enchantment, I could not say. It was he who groaned for his release each night, though, he who called out the names I taught him as his seed spilled into my womb. That much no one can or will deny. If he stood mute toward me the rest of the day, no matter; the truth of the nights was shield enough.

It has been six months now, and my courses have stopped. New life moves within me. I will bear his child, but it is not enough; I will also deliver his heir. His old queen's issue stands before my own, but that can be negated with time and effort. I have scarcely seen the children since the wedding ... a half dozen boys, I believe, and one small girl. To be honest, I have had no desire to see them. I am not their mother and will not pretend to be such a role.

Still, I know where in the castle they live. I found them a fortnight past and watched them at play, the sun glinting off their fair hair like sunbeams on water. My lord king was there as well, watching. We saw each other; he froze there like a bird before a serpent, watching me watch them. I wonder if he suspects I am with child.

No matter. I can be patient. There is a great deal of preparation to do regardless; enchantments of the sort I have in mind take time.

They were beautiful, really. The children, I mean. So fair and graceful as they flew about the yard. Almost like swans ...

MICHAEL CHOI

THOSE WHO LEAVE

MY FIRST MEMORY IS of the ocean.

The water was so cold. I cried and clung to my mother's neck.

Never be afraid of the sea, she said. *We are* haenyeo, *daughters of the ocean. In the water, we are home.*

Her warm lips pressed against my forehead.

I lifted my fingers from her neck. Her strong hands held me tightly in the water.

Kick, she said.

And my mother let me go.

My mother woke me before dawn on my eleventh birthday. Her hands smelled like the sea. As she did on all of my birthdays, she told me the legend of the Moon goddess.

"Every day, when the sun rises, the Moon goddess swims deep into the ocean and waits for the night sky to return. And if the goddess appears to a haenyeo on the day of a new moon, our year will be blessed."

"Have you ever seen her, *Oma*?" I knew the answer, but I asked the question with every telling, wanting to live in her tale as long as I could.

My mother leaned toward me, as if sharing a secret. "Mi Sun, when I was around your age, a terrible monsoon blew in from the west, the worst any haenyeo in our village could remember, ripping apart roofs and flooding the shore. When the storm finally calmed, the sea was barren, lifeless. For weeks, our nets were empty. Starving, I decided to swim far out into the ocean to hunt by the south wall. I dove down into the deep blue, and there, I heard the Moon goddess sing. Her song glimmered like sunlight through the water, her voice covering me. For the rest of our year, our nets were full, and the currents gentle."

I closed my eyes and tried to imagine the Moon goddess's song, wishing with all my heart to hear her on that morning's hunt. There was to be a new moon that night. But I knew better than to speak my birthday wish aloud.

My mother sighed sadly. "But that was when the ocean was still healthy and strong ... a long time ago."

She lifted her old gathering net from where it hung on the wall and handed it to me. "I was your age when my mother gave me my first net. This is yours now, my daughter. You are strong enough to carry your own catch."

I held her net close with both hands, as if it was woven of strands of fragile glass.

"Come, it's almost dawn," she said.

The edge of the horizon was just beginning to brighten as we left our small wooden home. A thin fog lingered over the sea like a mourning ghost, diffusing the distant lights from the mainland into a soft haze. I followed my mother to the rocky cove outside our village. I loved our dives on the northeast slope. It was one of our frequent hunting grounds, one of the few places on the island still ripe with shellfish. The wall was steep and the current always swift; few haenyeo attempted to hunt there, but my mother brought me with her, proudly proclaiming to other haenyeo divers in the village that I was already as strong a swimmer as she.

We walked across the seaweed-capped rocks, and I tried to match my mother's strides, much like I imitated her swimming stroke underwater. As the sun rose, I followed her into the water, feeling the sea foam tickle my chin. Our bodies rose and fell with the rhythm of the incoming tide. After we swam out past the break, I took six quick breaths followed by a long one, filling my lungs as my mother had taught me. Together, as if we were one body, we kicked down below the surface of the water.

I swam into the deep blue, listening for the Moon goddess's song.

I glanced at the time and cursed. I had missed another exam.

My mother hated the north end of our island, viewing the fancy resorts and department stores there as she would a festering wound. Once I was old enough to drive, I took the daily trips alone, stopping to sell our catch to the fishmonger at the port on my way to high school.

Our harvests had grown much thinner, and we often had to dive into the afternoon to fill our nets. In the past year, my class ranking had dropped from the top of my class to fifth as a result of all my missed exams. But more than my ranking, I hated being late because I wouldn't have time to rinse my body and would stink through my classes, not that the smell of shellfish ever truly left my skin.

I parked near the ferry dock and stepped out from the truck. The sound of tourists on the beach mixed with the thumping beat of pop music, so loud I could feel it in my sternum.

I had bought my mother a new poly-plastic net a month before, but she stubbornly refused to use it. I gathered our old nets and emptied them into a bucket. Our morning catch barely filled half of it. I bit my bottom lip and calculated what groceries we could do without.

The fishmonger smiled broadly when I entered his shop. He was a gruff, round man with permanent sweat rings beneath his armpits, but for all his ruggedness, his face was almost youthful.

"Baby Mermaid! What did you bring me today?"

Ever since I could remember, he had called me *Baby Mermaid*; it made me proud — I was eighteen, half the age of the next youngest haenyeo in our village. Through the generations, most of the younger women had left and taken jobs on the mainland.

I bowed. "The usual catch. Abalone, urchins, some conch, and a few fat oysters."

"Good, good. Let's hope for pearls."

While he sorted the catch onto two scales, I took my slate from my schoolbag. Over the past two years, I had secretly saved enough money to buy it, peddling polished abalone shell necklaces to classmates at school. I read under my covers late at night, only after I was certain my mother was asleep on her mat across our room. She hated anything new, seeing new as the enemy of *tradition*. Our house didn't have a computer or television. She even refused to use de-fogging diving solution in our masks, keeping to the traditional method of rubbing crumbled herbs on the glass instead. *This is our way. It has been our way for hundreds of years.*

I touched my slate, and the crystal surface brightened with the image of a pod of orcas swimming in the Pacific Ocean.

The fishmonger glanced over. "What are you reading about there? Whales, yes?"

"It's a book about a scientist. She studied whales before they were all extinct," I said.

"Another science book? Always reading, you are. Me? I was never any good at those little words."

The fishmonger opened the last of the oysters and shook his head. "No pearls today, Baby Mermaid." He weighed the meat and reached into the pocket of his apron. "It's a bit lighter than yesterday."

"Thank you." I politely accepted the thin fold of bills.

"Did you hear the news about Su Jin?" the fishmonger asked.

"No. What news?" Su Jin was a haenyeo girl from my village, several years older than me.

"Her uncle told me that she was accepted to medical school in Seoul."

Su Jin, a doctor. Most everyone who left our village to work on the mainland cleaned or cooked at resorts. Su Jin had graduated at the top of her class, not fifth. I would have to work harder.

Back at the truck, I saw that a ferry had docked at the port. Shortly after I was born, my father had left Marado Island on a shiny ferry like that one and never returned. Though I didn't remember his face, I always searched for him among the tourists, convinced that I would somehow be able to recognize him if he ever returned home.

There are two kinds of people on our island. Those who stay and those who leave, my mother told me that whenever I asked about him. *Your father left.*

On the raised platform beside the dock, a tour guide spoke to a group of visitors as they waited to board the ferry to leave the island. I'd heard the guide's talk so many times that I could lead the tour myself.

As I stepped close to the group, I smoothed my long salty hair with my fingers and straightened my shirt. I loved to watch the visitors from the mainland. I was captivated by everything about them — their bright modern clothes, which seemed to me so fancy and proper, their fascinating hairstyles, colorfully painted and styled as stiff as plastic, never bending in the sea breeze.

Several divers posed with the tourists holding their nets and masks. My mother didn't count them as true *haenyeo*, though most of them had once lived in our village. To her, they were now no more than trained animals, props for the tour companies to sell trinkets and souvenirs, putting on shows for the visitors for money, fetching shellfish planted in the shallow water the night before.

"Before we leave Marado island, have your photo taken with a real haenyeo, a Mermaid of Korea," the tour guide said. "As if frozen in time, their fishing methods have remained unchanged since the 1600s. Once numbering in the twenty thousands, there are less than three dozen of the diving women left in Korea now. Have your picture taken with a true *haenyeo* while you can before their way of life is gone forever."

I stood among the tourists, as if waiting to board the ferry. I couldn't stop staring at the girl beside me. I wanted to touch her hair — it was firmly styled but looked so soft, dyed blue and white, like a summer sky. She wore a glass band around her eyes. I had seen more tourists wearing these bands recently. She tapped the side with her fingertip, and it glowed with each touch. I tried to imagine being able to capture memories in glass like that, to hold onto things unchanged, forever.

The girl turned and our eyes met. I tensed as if caught stealing. For a moment, she looked as if she was going to speak, but then, in one motion, the girl looked from my unkempt hair down past my clothing to my weathered shoes.

She tapped the side of her band, then turned and boarded the ferry.

"I was accepted to a university."

My mother sat so still that I couldn't tell if she was breathing. Steam rose from her bowl of seaweed stew. After a long moment, she swallowed a spoonful of broth.

I sat on the floor across from her at the table. A gust of wind blew in through the open window. I pushed my hair away from my eyes.

"Oma, did you hear what I said? I was accepted to a university. It's in California. In America."

I had tried to tell her for months, but I could never push the words past my lips. I had sent my application as a dream. I knew we couldn't afford the cost, and I couldn't leave my mother — we had never been apart for more than a day. I don't know why I had even mailed it. Maybe just to imagine a different life for a brief moment, if only on paper. But then an official letter arrived at our house. When I read the word *scholarship*, a drop of blood fell from my nose onto the paper.

My mother put her spoon down and rested her hands on the table. "The outside world is not like ours, Mi Sun."

I know.

I was surprised with how quiet her voice sounded. She always spoke so loudly, nearly shouting, her eardrums damaged from years of pressure underwater. Instead she sounded tired, her voice wind worn and weary.

"I want to become a scientist. I want to save the ocean, to help our village. I want to help you."

"This is what you want?"

"This is what I want."

"Then leave." She exhaled slowly.

"Oma, look at me."

But she wouldn't. I took her hand. It felt cold. I listened to the sound of waves blend with the hum of an airplane overhead.

"I'll come back to see you often. I'll come back home soon."

She rose, her hand pulling away from mine.

"No, you won't."

I rubbed more sculpting paste in my palms and finished styling my hair, wrapping it around my head in a swirl, a fashion popular on the west coast. I added two streaks of dark blue dye and left it to set.

"Oma, can you hear me? Are you there?" I touched the glass control panel on the wall beside me.

"I am here," my mother said.

The room volume was set to its maximum level, but I had to strain to hear her over the noisy connection.

"Oma, I can't hear you. Did you get the satellite caller I sent you last month?"

"I did."

"Why don't you use it?"

"I don't know how to use it."

"There's nothing to know. You don't even have to charge the battery. Just leave it in the sun and —"

"When are you coming home?" she asked.

I heard Thomas pacing in the hallway. Even though we'd lived together for over a year, I had firmly instructed him to never come in the room when I was speaking with my mother. Long ago, I had promised him I would tell her about us, but I never could. But I think she knew. Somehow, she always did.

Thomas peeked into the bedroom. I knew we were going to be late for my graduation party at his parents' house, but I didn't care; it had taken longer than I thought to get a clear connection through a phone line. I waved him away. He shot me a sharp look.

"I graduated today, Oma. I have a PhD now."

I knew she didn't quite understand what a PhD was, but I needed to tell her. Somehow, even a decade after I had left, nothing felt real to me until I shared it with her.

"And Oma, I have more good news. I was offered a job as a geneticist at the Oceanic Institute. Isn't that great?"

"When are you coming home?"

I lifted the tint from the window and leaned against the glass. The full moon hung above San Francisco, dimmed by the city's bright skyline. I imagined where Korea lay in the distance, across the ocean. If I closed my eyes, I could picture our cove when I was awake, but I never saw it in my dreams any more. For years after I had left, I dreamt of the water every night — surrounded by the blue silence, feeling the breathing of the tide around me, in and out. But then my dreams stopped, and I couldn't remember when, like a lost limb I didn't know was cut off.

"Mi Sun, can you hear me?"

I touched my hair. It had hardened and was firm.

"I'll be home soon."

*

There was life.

I smiled and looked closer. Small bumps of coral rose on the sandy bottom inside the tank.

"I did it."

Though I was alone in my lab, I spoke the words aloud, *I did it*. The new strains of coral that I'd engineered were thriving in the same conditions that had killed most of the ocean's reefs — the same acidity, the same concentrations of iodine, cesium, and uranium.

At the Institute, I'd revived eight species of fish, re-engineering their DNA to survive in the ocean, but they had all died when introduced into the wild. Coral was the key to everything, I was sure of it. The reefs were the foundation for all sea life — to save the ocean I needed to start at the base, or nothing would be sustainable. And now, after three years, my coral polyps were ready to be relocated into the sea.

I rubbed my eyes. I couldn't see the clock, but I knew it was late. *I should call*, but I decided not to disturb Thomas's sleep. I would just stay in the lab again — I didn't mind, I slept better when surrounded by the tanks of salt water. It was the smell, I thought.

I took off my shoes and closed my eyes. *I did it, Oma. You'll see. It's not too late, the seas will live again.* I imagined the cove outside the village, as if I were young, my net tight with the weight of my catch, rising up through a shoal of fish.

For the first time in years, that night, I dreamed of the sea.

From the ferry, the island looked so small, no larger than my thumb. My hair blew across my face in whips and snaps. I hadn't styled it, knowing that it would upset my mother seeing it that way.

To the east, the waning crescent moon shone brightly against the dark sky. The new moon would rise in a few days. I remembered my mother's story of the Moon goddess that she would tell me on my birthdays.

The Moon goddess has abandoned us, I thought bitterly. *Her song has quieted and in her silence, the ocean has died.*

I couldn't stop it. All my polyp farms had died in the ocean. Every one. I'd altered the genetic makeup countless times over, each time letting myself believe that the sea would begin healing, but the reefs never grew.

When I stepped off the ferry, I could see how much the island had changed. A water amusement park and casino now covered most of the area west of the port. The air smelled like hamburgers. The old noodle house was gone. The tea-shop was also gone, in its place, a nightclub. The fishmonger had closed his doors years ago, driven out of business by the cheap shellfish being engineered on the mainland.

Our village had changed even more. The road was overgrown with weeds, and most of the old wooden houses were rotting and boarded up. As I approached our home with my bags, I was surprised by how small it looked. It had never felt small to me before.

I pushed the front door open. "Oma, I'm home."

My mother looked up from the table, sitting exactly where she had been when I'd left.

"You must be hungry," she said. She went to the stove and returned with a bowl of soup and a steaming mug of hot barley tea.

I sat on the floor across from her. I tasted her soup and was overwhelmed by the sudden rush of memories — my mother's hands holding me in the water when she first taught me how to swim, the glimmering sun through the waves, the taste of salt on my lips. I stirred the conch meat with my spoon. When I was younger, we rarely ate the seafood we caught, needing to sell it for money. But I knew that now there wasn't enough shellfish for her to sell, so she ate what she caught.

My mother's hair had turned completely white. Her skin, once dark and tough, was thin and brittle, like onionskin across her hands and neck. I took a sip of my tea and noticed a crack down the side of the mug. My old gathering net still hung on the wall, which was stained with water damage, the paint peeling off in flakes.

"Did you get the money I sent last month?" I asked.

"Yes."

"Maybe you could hire someone to fix up the house."

"Why?"

"Oma, you don't have to stay here. Come back to California with me. I have plenty of room. You'll like it there."

I said the words, but they were just continuations of all the lies I had been telling her. I knew she would never leave the island. I knew I wouldn't be in California either. Our house was already half empty, my belongings in boxes in a storage unit. Thomas and I had tried to make our marriage work, but in the end, there was nothing we could do. What was meant to fall apart could never stay together. Some people stayed. Others left. I was the one who left. *Throw away anything I left behind*, I wrote on a piece of yellow paper and put it on my pillow.

If this is how it all ends, why did I ever leave? I failed. I failed at everything. I'm sorry, Oma. I should have stayed. I should have stayed with you. I wanted to hear her voice tell me what to do. *Tell me to stay.* But I said nothing.

I felt my mother's eyes. I bit my bottom lip, forcing back my tears.

"Mi Sun, I was wrong to try to keep you here. Our way of life is dead, and I will die with it. But you are still alive. This life was never yours. I know that now. Find the strength inside, and go on. And do not stop. Promise me. Go further. Further than me. Sing louder than me. Your song will be different. I can hear it. I can hear you."

She placed her hand on mine. It was warm, like the summer ocean. With her touch, I felt full. I wiped my eyes and held her hand.

"Oma, can I dive with you tomorrow?"

My legs tensed under the weight of the air tanks as I stepped out from the warm Florida water. I disliked diving with tanks, but the polyp farm I inspected was too deep to free dive.

I walked across the shore to my campsite, the setting sun casting my shadow across the sand in the shape of a sword. I lowered my tank onto the ground and rinsed my face with fresh water from a canteen. Inside the tent, I marked down my notes from my day's inspection in my logbook; I kept my notes by hand, a part of me that was still traditional. For the past two years, it was always the same note. The polyp farms had not formed into reefs. There was no new growth. No life.

The tent's panels chimed as the satellite received an incoming signal. I glanced at the screen mounted on the side of the tent. The call was from the Oceanic Institute. I opened a connection.

"Hi, Sam. I'm sorry that my report's late. I had to delay the inspection of a few sites because of the current."

"Mi Sun, you need to turn on the news."

"What is it?" I opened another channel.

The storm hit suddenly. The ocean swelling, rising over the land, from Kochi to Shanghai. But the heart of the wave hit Korea, swallowing Pusan, Mokpo, and all the southern islands. I saw the water rush over Marado Island, the fancy resorts and our village, all crushed into splinters, washed away.

"Mi Sun, I'm so sorry."

It was as if all my blood had drained from my body, I felt empty, then my emptiness filled with cold. I stumbled out of the tent and ran to the water. I tore off my clothes and swam into the ocean.

My mother was the last mermaid of Korea.

I see her. Her body rolling as the wave crashes over her. Her legs kick and she rises to the surface. I know the ocean couldn't have taken her if she wasn't ready to die. My mother was too strong. She would have beaten the storm, fighting until the swell had fallen and the ocean was still. I should have been with her. She would have fought if we had been together.

I see her face as she decides to take in her final breath. Her body calms as if falling asleep. And she gives herself to the ocean. The water accepts her and takes her home.

I see her sinking. Her body silhouetted against the shimmering sun above. Slowly sinking.

I should have been with her. I should have been with her.

I swam until the muscles in my shoulders and legs burned.

I kicked below the surface. I wrapped my arms around my knees and held still in the water. Weightless.

I closed my eyes tightly. Salt mixed with salt.

I screamed until my breath was gone.

My first memory was of the ocean. Now the ocean is dead.

The rising sun broke over the horizon as I folded the tent and placed it into its shell. I had taken down the rest of the campsite the day before. That morning's inspection was to be my last dive before I left Florida, probably for the final time. I had run out of pages in my logbook weeks earlier, but it didn't matter. The notes never changed.

I started the engine on my small boat and steered it east. When I saw that I was above the site, I dropped anchor. It was a shallow site, a depth of about forty feet, so I ignored my scuba equipment. I put on my mask and fell backwards into the water.

I took six quick breaths followed by a long one, filling my lungs as my mother had taught me to do years ago, and kicked down below the surface. As I swam deeper, I was comforted by the stillness of the water that covered me. After all this time, the ocean was still the only place I ever found peace.

I had cut off all my hair the night before with a blade. I didn't know why, I just wanted it all gone. The tingling sensation of the salt water against my bare scalp was unlike anything I'd ever felt before, cool then hot.

Below me, I saw the white tags marking the location of the polyp farm. I pinched my nose with my fingers and sharply exhaled, clearing the building pressure in my ears.

As I descended, I closed my eyes and said a prayer — a nameless prayer — a single word. *Please.*

I kicked deeper, and upon reaching the site, I carefully searched the sand for any signs of growth. I saw only broken shells and rock. Dead skeletons.

I'm sorry. Oma, I tried. I'm so sorry.

I kicked up but stopped my ascent. *There.* Several meters north of the site. I swam closer. A small piece of staghorn coral rose from the sand like a budding tree. It was no larger than my finger. But it was alive. It was healthy. The polyps must have drifted during a storm. I kicked deeper and saw two more pieces of living coral, even smaller, but growing. But there was life. *There was life.*

And then I heard her.

A beautiful song filled the ocean like a warm caress of light, echoing in the water around my entire body. I heard the song again. The song of a goddess. *So lovely.*

A dark shape approached me through the shimmering rays of sunlight. My eyes widened as a humpback whale swam closer. She was strong and beautiful, her belly as white as a cloud. My heart leapt when I saw her calf swimming close to her side. The calf was slightly larger than me; she must have been born only weeks before.

The calf tried to sing, but she couldn't — her voice was weak and her song broke. The mother gently brushed against her daughter. The calf tried again, and her voice sang loudly, resounding brightly through the water.

Mother and daughter swam so close to me that I could have reached out and touched them. The mother whale's eyes were warm, smiling at me as she passed. As they disappeared into shades of blue, I heard them once more. The mother sang, and her daughter echoed her song.

NOUNS OF NOUNS: A MINI EPIC

ACT 1

Back in the time immemorial — before they invented the concept of time, or memories, or even ims — trouble was brewing. The Grand Earldom of Cliché was preparing to go to war against the fiefdom of Truism over a single handkerchief.

As in most dramas, the inciting incident of this conflict was a simple misunderstanding. With the best of intentions, the Grand Earl of Cliché had complimented the Baron of Truism on his almost-clean silk hanky as being "a lovely shade of green."

Since timekeeping hadn't been invented yet, the Baron of Truism had unknowingly committed the *faux pas* of imbibing large quantities of mead before five o'clock. His judgment thus impaired, the Baron responded at length. He opened with a rambling lecture about how lime should be considered a shade of yellow rather than green, proceeded to cast aspersions on the character of anyone who might disagree with this assertion, and closed with calling the Earl a stupid dick.

The Earl, quick with a retort as he was with a compliment, stated that lime was too a shade of green. He would have liked to point out that the Baron's accusation of stupidity was the case of the pot calling the kettle black, but idioms hadn't been invented yet, and the kettle was presently in use, brewing trouble. Instead he settled for insulting the Baron's lineage, personal hygiene, and finally his "gaudy green handkerchief."

Of course, this meant war.

ACT 2

The Baron of Truism called in a favor from the local chapter of the Necromancers Union, which furnished him with an army of two dozen undead.

Union zombies were expensive, slow-moving, and spent most of their time standing around and watching one or two of their number do the actual fighting or menacing. Still, they were a malevolent force of magical creatures, and the Grand Earl of Cliché would be damned if he'd let his foe show him up like that.

The Earl went on a long and laboriously described quest to assemble a preternatural fighting force of his own. He rode horses, and stayed at inns, and ate lots and lots of stew. He returned to his Earldom a little wiser, a lot sunburned, and with a motley collection of mystical warriors.

There was a flea-bitten werewolf who scratched incessantly at his mangy fur and smelled like wet hair, two slow-moving tree monsters whose bark was worse than their bite, and a half-elf bard who moonlighted as a town crier or, as she preferred to call it, a social media expert.

The Earl supplemented his fighting force with a regimen of farm boys, which were widely known as both the number one source of destiny-bound heroes in the land and the number four source of protein in an average dragon's diet.

The armies met at high noon, give or take a few hours — the concept of time still hadn't been invented yet. On the battlefield the farm boys brandished their cheap swords, the tree monsters molted, and the zombies whistled and catcalled for the half-elf to take off her hat and show off her large brain.

The battle lasted for twenty-four pages.

ACT 2.5

This is where the author took a seven-year-long break before completing the next act.

ACT 3

In the darkest moment of the battle (figuratively, not literally, since it was close to noontime), when the farm boys' sword arms grew tired, and the zombies were dangerously close to their union-mandated break, and the author was out of ideas as to how to resolve this conflict, a new threat emerged.

The Grim Lord of the Dark Murkiness, the infamous Duke of Ex Machina rode onto the battlefield at the head of an army of evil henchmen.

The Duke was once an accountant named Bob who found a magic portal to a fantasy land. The author spent a considerable amount of time figuring out his backstory, but chose not to share it with the readers, so he could feel smug and superior to them in his knowledge.

The Duke didn't care about the color of the handkerchief, but he was very interested in subjugating and/or slaughtering both the fiefdom of Truism and the earldom of Cliché because he was unspeakably evil (probably due to his pro-longed exposure to tax forms).

And so it came to be that the two foes banded together against a common enemy. The farm boys fought the henchmen, and the zombies fought the henchmen, and the tree monsters stood there and provided comfortable shade for everyone to fight in.

The evil henchmen were winning, and with only a few minutes left in the battle, it was dark tidings for the combined forces of the Baron and the Earl. (Figuratively, not literally, since it was still close to noontime.) But then the werewolf dodged the scimitar-wielding henchmen, gave wide berth to the spear-wielding henchmen, lifted his leg briefly to mark one of the tree monsters as his territory, finally ran up to the Duke, who was riding atop a corrupted unicorn, and bit him on the shin.

The Duke yelped in an un-villain-like fashion and rode off in search of tetanus shots, and also to leave a passive-aggressive review of the battle on Yelp: (Two stars. Wouldn't recommend). The evil henchmen shrugged, packed away their scimitars and spears, and left.

There was much rejoicing, and the Earl and the Baron hugged each other and apologized for their earlier behavior.

"I can absolutely see how lime could appear more yellow than green," admitted the Earl. "It's not worth arguing over. What's important is that it's a fine handkerchief, and it goes so well with your fuchsia cravat."

The Baron's eyes narrowed and he disengaged from the hug, already plotting retaliation for this grievous insult to his favorite necktie.

Which, of course, is the subject of the sequel.

Rahul Kanakia

EXCESS LIGHT

THE JONT SOCIETY HAD decided that all members ought to be uncovered when we heard her final revelation, so I woke up early in order to unzip my bodysuit and rinse the slime from my skin.

In the washing-place, I stared at my flesh — so harsh and grey — and made faces at myself while I did a little dance wherein my stomachfat and chestfat were allowed to swing from side to side. I chuckled, thinking of what my partner, Sanua, would say about this dance, and then I frowned and shook my head.

Today was not a day for antics.

After I was clean, I stood alone in the center of my living room, feeling the age all around me — the chairs made from trees which had lived and died long before I was born; the abraded edges of the stone countertops; the tracks that'd been worn into the plastic of the floor. Normally my smooth, gelatinous bodysuit kept me from making too much of an impression upon my apartment, but now I stood perfectly still because I was so aware that every smudge, every footstep, and every touch would make an indelible impression upon this ancient place.

When I was growing up within these very walls, my mother always said that although our people — modern people — could never have built this tower, we had a duty to preserve it.

I glanced at the far wall. The ancestor stone I'd made from my mother — her body compressed down into a fist-sized blue gemstone — lay in the soft light of her burial alcove.

A painful feeling blossomed in my stomach. All my life I had waited for Almeda Jont's final message, and today I'd finally hear it.

I knew, or thought I knew, what she'd say: Humanity was doomed; we would fall back beneath the waves and this time we'd remain there forever. And I felt the guilt of that indictment. I tried! I wanted to tell her! I tried to go into the stars, but the investors backed out. And yet I'd been willing, I wanted to say. Wasn't that enough?

But if she could answer, then I knew what Jont would say. "Try again. Try again until you succeed."

After an hour in the open air, my gills were dangerously dry, so I rustled around in the bedroom cabinets, looking for my fast-water patches.

Sanua woke up, and he watched me from behind his blank red faceplate, emitting tiny chirps as I carefully applied the patches to my neck.

"What's so funny?" I said.

"You are," he said. "I still can't believe you're going to all this trouble."

Sanua never missed an opportunity to tease me about my beliefs.

I felt logy and odd. My submerged gills were telling me I was still immersed in liquid, but my eyes and skin said I was in the open air.

"You still want to come?" I said.

"Of course!" he said. "As long as we can stop by my tower afterwards."

I stood up straighter. Would Sanua once again want to discuss the disposition of his now-vacant apartment?

He simply wouldn't let go of the absolutely insane notion that it was selfish for him to maintain control of an empty apartment when there were so many who were still forced to live down under the sea.

"Fine," I said. After he heard Jont's message, I was sure that he'd abandon all notion of uniting our ancestors within one set of walls. "We will go afterwards, if we have time."

Sanua bounded out of bed and refreshed the reservoirs in his bodysuit. Then he went along the far wall and touched each one of my ancestor stones while I waited impatiently by the door.

I used to keep my ancestor stones hidden behind a rejuvenation vat, but then, without asking me, Sanua cleared the space and changed the light and now they are always with us, shining quietly in their burial nooks.

Because I was uncovered, we could not travel by hookline or cannon-toss. Instead we sat in a spider-carrier, and my organs lurched around inside me as the vehicle scuttled from tower to tower.

The world outside our window was a vivid orange, shot through with streaks of excess energy that shot from exposed wires or flickered from within the heart of broken-down towers.

Here and there, I even spotted a few legacies from the uncovered times: a colorful mural etched indelibly on the side of a tower; a slew of signs for an entertainment program; and a few transparent walls that looked in upon lush, overgrown gardens.

But these colorful visions were rare. When I was immured within my bodysuit, the nutrient slime added so much to the taste and sound of the world. But when I had only my bare eyes and ears, I could not ignore the bleak sights that predominated:

above us, the pale white sunshroud that attenuated the light;

down below, the grey mist which veiled our ancestral oceans;

in-between, the people in black masks and body suits, scuttling up and down the outside of their towers; and, most of all, the towers themselves, with their coal-black faces and the long gouges that ran across worn, pitted surfaces, which could no longer be restored, but now, in these fallen times, were simply seared shut whenever the cracks became too large to ignore.

After the tarnishing of the air and the rise of the sea, humanity had retreated down beneath the waves, and stared upward, for centuries, at the silent relics that covered our planet. Only in the last several centuries had we gained the technology to crawl upwards and reclaim them from history.

Sanua took my hand. The skin of his bodysuit was moist beneath my bare fingers.

"I'm excited," he said. "I watched some of her pronouncements last night. It's something, isn't it, to hear a voice from so long ago?"

Because he loved me, Sanua thought he understood my feelings. But he interpreted everything through the mask of his personality. In his eyes, my interest in Jont was actuated by curiosity and a sense of wonder, because those were emotions that he could comprehend.

"Yes," I said. "I'm glad you're coming."

Sanua cooed, and his bodysuit grew soft, attempting to merge with me. The only other passenger in the carrier — a returned offworlder with golden thread for veins — was standing silently in the corner. These offworlders were such poor specimens. To Jont, they were the future, but none of them had lasted. Instead they'd limped home to Mother Earth, because even a sad half-life — forever marked as freaks because of the modifications they'd needed in order to live in another atmosphere — was better than the bleak nothingness that awaited them on Mars or the Moon or Europa or any of the half-dozen other worlds that mankind had attempted to conquer.

Most tried to ignore the offworlders, but I only stared. This could have been me. When I was young, the Jontian Society had come very close to launching its own spaceship. We'd assembled the money. The ship was under construction. We were selecting the crew. I was in the final phase of the interview process. They were even matching us for optimal genetic and personal compatibility. If selected, I was to father children with two women, I remember — Chem Andrey and Lin Hezin. Our plan was robust, and we expected to be fully self-supporting within a decade. And then, when the Earth finally fell, we would be humanity's sole foothold in the universe.

But then our plan had collapsed. And not because of some grand conspiracy, either. Simply bad luck. The ship cost twice what it needed to. One source of funds thought better of it and pulled out. Some of the crew moved on with their lives. A year of delay turned into three. And then ten. And then the ship had been laying half-built for so long that it became decrepit. And now the crew was too old — they'd need to be re-selected. Finally, everything fell into a quiescence from which it had never arose.

"What do you think she'll *say*?" Sanua said.

"There are several theories," I said. "The most popular is —"

"I know the theories. What do you think I was doing last night?" he said. "But I want to know *your* theory."

I touched Sanua's faceplate. There was a living human there, just a few inches under my fingers. someone soft and warm and alive. And when he looked at me, I had no idea what he saw. But my suspicion was that his vision of me was terrifyingly different from what I actually was.

And yet I was capable of loving him, and that by itself was an accomplishment. After emerging from hibernation beneath the waves, mankind lived and propagated itself for many centuries before regaining the ability to love.

So I said nothing, because I knew what would make him happy, and I knew what would frighten him, and I knew what I believed.

Almeda Jont was a writer and philosopher from the days of the Machine Democracy. In her time, mankind was immortal, and all of life's conveniences were produced by secret furnaces down beneath the sea. But Jont saw the signs of decay. She saw people becoming distant and detached from reality. She saw the disintegration of love and friendship, and the rise of tribalism. She saw how the speedrails were slowing, and the cannons were firing less frequently and the houses of science were using less and less energy each year. And, most of all, she saw the first stirrings of the madness and hedonism that would eventually drag us out of our towers and drown us beneath the sea. She saw that mankind had finally turned itself into an animal.

So she developed her own science. Carefully modeling human behavior as if each person was nothing more than a single cell in one vast orgasm, she created a robust history of the future.

Then, right before her death, she recorded a series of pronouncements: short, sharp messages that would echo through society at exactly the moment in history at which they would do the most good.

As the Machine Democracy degenerated and the Oceanic Ages began, her voice would occasionally bubble up, at preprogrammed intervals, from the mass-mind. And each time she spoke, her pronouncements were always exactly accurate. She predicted the mind overload and the abandonment of the towers and the irradiation of the Earth and the rise of the Rampants and the frothing of the seas and the return of death.

And her messages always ended with the same prophecy: Paradise will never return, she said. The Earth will never recover from the collapse. The only escape is to leave this tired planet and venture into space.

That was the sum total of her advice. The Earth is doomed. You must abandon it.

And then, as a tiny segment of mankind began to rise from the ocean, Almeda Jont said her work was almost done. There would only be one more message, she said, and it would not arrive for another thousand years.

In that time, the Earth stabilized. The towers were patched up and reactivated. Agriculture and engineering were rediscovered. We learned, once again, how to create new knowledge. A few ships even went to other planets. But that was where our progress ended. All of those expeditions failed eventually. Even a decrepit Earth was a thousand times more habitable than any other world within our reach.

"What is it?" Sanua said. "You still wish you were in space, don't you?" He pointed upwards.

"No," I shook my head, and then reeled from the strange sloshing of the water against my gills. "That plan is long-dead."

"What?" he said. "Then what? Why are you doing this?"

I could hear the edge in his voice.

"You did not have to come."

"Tell me." He muttered the words and put a hard edge on them. "Why are we here? What do you expect her to say?"

He was clutching my arm now. I drew away slightly, but he pulled closer. "Someone else can live in my apartment," he said. "Someone who'll need it more than me. It isn't right that it should be empty, you know."

"I know."

"That's the real crime," he said. "Not space travel." He shook his head. "Not space. There is space right here, and there are people who want to fill it. We're *lucky*. We are unified. How can you turn your back on ..."

"I already said that I would visit your tower."

I turned away, ignoring his importuning. This was so trivial and so slight — not at all the future that Jont would have wanted for us. We were supposed to be ascending for the heavens, not crowding ourselves closer and closer into these dry little spaces.

There were so many theories about what Jont might say, but most people ignored the simplest. What if she simply said, "It is time for you to go."?

What then? We had no more resources, and no more will. The Jontian Society was spiritually, financially, and intellectually inert. If Jont asked us to go to the stars, then we'd be revealed, once and for all, as a bunch of ineffectual crackpots.

The hall was not crowded. Once Jont had commanded millions of adherents. Now only a few dozen of us were gathered in a rocky amphitheater carved into a mountaintop whose peak was just a few hundred meters above sea level.

I knelt down and ran my hands over the muddy dirt. A few meters away, the sea hissed and popped, exuding strange gases.

The sun was blocked, and all was dark, except for that which lay within the aura of the lights that we carried. Up above, the towers emitted a terrible grinding sound as they swiveled atop ancient gears.

Most of us had never met each other in person, so we mingled in small groups and speculated about Jont's final revelation.

The optimists, few in number, believed Jont would say the danger was finally past and that mankind was saved. Her focus on space travel had been a feint, they said—a red herring designed to unsettle and misdirect mankind in some fashion that only Jont herself would ever understand.

"Oooh, I like that," Sanua said. "So crafty."

Others, the cynics, thought she'd be completely wrong. No one can truly predict the future, they said. Surely she'll babble some nonsense that will in no way reflect the more-or-less fine state of the world.

Although I didn't believe in this, I think a part of me would've been relieved to discover that Jont was a false idol. And, to my surprise, Sanua was somewhat intrigued by this possibility.

"Well, wouldn't there be something quixotic about that?" he said. "Something quite lonely and beautiful and heroic?"

The pessimists — the largest of our number — thought Jont would tell us that we had missed our chance. The Earth was doomed, and it was too late to leave.

To that, Sanua emitted a loud beep. "Why go through the trouble then, of setting up this millennia-long project?"

I didn't know. Perhaps there were many messages, and this one would only play if the conditions were met. Or perhaps Jont was like a doctor whose only remaining course of treatment is to gently inform the patient that the end is near.

Finally, the sentimentalists thought that Jont's final recording wouldn't address the entire planet. Instead, she would have some message meant only for us, the few who had kept the faith.

I detested that theory. Jont had no time for the obsessives and fanatics that made up the Jont Society. If she was to address anyone, then it would be the real doers: the builders and the scientists and the interplanetary explorers.

When I voiced that opinion, I got a chorus of agreement, but Sanua chirped derisively.

"You need to have more faith in your own value," he said.

I knew this was the prelude to a very familiar argument. "Please," I said. "Not today."

Sanua's family had controlled an apartment in Agrath Tower for seven centuries. Currently it stood empty, because he preferred to live in mine. But his ancestors were there — it was his home. And he wanted to give it up.

Not sell it, since that was illegal, but, rather, simply disengage the locks and leave it open for whatever oceanborn person decided to climb out of the water and occupy it.

I was absolutely opposed to this unbelievably sentimental notion. After all, what if the two of us parted ways? What would happen to him then? The trust that Sanua had in our relationship was ... it was simply chilling.

The final group of Jontians were the nihilists. They believed that the equipment was broken, and that the recording wouldn't play.

If they turned out to be right, I'd be saddened but unsurprised. Jont lived ten thousand years ago, and if there was anything she had taught us, it was that nothing lasts.

Finally, we took our places on the warm stone benches of the amphitheater, and, after a few moments, a hologram appeared.

The ancient projector had produced a shimmery and unreal image, but its eyes were very alive. And as they moved across the amphitheater, I had the disturbing impression that she was staring at each of us in turn.

Jont had claimed her technique could only predict the fate of whole planets. She'd written that the uncertainty and randomness made it impossible to predict the future of individual humans. But if that was true, why did I feel like she was staring directly at me?

"Friends," she said. Her voice was strong and low. "You would not be true followers of mine if you were willing to accept my words on faith alone. So please know that the details of my theories have been stored in several vaults that are hidden inside the ocean-mind. When this recording is finished, I ask you to go forth and find my proofs and recalculate everything to your satisfaction.

"Now, as for the grosser sorts of evidence, allow me to demonstrate that my predictions are still robust. Exactly 10,341 years have passed since the creation of this recording, and the world is better now than it has been in many years.

"Although trillions of men still lie under the sea, vegetating uselessly, there are some eight hundred billion who have managed to regain sentience, and now you reoccupy the world-city. You've learned to shield yourself from the sun. You've rediscovered art and science and leisure and love. You are organized into self-governing units that are largely at peace."

I felt a shiver run through us. We had not worshipped a false god.

"And yet you live in perpetual darkness," she said. "Your lives are short and nasty, with each generation killing itself off to make room for the next, and your planet is a foul, stinking mess.

"Most of your country people have accepted the myth of progress. By gradually rising from the ocean and improving themselves, they hope to usher in another age of Machine Democracy. But you, my followers, know that will not happen. The cheap energy locked in the Earth's waters is almost gone. The sun's energy is fully utilized. The iron and gold one would need to construct more Machine Minds are instead being used to domicile more and more of the ocean's transient souls. This is all there is and ever will be. It is the last efflorescence of humankind before we are lost forever."

She took a deep breath. We were transfixed. One man stood and left, but the rest were not ... well, I at least was not frightened or scandalized. No. I was excited. I no longer had to be anxious. Now I knew. The Earth was doomed, and there was nothing left to do. I looked at Sanua. Did he understand what this meant for him? We could finally join ourselves together.

But her next words destroyed my sense of peace.

"And yet there is hope," she said. "At this moment in time, the will and the capacity for space travel still exist. In the past, the time was not right: the human race was too afraid of death. But now you have forgotten what it meant to live forever. And that means you can still act. All you need is for all hope of safety and progress to be stripped from you."

My limbs felt heavy and sore. What fresh burden was Jont about to place upon us?

"And that is why you must destroy the towers."

She paused. A huge bubble rose from the waves beyond her shoulder, and then it popped, releasing a cloud of sweet-smelling gas that drifted down over us. I do not like to come to the ocean, because even though I was born above-ground there is something within me that yearns to sink down under the waves.

"The towers must fall," she said. "And you must bring them down. Go home and tear up whatever it is that protects you from the sun. Disrupt the elevators. Massacre men in the promenades. Make them afraid. Become the cancer within the marrow of human society. Run amok and let the fear spread and spread until everything comes to a halt. Then and only then will mankind finally be motivated to leave.

"If you heed my call, your neighbors will revile you, and, in their stories, you will be turned into the madmen and monsters who drove them from their homes. But they will tell those stories on a trillion planets in a million galaxies. Because of you, humankind will be safe forever.

"Whereas if you ignore me — if you go home and forget — then you will lead peaceful and prosperous lives. As will your children, and their children, and on and on for a hundred steadily-dwindling generations, until mankind finally sinks down beneath the waves forever. Because this is truly the one and only moment. Even one generation in the past, it would've been too soon, and one generation from now, it will be too late. If the collapse comes now, we will escape it. If it comes in ten thousand years, humanity will die."

That last word hung in the air as her image dissipated, and we looked at each other, unsure of what to say and what to do, until the silence was finally interrupted by Sanua's laughter.

Afterward, some few of us — the archivists and the scientists and the historians — rushed to examine the recording for clues as to the whereabouts of Jont's other caches.

But Sanua and I headed west to his home tower: a squat oval that lay half-submerged by the sea.

When we entered, the hip of his bodysuit expanded and created a hollow space into which he put a few of his knick-knacks. The apartment was clean, still, and bare. Through the window, I could see human shapes lying beneath the still waves. It was their hands that stood out — the forest of hands, fluttering bonelessly in response to the slight current. Growing up with such a sight, it was no wonder that Sanua felt such compassion for them.

I said, "You don't want to talk about —"

"One minute," he said.

He was going through his burial alcoves, picking up his ancestor stones and putting them in the pouch at his hip.

"Is *that* what we came for?" I said.

"I want to be near them."

"Sanua, you have to listen. I can't promise you that we will be together tomorrow, much less a hundred years from now."

"You shouldn't worry so much," he said. "I won't give up the apartment until you agree with me that it's the right thing to do."

I imagined detonating a bomb that would rip Sanua to pieces and destroy this entire tower, and I knew then that I was capable of it — capable of enacting Jont's plan — because the fantasy did not fill me with disgust or horror. This was my purpose — the reason I'd been left behind and denied the stars.

"They *will* eventually authenticate her recording," I said.

"Hmm," Sanua said. One of his ancestor stones was large, gnarled, and green. "Do you know who this is?"

"Your uncle, on your father's side. I've seen him before."

"Should I put him next to your mother, do you think?"

I caught Sanua's arm. "Please, this is not a good idea. Leave these here."

He turned and very slowly pressed his faceplate against my bare face, so that I felt a moment of disorientation, and then a pair of lips popping through the viscous medium.

"Let's walk along the sunshroud before we go home," Sanua said.

And that's what we did.

The air was so thin that it left me gasping, and when we finally got home, I collapsed, blue and sick, into the rejuvenation vat.

When I awoke, Sanua's ancestors were paired with mine on the alcoves. At first my burial places looked strange and overfull, but over the coming months I got used to them.

The years passed, and one day Sanua said, apropos of nothing, "Who was recording her?"

"What?"

"When Jont was creating her messages, who operated the holographic recording device?" he said. "Would she have trusted anyone with her messages ahead of time?"

I hadn't thought about Jont in ages. Somewhere in my messages, I still had the report produced by the Jontian society: they'd decided, after considerable study, that her final message had been real, and they were now in the process of forming a committee to discuss its implications.

Why had I abandoned the idea of enacting her plan? It wasn't the violence or the mayhem that had dissuaded me. I shook my head. It was something else. Perhaps just inertia.

"Maybe she operated the camera herself," I said.

He snorted. "Well, if so, her stage presence was shockingly good. How many times did she re-record each message, do you think? And did she do any post-production editing?"

At the time I cut him off with a frustrated hiss, but I was actually quite amused. For a few minutes I played through a mental image of Jont watching her own speech on the holographic recorder, and then shaking her head and thinking, *no no no, I need to train myself to look at the empty air right above the stone benches, because that's where their eyes will be.*

SUNIL PATEL

THE ORIGIN OF TERROR

Channel 12 News Report, March 21, 2036

[Smoke fills the screen. It wafts away to reveal a Chinese woman in her early fifties, holding a microphone. Behind her is an ornate cathedral. The sounds of people screaming can be heard.]

Marjorie Huang: This is Marjorie Huang, International Correspondent reporting live for Channel 12. It was only thirty-five minutes ago that Terror appeared in Prague, but she has wasted no time in her destruction. You can see her trademark steam everywhere throughout the city, though we cannot determine how much she is varying the temperature.

[A dark cloud bursts from behind the woman and engulfs her, obscuring our view. After a few seconds, it clears. The woman coughs and shivers.]

MH: Terror is currently unleashing ice cold vapor upon the city. We know in the past she has been able to freeze pipes and expand cracks in the structural support of buildings in order to —

[The building behind the woman topples, the rubble kicking up dirt to create a rival dust cloud.]

MH: The St. Vitus Cathedral has fallen. I repeat, the St. Vitus Cathedral has fallen. Terror is now making an announcement. She is saying, "Do you not see how easily you fall? How complacent you have become, ensured of your own safety? You are not safe, and you will never be safe, as long as Terror reigns!"

[The woman puts her hand to her ear.]

MH: I am getting word that we have exclusively in the studio Bonnie Baker and Cliff Curtis, better known to the world as Ignite and Chill, superhero parents of the supervillain Terror. We now take you —

[*From the top of the frame descends a woman riding a puff of steam. She is Caucasian, in her mid-twenties. As she lands, she looks sharply at the reporter, who fiercely stands her ground. Terror raises her hands to the camera and shoots a steady stream of steam until nothing is visible. The feed cuts out and cuts to a live feed of the news studio. An African-American man in a suit sits behind the desk. At an adjoining desk are a couple in their mid-fifties, the man with salt-and-pepper hair and the woman full grey. They wear jeans, work shirts, and boots.*]

Keith Stanton: Marjorie? Marjorie? We seem to have lost Marjorie, but we'll check back in on her. I'm Keith Stanton, and we have here in the studio Bonnie Baker and Cliff Curtis. You might know them as Ignite and Chill. Thanks for coming in.

Bonnie Baker: Thank you for having us, Mr. Stanton.

KS: Please, call me Keith. Now, Ms. Baker, Mr. Curtis, have you seen the footage coming out of Prague?

BB: Oh, yes, it's just awful.

Cliff Curtis: It's some bad business there. No denying that.

BB: Our hearts go out to the city.

KS: Is there anything you would like to say to Terror?

CC: Are they still calling her that?

BB: They're still calling her that, dear.

CC: She was such a good girl. Do they know that?

BB: Such a good girl.

KS: My apologies. Would you like to say anything to Tera?

BB: Call home, pumpkin!

CC: Just a short phone call, a little hi, a little hello, your mother's worried sick about you.

[The feed flickers and cuts back to the scene in Prague, where Marjorie Huang stands, completely scalded from head to toe, covered in blisters. The microphone falls from her hand, and then she collapses to the ground. The feed cuts to the studio.]

BB: We love you, dear.

Raw Footage from *The Huang Interview*, June 9, 2039

[A tall white woman with long black hair sits in a cell behind glowing green bars. Red light bathes the cell, making the true color of her prison uniform indeterminate. In front of the bars sits a Chinese woman holding a notepad.]

Cynthia Huang: Tera Baker-Curtis, a.k.a. Terror, has perpetrated some of the most monstrous crimes of our generation. The San Francisco Incident. The Obscurity of Prague. 8/14. But she has finally been brought to justice, and in a few short hours, she will be executed. I have been granted exclusive access to record a final interview with the woman *TIME* magazine called "The Villain to End All Villains."

Tera Baker-Curtis: There will be villains after me. I am not the end.

CH: Let's start at the end, then. With your capture.

TBC: It is fitting that it was Twindian. He has a bright future. A television special, perhaps.

CH: It's airing next week.

TBC: A pity I will not be able to view it myself. What will he say about his great victory, capturing the arch-villain Terror? What would he have done, were I not here to be caught?

CH: Interesting questions, but I'd like to focus on you. You're facing the end of your life. It's certainly been a memorable one. A deadly one.

TBC: I believe my body count is in the high tens of thousands.

CH: 87,126.

TBC: I only hope it was enough.

CH: Enough for what?

TBC: To change the world, of course. Do you think I mean to leave this life without having affected it?

CH: There's no question you have affected countless lives, if only by ending them.

TBC: A callous use of cleverness, Ms. Huang.

CH: One of those lives you ended was my mother's.

TBC: I wonder what number she was. 50,005? 63,487? I lose track. You must know. So clever.

CH: We're not here to talk about me.

TBC: You brought your mother up, not I, Ms. Huang.

CH: Moving on. I'd like to discuss what many consider to be your most heinous domestic attack.

TBC: Do enlighten me as to the hierarchy of my heinousness.

CH: Every American knows where they were on 8/14.

TBC: Of course, of course. I was experimenting then, to be honest. I did not know the range of temperature I could work with. People are so obsessed with the power of steam, with "steampunk," machines powered by the pressure of steam, but few consider the *heat*. In its gaseous state, it can become a far more powerful conduit for heat than a liquid, infiltrating cracks in buildings. Seeping into the skin. I didn't think it would be so effective, if we're being frank, and I think we are.

CH: Do you regret your experiments?

TBC: I foresee a repetition of this question, so allow me to answer in the negative so we may concentrate on the more salacious details I am sure your viewers desire.

CH: Do you regret the Obscurity? That was no experiment.

TBC: Truly, the Obscurity fills me with deep remorse. If I could bring all of those men and women back to life, I would, I assure you.

CH: It heartens me to hear you say that. Finally, some words of ... dammit, Tim, edit this bit out.

TBC: You are quite gullible. This will be fun. Continue.

CH: Your childhood. Your parents. What our viewers want to know is: where did Terror come from?

Channel 12 News Report, July 6, 2011

[Paul Taylor stands in a hospital room, microphone in hand. On the bed lies Bonnie with a bundled blanket in her arms. Cliff stands on the other side of the bed.]

Paul Taylor: It's an event as momentous as the birth of the Royal Baby: popular superheroes Ignite and Chill have had a child, and the world is watching! I'm here with the proud mother. Now, Ignite —

Bonnie Baker: Oh, please call me Bonnie.

[Bonnie pulls back the blanket to reveal the newborn's head.]

BB: And this ... this is Tera.

PT: Tera, what a beautiful name. It's a girl, folks!

Cliff Curtis: Most beautiful girl I've ever seen. Next to Bonnie, of course.

PT: What does this mean for you two? Will you be settling down, retiring from a life of saving people from burning buildings and chasing down teleporting monkeys?

CC: Ha, those monkeys, that was a trip, I tell you.

BB: We haven't quite decided yet. I don't think our work is done, but right now we have a more important job.

PT: Has she exhibited any powers?

CC: She's a good crier. Real good crier.

BB: It's too soon to tell, but I'll say this now so it's on public record for her to know forever: Tera, we will love you, no matter what, powers or no powers.

CC: Would love her to carry on the family business, though. Teach her the ways of us heroes.

BB: There's no question she'll be a hero, Cliff. Our little superhero.

International Superhuman Database Entry, Cached February 4, 2038

Name: Tera Baker-Curtis
Alias: Terror
Race: White
Gender: Female
Nationality: American
Birthplace: Hutchinson, Kansas
Birthdate: July 6, 2011
Height: 5' 9"
Weight: 140 lbs.
Eyes: Brown
Hair: Black
Powers: Steam/smoke/vapor. Can vary density and temperature of gas from intense heat (burn and melt) to intense cold (freeze).
Status: Alive, uncaptured

Raw Footage from *The Huang Interview*, June 9, 2039

Cynthia Huang: We all know the story of the Annihilator, how his parents locked him in his room if he didn't say his prayers before bedtime, how children at school teased him for the birthmark on his forehead, how his beloved dog was hit by a car on his eighth birthday. Many speculate these events shaped him into the man we knew.

Tera Baker-Curtis: While I am loath to speak ill of such a great man, I find him weak, in retrospect. Anyone can become a supervillain with a bad childhood, but it takes true strength and dedication to choose that path from a childhood such as mine. My parents did not lock me up. They gave me all the freedoms they could.

CH: What kind of freedoms?

TBC: They allowed me to roam around the ranch unsupervised, trusting that I would come back to them safely. This was before they knew I had powers. I had free rein over the countryside, an idyllic landscape. Did you grow up in the country?

CH: I'm a city girl, myself.

TBC: I grew to love cities. So much more to destroy. But the country was so open, as if the world was a much bigger place than my simple home. My parents understood that. No dog died on my eighth birthday. Do you know what happened on my eighth birthday, Ms. Huang?

CH: I'd love to hear it.

TBC: They bought me a pony. My parents loved me more than any parents have ever loved a child, and I shall brook no argument to the contrary.

CH: Would you kill them?

TBC: My parents, or a person foolish enough to denigrate them?

CH: I actually meant the second, but the first is a much more interesting question.

TBC: My mother sang me a lullaby at night. I still remember how it goes.

[She hums a lullaby.]

Message from the Hutchinson Emergency Broadcast System, December 14, 2032

ALERT!

ALERT!

ALERT!

We interrupt this program for breaking news. There has been an attack on the Reno County Courthouse. While details are still coming in, the attacker is said to be a white female with as-yet-unidentified powers. Some reports indicate she can fly; others indicate a massive amount of smoke issuing from the windows. A source close to paramedics reports serious burns and frostbite. Approximately a dozen casualties have been reported, with numerous others severely injured. This superpowered individual is uncatalogued, and she may still be at large. Stay in your homes until further notice. We repeat, please stay in your homes until further notice.

Excerpt from *An Oral History of Terror* by Rachel Westinghouse

Kevin Halloran, *neighbor*

Tera? Aw, Tera was just the cutest little girl you ever did see. She was always up to something or other. Bonnie and Cliff, they let her go where she wanted, and sometimes she'd show up on my doorstep. "Misser Halloran," she'd say, "can I have some lemonade?" And you couldn't say no to that face, no way. Puppy dog ain't got nothing on those eyes. Yeah, I loved getting a little visit from Tera. They raised her right, that girl. Good, traditional American values. I know some people look a little funny at folks with powers, and maybe that's not so traditional when it comes to America, but given all they do for our country, I say they're as American as any soldier. Oh, Cliff and me got along like the fox and the hound, you know, like in that old movie? Good people, Bonnie and Cliff. Good girl, Tera.

Raw Footage from *The Huang Interview*, June 9, 2039

Cynthia Huang: So you were a happy child, then.

Tera Baker-Curtis: The happiest, you might say. I used the word idyllic earlier, and I would like you to fixate on the connotations of that word. Imagine an *idyllic* life, a veritable utopia, like a dream. Know that, as a child, the world you know is the world you experience. It is also the world you are told about. Not long after my eighth birthday, I learned of the Annihilation.

CH: I think I was twelve when my parents told me about it.

TBC: An entire country wiped off the map. Millions dead in a matter of seconds. Such power Winston had. Such power. It was in that moment that I knew the world was not *idyllic* after all. You might say that my belief in a good, kind world was annihilated.

Excerpt from *Major Superhero Events of the 20th Century* by Michelle Buckle

Annihilation, The: On April 18, 1967, Winston Wyndham, to be known afterward as the Annihilator, unleashed a burst of psychic energy that extended to the borders of Switzerland. This burst affected the minds of all five million humans within the borders — including tourists from eight different countries — and shut off their brains. Notably, the burst also reached into the skies, crashing two planes, but experts agree that the passengers were dead before impact. Wyndham gave no warning or explanation of this attack, and, immediately following, disappeared. The United Nations organized the world's first global superteam, consisting of Brawn, Pyrette, Incredible Woman, Hyperboy, and Madame Fury. The Champions were able to track down and defeat Wyndham before he could attack again. Although the team had been given instructions to capture him alive, he perished in the battle, and the reasons behind the Annihilation remain unclear.

Raw Footage from *The Huang Interview*, June 9, 2039

Cynthia Huang: So the world wasn't what you thought it was, then.

Tera Baker-Curtis: It was far more complex and twisted than I had imagined. As a child, I did not comprehend the depths of that revelation, but as I grew, I became acutely aware of what I had, in relation to what others did not. Not all daughters received a pony on their eighth birthday.

CH: I sure didn't.

TBC: By my ninth birthday, I didn't either. Things happen, you know. To ponies. And mothers.

CH: Don't you dare talk about her like that again, you soulless piece of shit.

TBC: Now, now, I have a soul. When my mother saw what I'd done to poor Smokesy, she tried to appeal to that soul with a muffin. Encouragement or deterrent, Ms. Huang? Mothers do the strangest things.

CH: Tim, cut everything after "I sure didn't."

TBC: I had a neighbor. Kevin Halloran. His daughter Kathy was three years older than I, but we often spent time together. She was a naïve girl. They were all of them naïve, ignorant of the world, or, if not, refusing to acknowledge what it truly was. Simply because they were in no danger, they believed themselves to be safe. Did the Swiss think they were safe, Ms. Huang? Did visiting Australian scholar Thomas Buckle believe he was safe? Do you believe *you* are safe, Ms. Huang? Right now, at this very moment, with these bars between us?

CH: Yes. I do. The dampener's on.

TBC: You have that privilege, don't you? I saw these mortals in their complacency, taking the world of good for granted. The Annihilator is ancient history, they said. All is well, they said.

Channel 12 News Report, July 30, 2017

[Bonnie holds Tera up to the camera, bouncing her up and down. Cliff tickles Tera's side. Pan left to Scott James.]

Tera Baker-Curtis: Put me *down*, Mommy!

Scott James: That's right, put her down, Mommy! She's not a baby anymore!

[Bonnie puts Tera down. The camera follows the child.]

SJ: Tera Baker-Curtis, the Super Baby, is now a Super Kid, and she is, I gotta say, *super* cute.

Bonnie Baker: Thank you very much, Scott.

SJ: She seems like a real handful, but I know all of us here at Channel 12 are glad she's not taking up *all* your time.

BB: Cliff was kind enough to watch her while I came to your rescue. The Mantis Wasp doesn't seem to like you folks, now does he?

SJ: No, Bonnie, he doesn't. So tell us about Tera.

BB: Couldn't be prouder.

Cliff Curtis: She tried. She tried to be prouder, and she couldn't. I was there.

SJ: The whole world's wondering … does she have powers?

[Bonnie and Cliff exchange a look.]

BB: Well …

SJ: A Channel 12 exclusive reveal, maybe? A demonstration?

CC: Oh no, that ain't happening. Not until our girl decides what she's doing with them. Secret identity and all. That's a sacred trust.

TBC: Annihilate!

CC: It's her new favorite word. She likes the sound, don't know what it means yet.

BB: We'll tell her when she's older.

Transcription of Video Chat, superheronews.com, November 13, 2035

Tariq Ahmed: The world is still reeling from the reveal of the supervillain Terror's identity by blogger Kamera Obscura. Did you know?

Bonnie Baker: Don't you call her that. That was *our* name. Our little joke. She was so well behaved, we called her that with *love* when she was a kid. And you people picked it up and spun it around. And then she started to believe it herself. That word. Everyone so afraid of our little girl.

Cliff Curtis: Calling our daughter a supervillain? Look, now you even made me say the word.

BB: We never dreamed she was using her talents like that. We taught her the right things, I promise you.

CC: Someone at the market spat at me the other day, can you believe that? Like I told my girl to go kill people, what kind of poppycock is that? We raised her right, you hear me? Food, shelter, good values, the works.

BB: We know she must be doing these things for a good reason. I have to believe she is the girl we knew, the girl we made, deep down.

TA: I understand you have both considered yourselves retired from the superhero life for several years now. Will this spur you back into action?

BB: To what? Go fight our *daughter*?

TA: Kill, preferably.

CC: We're not gonna kill, Tera, what kind of poppycock is that?

TA: Someone has to.

BB: Oh no, not my little girl. Don't you understand she's still my little girl?

CC: Gotta be another way. Something. Can't even think about that.

TA: Terror talks about safety. Killing her would make us safe.

CC: You have kids?

TA: No.

CC: What do you even know about this then?

Raw Footage from *The Huang Interview*, June 9, 2039

Tera Baker-Curtis: Many don't know this story, but there was a boy. This was a few months after Chill finally defeated the Mantis Wasp. His brother, Moth Wasp, went on a rampage, but this was before that. Like me, I feel he was new, testing. And he saw this boy, and he attacked. The boy fought admirably, I must say, avoiding the stinger, beating at the hairy wings.

Cynthia Huang: Moth Wasp put my wife's cousin in the hospital.

TBC: That's nice. This was not your wife's cousin. I watched the battle, determining whether to intervene. I ran to them and shot a cloud of smoke into Moth Wasp's eyes, and he flapped his wings furiously to clear it. I grew the cloud and froze it. That stopped his wings cold, as it were.

CH: You saved that boy. He would have died.

TBC: I felt no satisfaction about this.

From the Notes of Hutchinson News Reporter Jonathan Pak, September 18, 2029

Manuel Herrera, *survivor*

That thing was coming right at me, man, you know? Big-ass monster like I never seen. But my dad and me, we spar in the garage, and I boxed the hell out of that thing. Yeah, I coulda maybe taken it, but I had to watch out for the stinger. Float like a butterfly, sting like a motherfuckin' *wasp*, you know what I'm saying? Then there's all this smoke, and this white girl comes running. She's fine, dark hair like I like it. And she freezes the damn thing's wings! Two super people in one day, just on the way home from school. She asks me if I feel safe now, and I say I do, and she just sort of grunts. She looks at me, and the sun's making her look like a damn goddess, and I was gonna ask her out, but then she just leaves.

Raw Footage from *The Huang Interview*, June 9, 2039

Cynthia Huang: Tell me about your first kill.

Tera Baker-Curtis: Of course. The loss of innocence. Crossing the line. The kind of salacious details your viewers are looking for.

CH: It's now or never, after all.

TBC: I owed it to myself to see the other side. Have you ever killed anyone, Ms. Huang?

CH: No.

TBC: How do you know you wouldn't like it? It is a particular pleasure to envelop a human being, to be both in my own body and floating in the steam. I can feel each particle caress her skin, and the microphone, which I superheat until it scorches her palm. As I raise the temperature around her, I consider each smoldering blister a message. Her breathless gasps, a reply. It is, as they say, a pleasure to burn.

[Cynthia clenches her fist in silence.]

CH: If you pull anything like that again, this interview is over. You … *you* monster. Tim, edit that out. Edit. That. Out.

TBC: But you wanted to know about my *first* kill, not my 50,000[th] or whichever she was. I found my victim in secret. This was not to be a debut of any sort. This was new, this was testing. He coughed as the smoke filled his lungs. He could not scream when I superheated that smoke, searing them from the inside. I had not practiced that technique; it was a spur-of-the-moment invention. When he fell to the ground, I held his hand and felt his body go from warm to cold, from Ignite to Chill, and this, *this* felt like something earthshattering. This was interesting.

Obituary – Manuel Lito Herrera (July 6, 2011 – September 24, 2029)

Manuel Lito Herrera, 17, passed away on September 24, 2029. Manuel was born in Hutchinson, KS and was a lifelong resident. He was an exemplary student at Hutchinson High School, where he was praised for his animated personality. Manuel also founded the Boxing Club. He is survived by his father, Alfonso Herrera, and his husband, Hernando Esparza; his mother, Daniela Acevedo, and his stepfather, Joaquin Acevedo; and his two sisters, Rosario Acevedo and Juanita Acevedo. Services will be held on Thursday, September 27, 2029 at Old Mission-Heritage Funeral Home.

Raw Footage from *The Huang Interview*, June 9, 2039

Cynthia Huang: The courthouse attack was your debut.

Tera Baker-Curtis: It was no Annihilation, but it was a start. You must understand, Ms. Huang. The world grew complacent in a post-Winston time. No one else saw it, but I did. And a world like that, a world that felt safe, *was not safe*. Ignite and Chill stayed home to take care of me, allowing others to tangle with any villains more threatening than those pesky Wasps. The Annihilation was a wake-up call, a reminder that there was true evil in the world to be vanquished. You saw the effect it had.

CH: I have a Champions T-shirt like everyone else.

TBC: Don't you see, then? Don't you see that the world *needed* me? Why is light needed but to drive away the dark? My rustic reveries would not have been possible had they not been defended. History will remember me as a monster but I will know me to be a savior.

Channel 12 News Report, August 12, 2026

[Bonnie, Cliff, and Tera sit opposite Scott in the Channel 12 studio. On the screen behind them is a title card reading, "SUPER TEEN."]

Scott James: It's good to see you again, Tera. You're looking more and more like your mom.

Tera Baker-Curtis: Thanks, Scott! That's a real compliment.

Bonnie Baker: Very sweet of you to say, Scott.

SJ: Now that you're older, have you given any thought to whether you'll be joining, uh, the family business?

TBC: I don't even know where I'm going to college yet.

Cliff Curtis: You've still got time, honey. No one's forcing you to make choices now.

TBC: Everyone's got to make a choice sometime, huh?

BB: We're defined by the choices we make.

SJ: This is real heavy stuff!

TBC: Guess the Annihilator made a choice one day.

CC: Wasn't a good choice.

TBC: Maybe it's not that simple.

[Bonnie reaches into her purse and pulls out a muffin.]

BB: Have an orange spice muffin, dear.

[Tera takes the muffin.]

TBC: That's a good choice. You're right, Dad, Winston didn't make a good choice.

Raw Footage from *The Huang Interview*, June 9, 2039

Tera Baker-Curtis: That is an absurd question. You ask some absurd questions, has anyone ever told you that?

Cynthia Huang: Just imagine if things were different. What if your parents had been like his?

TBC: I *imagine* things may have gone differently. I *imagine* I would have become a hero, a rebellious act against such mistreatment.

CH: But that's not what happened with the Annihilator.

TBC: You seem incapable of comprehending the nuances of human behavior, Ms. Huang. As if each person will react to adversity in the same way. As if each person will react to comfort in the same way. My parents nurtured who I was, though they did not know who I was. They ignited my true self, chilled my false one. Love, respect, admiration — I fed off of them, Ms. Huang.

CH: And these *nuances* resulted in the deaths of tens of thousands of people.

TBC: I could express remorse but I've already negated such trifles.

CH: We really mean nothing to you, do we?

TBC: On an individual level, only two of you mean anything to me.

Channel 7 News Report, October 1, 2033

[Two identical Indian men stand side by side. They give each other a high five, and a blinding flash of light emits from the impact. When the light fades, only one young man remains. Chyron on screen reads, "NEW HERO(ES) IN TOWN?" Zoom out to show African-American man with microphone.]

Don Harrison: Don Harrison, reporting live for Channel 7 News, and I'm here with ... what should we call you?

Govinda Sharma: I haven't come up with a name yet! Sorry, didn't know I was going to be on TV. I just wanted to help. I'm thinking something Rama-Lakshmana-y. Laksh-Man? I don't know.

DH: Well, at least five people will be calling you their savior after what you just did.

GS: I can't believe I really did that! I'm still alive! They are too! Because of me. Wow.

DH: I know they're grateful.

GS: After 8/14, that was a wake-up call. I saw Terror on the news and I just knew I couldn't *not* use my powers for something more. There are other super-heroes out there, sure, but there's also me. It's my duty. Look at what the world is, right? It needed me, so here I am.

From the Notes of *Chicago Tribune* Reporter Anna Wilson, October 1, 2033

Juanita Herrera, *survivor*

The dude just *split himself in two*, it was the most amazing thing I'd ever seen! Like, I've totally seen super people before, but nothing like that. And both of them, or both of him, or whatever, they pushed the car out of the way, like he must really work out. The train went by and we still screamed because, like, we almost died. But he saved us. I need to call my sister now. She's gonna *flip*.

Raw Footage from *The Huang Interview*, June 9, 2039

Cynthia Huang: So that's your story.

Tera Baker-Curtis: You wanted my story. You have my story.

CH: The secret origin of Terror herself.

TBC: May it enlighten the populace and win its timeslot. Perhaps the world will change its mind about me. But that is irrelevant. What they think is of no import; what matters is how the world changes. I've made an impact. What have you done?

CH: I've gotten your story, for one.

TBC: You *got* nothing, Ms. Cynthia Huang, daughter of Marjorie Huang. I gave you this story. And some lovely family memories.

CH: They said you wouldn't talk to anyone but me.

TBC: In you I can see the real impact I have had. Poor thing. I hope you treasure our time together.

CH: Allow me to give you something in return. Tim, bring them in.

[Bonnie and Cliff walk in. Tera stands abruptly.]

TBC: Mom? Dad?

Cliff Curtis: All this time out in the world, and you never called! No hello, no goodbye.

Bonnie Baker: We missed you, honey.

[Tera paces in the cell.]

TBC: Have you been listening all this time?

BB: You said such nice things about us, pumpkin.

CC: Little less nice about you, though.

CH: Ignite, Chill, and Terror, together again after a decade.

TBC: I was always thinking of you. I want you to know that.

[Bonnie reaches into her purse and pulls out a muffin.]

BB: I brought you an orange spice muffin.

[Tera sits down.]

TBC: It's too late for muffins.

BB: We just wanted you to make the right choice.

CC: Don't know about these choices, Tera. Thought we taught you better than that.

TBC: Ms. Huang, please send them aw —

CH: Bonnie, Curtis, your daughter will be executed in hours. Is there anything you would like to say to Tera?

BB: We love you, dear.

CC: But we wish you wouldn't have killed so many people.

THE TANGLED WEB

HE WATCHES ROMANTIC COMEDIES as most men do: alone, knife in hand, wedging the tip underneath his carapace until his gray skin wells up with blood. He itches to shove the knife in, to unleash those luscious endorphins that simulate love, but a wound deep enough to provide release might cost him his job.

If this film is good enough, he promises himself, he'll allow himself a taste. Not too much. The skin beneath his exoskeleton is already crisscrossed with shamefully straight scars — not ragged curves from a proper set of fangs, no. He covers his female-given scars with layers of makeup, outlining his wounds proudly in bright-colored swirls only males can see, yet hiding his failed love affairs from females' weak eyes.

He hates touching the good scars. All he feels is what was taken from him.

As the opening music starts up, the television droops in the cheap webbing of his wall; he scuttles to follow the cracked screen, ignoring the hitch in his step from the old, good wounds.

That's when he notices the male in this comedy shares his name: Mesoth.

Excited, he cuts shallow trails under his belly. It's not unusual for the lead to share his name — there are only so many names anyone bothers to give a male — but any connection to this fantasy sets his pedipalps quivering.

He settles in to watch, cutting off last night's scabs in anticipation. The two leads are introduced: Mesoth, a plucky meat-harvester, and the Female, a cunning trader. The two have separate adventures, coming so close to meeting that his knife quivers as he prepares to ram it home —

Yet fate conspires to interrupt the two lovers' predestined meeting: a webbing collapse, an incursion from a rival tribe, a fungus-plague that clogs Mesoth's best friend's lamellae until he suffocates. Mesoth doesn't even get to watch his friend die: he stumbles over the shriveled, mold-furred body, the meat having rotted enough to burst the shell.

A bad death. Useless.

For the sixth time this long evening, he frets that perhaps this is a horror film. Maybe the film-Mesoth also rots alone. But no! Finally, Mesoth comes within scenting-distance of Female!

They exchange no words; they cannot. They share no common language. Yet Female's tricobothric hairs prickle at his scent.

She whisks him up in her great jaws, carries film-Mesoth back to her birthing chambers. Real-Mesoth's breaths go shallow as he readies the knife, imagining a woman taking him.

Female removes Mesoth's robe, removes Mesoth's jewelry, removes Mesoth's head with one clean bite. She strips his exoskeleton off as he quivers rhapsodically in her web, stabbed deep with her eggs. Good eggs, firm eggs, eggs that will grow strong.

Time passes. The younglings hatch, Mesoth's body given fine purpose, the little ones chomping eagerly upon his flesh. As the credits roll, montages of Mesoth's beautiful children blaze across the screen: them hunting rival tribes, spinning great bridges, flying high into the air on exploratory parachutes …

By the time the screen darkens, Mesoth — the real Mesoth — realizes he was so caught up in bliss he forgot to cut himself at the film's climax. It is getting late. He has to go to work tomorrow. He can't oversleep, it's hard enough for a male to find employment …

The screen flares with an advertisement for the next film: another comedy. This one is historical, not his favorite genre, but …

His belly itches to be eaten.

This knife feels so good.

As the next movie sends lambent light flickering across his web, the entire complex pulses as one: a hundred bachelors watching hungrily, shamefully, in silence, each pretending the others don't exist.

The next morning, he's trying to save the lives of two males before they float away. He orders the other workers to daub fresh webbing onto the base of two quivering tethers stretched high in the air, attempting to stop it from pulling free.

The males are brown dots against a vast blue sky, their white webbed canopies pulled out behind them in the wind. Mesoth can feel their panicked scrabbles vibrating down the taut line as they try to crawl back to safety.

Gentle breezes were supposed to carry them to rocky outcroppings on the far side of the abyss, where they'd set a tether line; Mesoth and the other webgineers would use that filament to set up sturdier anchor silk to expand the empire outwards.

Instead, an unexpected squall swept them far out over the empty drop. He wants to tell them to ride the breeze, not fight it: spin out more thread, let the wind carry them as far as it needs to until this bluster passes ...

The first canopy shreds apart.

The first male drops into darkness.

Mesoth orders his workers to swarm the second tether, piling sticky webbing up until the smaller males are caught in it, but soon the second male's canopy ruptures. He falls, trailing his tether behind him, a thin gray arc marking his demise.

The remaining worker-males press their bellies against the ground, going flat with horror.

Mesoth alone stares into the abyss, longing for love.

Love would have prevented this, he thinks. Love would have given them a clean time of death, a use for their bodies, a last embrace to tell them how badly they were needed. Smashing against rocks brings no rhapsody; only a lover's sharp bites can suffuse a male with exhilaration.

Why didn't some female give them beauty? Why were they abandoned to die at nature's whims, when a female — any female — could have gifted them with a perfect ending?

Why are they so unworthy?

He turns to the weatherman, signaling angrily with his smallhands. *You should not have let them go out today.*

The weatherman blinks his many eyes in slow derision. *They wanted to smell clean. If you want safety, take a job at the chemical factories.*

Mesoth's spines bristle. The jobs available to males were menial or dangerous: who would waste time training someone meant to be eaten? The saddest cases — males with half-devoured legs — tended vats at the chemical plants, where sulfuric odors clogged their setaceous hairs, made them stink so badly no female would court them.

Whereas webgineering was considered a fine job. The clean outside air would, it was said, make you alluring. Though if this were a female profession, they'd be stocked with scientific tools to check for incoming currents. Instead, they were left to peer at clouds and live in fear of an uncertain death.

Go down and hire four new fliers, the weatherman says. His trim exoskeleton is draped in shining silver beads displaying his house's crest, flashing metal designed to catch a female's weak eyes.

Four? Mesoth says. *It's not safe to fly yet.*

It will be soon, the weatherman replies. Then, when Mesoth pauses: *We can do this without you, you know.*

Mesoth unsheathes his fangs — not quite a challenge to combat, but enough to let the weatherman know Mesoth can be pushed too far. The weatherman averts all eight eyes despite his tiny size, telling Mesoth he is so unworthy a threat that he does not need to be watched.

Mesoth hisses and scuttles down the mountaintop, headed for the gates.

He understands why the weatherman is pushing so hard: if they claim the outcropping by week's end, rumor has it the weatherman's family will parade him through the next swarming party, where perfumers will alter his scent to appeal to high-born females. A tender young boy like that will be devoured before sundown.

While Mesoth still grieves for the two high-fliers, he wonders: If they had offered him a firm date for his death, a chance to fulfill life's dream, how many would he sacrifice?

He wants to think he'd be kind, but nobody has made him the offer.

As he approaches the low gate where the petitioners clamor, tides of crawling males perch up on their legs. They rush the gate, gesturing with frantic motions: *I'm strong, I'm fearless, my webs are second to none.*

As always, his eyes pass over the flawless young males, the ones still gleaming from their last molting. No, Mesoth hunts for scars smeared beneath bright makeup, the prosthetic limbs, seeking the ones marked by love.

And as he points at the first worker, he —

Jaws clamp around his abdomen.

Mesoth goes limp with ecstasy.

The other males dance upon their hind legs, trying to get the female's attention, but it's no use: she lifts Mesoth up, her great fangs cradling him, so beautifully huge she rivals the mountain.

Then he sees the expensive silver jewelry dangling from her legs: the same crest as the weatherman's. Mesoth's pedipalps vibrate as he realizes she *owns* this mountain, she'll breed such powerful children within him. His thoughts dissolve in bliss as his flesh parts under her sharp fangs …

She opens up her second-jaws, patting him down with her pedipalps from chelicerae to spinnerets, licking every inch of his body. *Come on,* Mesoth begs, riding joy, *haul me back to your birthing chambers, have your way with me …*

Of course it's never that simple.

She places him onto on the ground, straddles him. She is so large that her abdomen's shadow covers him like an eclipse, having grown gorgeously monstrous over long years. The crowd flattens respectfully as She exposes her scentglands, rubs them all over Mesoth's body, marks him as Her own.

She wheels around to glare at Mesoth. They speak no common language; he is too small for Her to see his smallhands gesticulating, and She knows no one would have bothered to teach a male how to write. She has daubed him in the complex language of Her scent, an ephemeral grammar he lacks the odor-hairs to comprehend.

Instinct tells him the action means this: *I want you*. Yet he wishes he could speak the air as She does, comprehend the complex emotions conveyed by short-chain carbons and amines and hydroxycitronellae, so he could understand what about him she finds desirable.

She lowers herself to his level, descending from great heights, to nudge him. This gesture, he knows from long experience: *do you have enough of my scent to find me?* And yes, slathered in Her, even his substandard odor-hairs could track Her lair anywhere in the city. It is an invitation to stop by after work hours.

To court one of the most fecund females in the land.

He manages a weak nod through the drugged rapture of his shallow wounds. She bumps him affectionately, then scuttles up the mountainside to give orders to her son, the weatherman.

And when She has vanished from sight, they flock to him. The younger ones trace the outlines of his wounds, as if touching the injuries inflicted by a female might teach them some great secret. The older ones press their legs up against Mesoth's chitin, impregnating themselves with Her pheromones before slackening in gratitude: they thought they'd never scent a woman again.

You did it, they say. Except Mesoth doesn't know what he did. She chose him, and he never knows why.

This time. This time, he will go all the way.

Every night, after work, Mesoth eats a banquet and is eaten.

Her birthing chamber is a vast tapestry of elaborately-knotted webs, providing tiny footholds for clumsy newspawn. The knots are all spinnerette-white, freshly extruded; She must have many talented servants who clear away the dusty webs and weave new ones every morning.

There are great heaps of violet leaves for him to eat. She waits next to them, flexing Her odor-hairs anxiously. She makes space for him to sit beside Her — a mark of respect so great, his legs weaken.

He does not know what the leaves are, and has no way to ask. He might not even have a word to describe them: females have expanded responsibilities and expanded vocabularies. The sap oozing from the cut stems is sharp and piney.

Still, the room is wreathed in perfume — Her whispered reassurances to him in a language he cannot understand.

She reaches over with her smallest limb to push the leaves towards him.

Eat them, that shy gesture says, *so I may fall in love with you*.

Mesoth tucks into them. His natural odor is alluring, but not alluring enough: She is trying to help him, changing his chemistry to trigger Her lusts. She wants to want him, and doubtlessly She has paid greatly for these exotic herbs.

It is an honor. A brutal honor, as the leaves swell in his stomach and the drugs pulse through his lymphomatic systems.

She strokes his back as he convulses. Her touch is intended to comfort him, but Mesoth worries her caresses will wipe off his makeup. If She saw the marks from all the females who'd courted him before, She'd be revolted at how hard-used his body is …

She gathers him up tenderly to take little bites of him. She trembles with elation as She nips tiny segments out, snuffling his body as though searching for the treasure within him.

His flesh is made exquisite by Her attention; he never feels more alive than when he is in his lover's jaws, his impending death filling him with appreciation for the beauty She has provided.

He angles his body so She will not eat the hard knots of scars left by past lovers. He soars high on endorphins: She bites harder, deeper. Her stinger pokes out of its sheath, ready to impregnate him …

She collapses to the ground. He tumbles from her slackened jaws.

Is She embarrassed? Angry? Self-reproaching? He cannot tell. He would have had to be around enough females to read their body language. And what female would be with a male without a mating instinct to pull them together?

He inches toward Her, thoughts muddled by the herbs, gently tapping Her tarsus: *should I return?*

She sweeps her scent-gland across him: *yes. Return.* Her touch lights a new hope within him: when he returns tomorrow, She will have new remedies to solve the puzzle of his foul flesh.

They are united as one: him needing Her, Her needing him. Together they will forge a path to love.

And he is still filled with hope the next morning, when he arrives at work to discover another three males have sailed off to their deaths in the night.

The weatherman shrugs.

They died because of you, Mesoth says, raising his arms high so all the workers may see him speak. *Before we work again, you will get proper equipment to sense the changes in the wind.*

The weatherman cringes, reluctant to face down an incubated. The request will take many days —

Then the bridge will wait days! Mesoth waves. *Not another strand will be spun until these males are safe! Do you think their fathers sacrificed themselves so they could die to chance?*

The workers chase the weatherman out onto a thin ledge. The weatherman makes high-pitched keening noises, promising to send soldiers in to quell this rebellion, knowing it will be of no use: who would resist a beloved male in his last days?

To be a male in love, to have the end so dizzyingly in sight, is strength. Mesoth would have feared for his job before; now, he is intoxicated by death's proximity. He is already sacrificing himself for great causes; why not greater ones?

No great change ever came about but for a father's love, the saying goes. And as the weatherman pleads weakly that he can't get the equipment in, making concession after concession as the males riot, Mesoth understands the power of passion.

After weeks of experiments, Mesoth enters the chamber to see Her standing next to a pile of violet leaves.

His heart slows. Still, he shambles towards the leaves, shovels them into his mouth, hoping against hope.

The violet leaves are, at least, comparatively good to eat. Over the last few weeks, She has brought him increasingly pestilential concoctions: a crusty white bark that made his hairs fall out, acidic seeds that pockmarked his fangs, black mushrooms so vile that Mesoth coughed dark spores for weeks afterwards. He crawled to work, belly scraping the ground, keeping his job only by Her forbearance and the natural deference to sickly fathers.

And now, back to the first herbs.

He crunches the leaves down. Except when he convulses this time, She palpates him in confusion, searching him for answers.

Why is he so unworthy?

She heaves him off the ground, taking larger bites than ever before, the air pungent with Her frustration. Before, Her bites were precise wounds, weaving Her way delicately around his anatomy. Each puncture felt like a strand placed in a web, an elegant rising towards mortal injury.

These injuries feel random, angry, a murder instead of a pregnancy.

He struggles in Her grasp for the first time; She tears into him, hoping to find something delicious deeper inside him, some small place to lay Her eggs ...

Finally, the air stinking of rage, She sinks Her fangs deep into his cephalothorax. She bites deep into his shoulder's root, tearing his left bigleg free — not a clean disseveration, but a ragged chunk, the way you'd eat prey.

Mesoth flails his smallarms. *I'm being devoured*, he thinks, horrified, *not loved*. He grapples at Her maw, his reflexes jangled by his missing leg, his hemocyanin spilling out of the wound into sickly green puddles on the floor. She rips his midleft leg out …

Then flings him into the knotted web, collapsing in frustration.

Mesoth spasms as the wounds pucker, an amputation so deep the legs will never grow back. She champs her jaws on his severed legs — *my legs are over there,* he thinks, *not attached to me* — before crunching them into fragments.

Despite his maimed body, Mesoth tumbles out of the web. He no longer knows how to walk, with only six legs; his gait is a clumsy thing, smashing his jaw into the floor as he stutter-limps over to Her.

He feels sorrow for Her, for himself, for them. They wanted to make something grand. But he wasn't what She needed, and She had given him every last chance: even those final dismemberments had been Her last attempt to find the goodness within him.

She has changed color, so saddened her shell has turned a mourner's white.

He taps Her tarsus.

She flicks Her underhairs at him, filling the air with poison. *Get out.* Even that is a kindness: She could consume him in Her rage, no one would blame Her, Mesoth had wasted Her time with his polluted, eggless flesh.

And neither of them know why this didn't work.

Mesoth hobbles off, leaving hope behind.

Getting to work the next day is a labor in itself: climbing the mountain is near-impossible with fewer limbs, and more than once he reaches out with a phantom limb. He slides back, hanging unceremoniously from three legs.

The other workers climb past him, pretending he doesn't exist.

As he struggles onto the mountaintop, the weatherman is assembling the newest devices brought in: windsocks, glass tubes filled with air pressure-sensitive fluids, brass telescopes to view the horizon.

Such expensive equipment, the weatherman says. *I've been asked to find other ways to cut costs.*

He trains his many eyes on the gaps between Mesoth's legs, his hairs rippling with pleasure. Mesoth begins to protest that he could teach the new workers how to set strong anchor-webs — but he is no longer a father. He is a meek male who hopes to get a kind reference, and so he slinks home.

He almost has the hang of walking again by the time he climbs home.

Things aren't so bad, he thinks. His rent is paid up through the season. He's not so crippled yet that he needs to work at the chemical plant. And if the weatherman gives him a good reference — what male would blame a father for an exuberance of caring? — then he can probably get a job stringing prey-webs. With luck, he might even afford some prostheses — fake legs would never fool a male, but the females, well, they don't look much beyond the abdomen.

He settles into his wall's rough weave, stumps aching. At least he has his scent. Males with better-developed odor-hairs than he have told him his scent is alluring, he'll find a mate someday.

Speaking of scent …

He gulps down a packet of molting-herbs to help his broken shell loosen. His exoskeleton is too suffused with Her scent. He carefully plucks off the shattered portions She bit through, his remaining legs hitching painfully around Her wounds …

He piles the jagged chunks of chitin next to the other shells he has molted to move on, each saturated with the exotic aromas of all those who had loved and left him. There's the adolescence-soft shell he wore when he met the golden weaver who drew his first blood. The sleek shell he wore for the sequined mirror-mate who glittered so beautifully at dawn. The punctured shell from the tufted recluse who had leapt at him out from her lair, dragging him back to a whirlwind romance.

And now, placed carefully next to the rest, the jagged chunks from the immense socialite.

He shuffles the shells around with his remaining frontleg, stirring up miasmas of memory. He doesn't know why they left him, and they always leave scars.

He wonders whether he'll ever be enough for someone.

So much to do. He needs to see a physic, to see if the herbs She gave him has done long-term damage. He'll have to hunt for jobs, to figure out what swirls of makeup will cover his new wounds, to practice new weaving techniques to compensate for his lost limbs …

The television screen glows with yet another romantic comedy — and though he intends to practice weaving, Mesoth instead tucks his legs underneath himself and watches.

Somewhere, there's a female who wants him for who he is.

Somewhere, there's a connection so powerful it transcends language.

Somewhere, there's a love that sweeps aside all excuses, a romance so certain there's no need for courtship, just a life-long bond that gives both partners perfect meaning.

Mesoth watches the romances, his breath shallow, hoping against hope that one day he too will find perfect love.

ALISA SCHREIBMAN

HAMSA, HAMSA, HAMSA, TFU, TFU, TFU

"SIM, PAPAI." YES, DAD. Gabriela Costa Barros waved to the server ten chairs down the white sand beach from her and mimed signing her check. *"Vou chamá-lo quando eu chegar lá."* I'll call you when I get there. If she hurried, she'd just make the 11:41 flight.

So much for her sun-and-Metaxa-soaked compassionate leave.

The sun rose at the excruciating hour of 5:21am, Adana local time. Four hours, seventeen minutes, and 370.9 km later, Gabi exited the "taxi" she'd commandeered at the entrance to the excavation site at *Göbekli Tepe*.

Impatient with a raki-induced hangover, Gabi stopped the official guarding it with an upraised palm before he could say anything that would piss her off.

His eyebrows pinched tightly over the long hook of his nose.

She brandished her badge and then shoved it across the space between them.

Seeing the official *hamsa* that all signatory nations to the Treaty of Gehenna Basin recognized, he sighed. "Good morning, Agent Costa Barros. To what do we owe the pleasure of your visit?" he asked in English of an indeterminate origin.

Aside from the fact he'd obviously been watching American spy movies, it wasn't a bad choice. Even though they required operatives to speak at least one Middle Eastern language, the Department of Supernatural Operations conducted its official business in English.

Rather than playing guessing games with complexion and surnames, Gabi replied, "Demons," in kind, in the heavily accented, sixth, and least fluent of her working tongues. "There was a report?" Never mind that it wasn't an official report.

"If you will just wait —"

"Think about that a second."

A worried frown creased his entire face — *there you go* — and he handed her back her badge. Nervous now, he shifted his weight from one foot to the other.

"Will you require —"

"I'll be safer without, thanks." An escort would only complicate matters.

Curiosity got the better of Gabi while she wandered the stone rabbit warrens of the Neolithic site. What kind of people had lived here? Had they looked like the site-workers dressed in various shades of beige rags with their black hair and dark eyes?

A football bounced from an embankment into Gabi's path. At a wave of tittering laughter, she glanced up at the band of dust-caked children. A woman stood from a trench where she'd been sifting dirt. While reversing the bow in her back to stretch, she scolded them.

"*La bas*," Gabi replied in Arabic. *It's fine.* With a smile, she drop-kicked the ball back to the children.

Leave it to Amélia Graça da Costa to populate her dig-team with Syrian refugees. If she knew her father, whatever pests her grandmother had wanted her help with didn't worry him near as much as the refugees.

He worried too much. At nearly eighty, her grandmother scared soldiers to a stand-still with a single, withering glance. Yet, as the sun rose higher and sweat collected in uncomfortable, hard-to-wipe places, Avó's unfairly unlined face was no more in evidence than blue-eyed blondes.

She hadn't wanted to call attention to herself or Avó, but after a half an hour more of not finding her, Gabi broke down and asked a sketchpad-laden postdoc if he'd seen Dr. da Costa.

"Try her tent," she was informed and given no chance to inquire further before he hurried away.

Since when did Dr. Amélia Graça da Costa rest in her tent while others labored?

"¿Avó?" Gabi called quietly from the courtyard of the beige-on-beige Tent City that served as basecamp for her grandmother's excavation. "¿*Onde está?*" *Where are you?*

No one answered, and the hair stood up on the back of Gabi's neck. "He that dwelleth in the secret place of the Most High shall abide under the shadow of the Almighty …" she began. The 91st Psalm offered protection against the *mazzikim* most likely to be in a barren place like this if the "pests" were supernatural.

"¿Avó? It's not funny now. *Papai* said you needed my help."

A tent flap moved aside to let out her grandmother's voice, her native Portuguese long since weathered soft by the pronunciations of a dozen different towns: "Gabriela Lúcia Costa Barros, is that *fear* in your voice?"

Gabi let out a breath of relief and then scoffed. "As if. Now, what are you doing in your —"

Her grandmother emerged, the long, barely-silvered braid pulled over her shoulder doing a poor job of hiding an arm in a sling. Her sun-darkened skin did even less to hide the vertical split and yellowing bruise on her cheekbone or the still-shiny black eye above it.

"¡Avó!" Gabi dropped her bag and sprang forward like a gazelle; her heart pounded like a young rabbit. "What the hell happened?"

"Gehenna, *meu bem.*"

"Seriously? You're going to argue semantics at a time like —"

But her grandmother was shaking her head.

"Oh. You actually mean that." Carefully, Gabi embraced her grandmother. "Papai said ... but he didn't want me to call DSO to send in a team, so I thought —"

Her grandmother smoothed a hand against Gabi's cheek, bruised eyes soft with sorrow. "*Sim.* I'm sorry about Piotr, *carinho.* I liked the boy."

Only her grandmother would want to console her for the loss of her partner when she'd just been battered by demons.

"We can talk about my problems later." She scooped up her bag and held aside the tent flap for her grandmother who looked about as fragile as a tank. "Tell me everything."

"I know you can handle this, Costa Barros," came Wellesley the Weasel's response to her detailed summary of her grandmother's dealings with, at the very least, a pack of minor mazzikim and possibly worse. "It'll be a good way to ease back into things."

Gabi bit back a strangled scream. Twenty-four hours ago she'd been on indefinite compassionate leave. Now she was back in the field without so much as a psych how-do-you-do?

"Just let me know if anything comes up."

"I *am* letting you know, sir!" she all but shouted. Fortunately, or unfortunately, her boss at DSO had already rung off. Gabi growled and jerked irritably at her ponytail.

"I'm sure they know what's best, meu bem," Avó soothed from a rocking chair on the porch of a generously called "inn" in the nearest town.

"DSO doesn't know *dick!*"

Her grandmother barely batted an eyelash at the language, but somehow Gabi still felt like she'd been hauled to the headmistress's office. Perversely, she elaborated, "Fine. They know slightly less dick than most people."

Amused, her grandmother lifted an eyebrow over her unbruised eye. "I wonder ... maybe that should be *more* dick?"

Snorting back a laugh, Gabi paced the length of the porch and then went inside to exchange her euros to Turkish lira. Since she'd been on *compassionate leave,* she didn't have a fully-stocked exorcism kit with her.

When she returned, she knelt at Avó's side and scanned her face for signs of fear. Before she could say anything, Avó poked her in the shoulder with one very pointy finger.

"Go on. I'll be fine." She held up her cell phone.

"You didn't call me before."

"You'd have asked questions."

"So why didn't you at least tell *Papai* that you'd been hurt?"

"Oh —" Avó waved dismissively. "You know how your father is. He'd have insisted on coming down here."

"And he could've dealt with the mazzikim, too." Gabi gave her grandmother a pointed look, but she knew better than to expect an answer to the question: *So why did you insist on me?*

She'd come no closer to an answer when, as she walked around the picnic bench that had fractured her grandmother's radius and ulna, an invisible force rushed past her, catching an arm and spinning her around. The small bells braided into the ends of her hair tinkled faintly and the pressure on her arm ceased.

Invisible. Capable of physical contact but moved like the wind. Probably mazzikim.

Gabi raised her hands and turned them outward to display the hamsas inked in black, and all important blue, on them. Since the fingers of the design mapped to her own fingers, the tattoos effectively turned her hands into the powerful ancient symbol used to ward off everything from the Evil Eye to crib death — and from the deepening shadow of the tent opposite Avó's, the being responded in a whiny wail.

"Knock it off," Gabi commanded, and compelled by the power of her blood, her faith, and the color blue, it stopped. "Tell me your name."

The *shush-shush-shush* of a subtle body of air and fire shaking its head was the only answer.

"Fine." Worth a try, but the mazzikim, the pickpockets and sneak-thieves of the demon world, traded on their wiles.

So did Gabi. She poked around in her pack while she hummed a little Miranda Lambert, "Gunpowder and Lead." Neither of those were effective against spirit bodies, but it sounded the right kind of badass. "Hm. Salt, indigo ink, parchment ..."

"Noooooo!" it wailed again.

"Well ..." *Got you.* "Okay. You tell me why you're harassing Dr. da Costa, and I won't bind you."

"Truly, you are righteous."

They had such ingratiating voices. Even knowing they *could* do immense damage if motivated, Gabi had a hard time taking them seriously. She gestured with one hand, hiding the hamsa to allow it to move.

The demon didn't take that bait, but it did answer, "Dybbuk!"

... fuck.

Gabi drew a slim blade from a sheath in her bag and pricked the tip of her right forefinger. She squeezed it until a drop of thick crimson welled up and then smeared it on the bench, something the demon had touched. "By blood and by faith, I adjure you: Leave this place forever and pay Dr. da Costa and her people no further heed."

"LIES!" the mazzikim screeched. "LIAR!"

"I didn't lie." Demons thought like lawyers. And if you didn't keep your word, they didn't have to keep theirs. "I said I wouldn't bind you, not that I wouldn't banish you." Gabi took a long breath and began again. "By blood and by faith, by truth and by will, I compel you ..."

The demon keened its fury. From the rush of wind, Gabi knew it had propelled itself upwards.

Don't think about it. Don't think about it. First get rid of any more mazzikim. Then worry about the –

Don't think about it.

"I heard a scream." The postdoc she'd spoken to before, minus his sketchpad and plus a healthy five o'clock scruff trotted between two tents from the hillside *Avó* had 'tumbled' down. "Are you all right?"

How could she be? Piotr had been killed by a dybbuk.

"Did you push Dr. da Costa down the hill?" Gabi demanded of the student who'd just introduced himself as *Omer Ital Barzani, but I prefer Ital.*

"What?" His expression shuffled like a CD changer looking for something to play. It settled on wide-eyed, appalled indignation. "No!"

No, outright. Said once only. Uncertainty without looking away: multiple emotions, not fabrication. Good.

Gabi's expression, on the other hand, never wavered. As far as she knew, she didn't even blink; something she got from her grandmother. "Are you lovers?"

His long slender nose seemed to curl along with his lips. "No."

No need to be offended, jerkface. "It wouldn't be the first time she's had a much younger man. Were you jealous of someone?"

"No!"

No hemming, no hawing. Straight-up denial. Also good.

"Are you sure you didn't have some reason to want her out of the way? Advancement? A failing —"

"No." Jerkface pinched his brows together so hard it looked like it hurt. "Listen. I don't know who you are. I don't actually care. But for your information, Dr. da Costa is one of the finest scholars of Middle Eastern archaeology in the world. I'm honored to work with her. She's been nothing but supportive of me and my work —"

"Just what exactly is your work?"

"Combat archaeology if you must know," he said, obviously peeved to have been cut off before clearing his name.

It didn't need clearing any more, though. She read people. It was her thing. One of three skills responsible for her being solicited by DSO. "So you're interested in weapons and tactics, how to cause maximal damage with minimal effort?" Now she was just goading him.

Before she could profile the calculation in his eyes, he'd caught her around the back of her neck and his mouth crashed down over hers. His tongue pushed into her mouth —

Her fist connected with his jaw.

"Ow." He sounded like a man who'd just bitten the hell out of his tongue.

Gabi flipped open her badge. "Special Agent Costa Barros, Department of Supernatural Operations. What the hell were you thinking?"

"That a pretty woman would be easily distracted by sexual attentions," he oozed.

Just the tone made her feel like she'd kill for a bath. It sounded nothing like the cultured, polished Arabic they'd been speaking a moment before.

Gabi blinked.

Fuck. Fuck. *Fuck.*

She reached for the bloody blade still resting on the picnic bench. "What do you want, *dybbuk*?"

"I thought we'd established what I wanted." More oozing. She was surprised he didn't slither right onto his ass with all that oil and smarm.

"Not from me." Her mouth felt drier and more inadequate than all the beige in *Göbekli Tepe*, and if it didn't slow down, she was going to vomit up her own heart. "Here. With the doctor." A jerk of her chin was pure bravado, especially since everything else had turned to salt crystal (she knew she shouldn't have looked back on Piotr).

The dybbuk tilted its head, almost birdlike, in curiosity; Ital was clearly no longer in charge. "Why do you care?"

Care. Her? *No.*

Except it was a clue. It wanted to be heard. It wanted her to care. "Why wouldn't I?"

"You're here. Helping her." It cast its hand out toward the dig, well outside her field of vision even if she dared turn her head. "Helping *them.*"

Gabi took in a long breath and then released it, easing the tension out of her body the best she could. Hopefully, the dybbuk didn't have her profiling skills. "Helping them with what?"

"Helping them get out!" The dybbuk roared, like a lion in pain.

Maybe she could pull its thorn. Get rid of it without having to hurt Ital. "The Syrians?" she asked, almost gently, almost as though she cared.

The dybbuk flinched; Ital's proud, straight carriage all but imploded.

"I'm not helping them." Gabi shook her head and took a step forward, even attempting a smile. "Like I said, I'm with the Department of Supernatural Operations. Syrian refugees aren't my concern. Dybbukim are." *Carefully, carefully.* "How can I help you?"

"You would do that?" Suspicion joined the vocal slime.

"As long as it doesn't involve hurting them myself," she assured it and then sat down on the bench, making sure to leave the smear of blood between her and the dybbuk. "Come tell me why you're here."

Cautiously, gaze sliding to her blade, the dybbuk moved Ital's body forward to the bench.

Telegraphing every move, Gabi shifted the blade to her outer hand. "If you don't talk to me, I can't help you."

The dybbuk scowled but sat, then scooched away from the blood like it burned.

It might, actually, but now wasn't exactly the time to ask. She kept her gaze steady on what had been a handsome face with its owner in control.

"They blew me up," the dybbuk finally said.

"The Syrians did?" Not impossible. There was a war going on. Or three.

It nodded.

"Why?"

"I don't know!" If it was possible to whine while shouting, the dybbuk did. "I was just a barista!"

As tempting as it was, Gabi held off asking its name. Too soon and it might bolt or turn on her. Then this exorcism would get messy. Instead: "Where?"

"Golan Heights."

Ah. "You're Israeli."

It nodded and folded its hands in its lap.

She almost felt sorry for it. Almost. "Did you know them?"

A shake of its head this time.

Even as disembodied spirits, dybukkim possessed some level of intelligence. Once in a body, it would have sought answers. "They were never caught?"

"No."

Gabi forced herself to brighten, smile, and hold out a hand to it. "Then I can help."

Another birdlike head-tilt made the former-barista-in-the-scholar's-body seem childlike, almost. Clearly not as intelligent as Ital, anyhow. "How?"

"I may work in Supernatural Operations, but I have access to everyone's databases. Interpol, Israeli security, Saudi security …" Technically true, though she rarely needed it. "If there are records, I can find them."

Now the dybbuk straightened up, pulling Ital's shoulders back into a semblance of the scholar's strong posture. "Really?"

"Yes. Really."

"Why would you?"

"Would it stop you from pushing helpless old women —" *Snort.* "Down embankments for employing Syrian refugees?"

The dybbuk started to speak but then paused to reconsider.

"Wouldn't you rather have your real killers punished instead of hurting people who have nothing to do with it?" Like they did to you, she left unsaid, rather than risk pissing him off.

He seemed to hear it anyway. "It would be better. An eye for an eye, instead of an eye for any eye."

"Exactly." Now Gabi did offer a smile. After all, dybbuks were people, too. Sort of. "So, I help you, you stop hurting people who had nothing to do with how you died?"

He nodded. "Deal. What's next?"

"Just tell me your name so I can search the records." Casual. Super-casual. Doesn't mean anything. Totally irrelevant. Ho-hum. If Gabi could whistle tunefully, she would have.

"Eitan Ben-Reuven," he answered almost cheerfully.

Gabi bit the inside of her cheek to stop herself from crowing. "Hello, Eitan Ben-Reuven. I'm Gabi." She reached into her bag, hoping Eitan would think she'd gone for a notepad or a tablet.

"I'm not sorry I kissed you," he said while she rooted around for what she needed. "You're nice. And pretty. Ital doesn't have a girlfriend, so there's been no knocking boots since I died."

"I'm not sorry you did either, Eitan Ben-Reuven." Gabi produced a flask, a white candle, and a lighter which she very quickly put to use. She brandished the lit candle like a villager's pitchfork. "I wouldn't have known you weren't Ital if you hadn't."

Eitan hissed and pulled back, fury darkening already dark eyes and drawing strong brows into vicious slashes.

"I command you to leave the body of Omer Ital Barzani and trouble him no more." The pure force of Gabi's will wrapped around the possessed body, holding both Eitan and Ital in place.

"The deal is broken!"

"No, it's not. I said I'd help you get justice and I will. *After* you give Ital back his body."

Eitan's skill with head-whipping might've given Linda Blair a run for her money, but Gabi flipped the hand with the unstoppered flask and her hamsa ended the agitation. "I adjure you, Eitan Ben-Reuven, to leave that body at once. It doesn't belong to you."

The flame guttered on a blast of spirit-wind. A chill crept over Gabi's hands and arms. She shook her own head until the bells on her ponytail tinkled. For a timeless instant, the world seemed to hold its breath —

The flask glowed red.

"I will find out who did this to you, Eitan," she promised softly. An exorcist's strength came from her will and her belief in her own righteousness; of course she would.

A tear trickled down Gabi's cheek as she stoppered the bottle and put out the flame.

Piotr.

"Who *are* you? And why does it feel like I ran into a left hook?" came a cultured voice at her side.

"Right, actually," she said to no one in particular.

Ital had already passed out.

"I really kissed you?" Jerkface asked a few minutes into her recitation of the events leading to his collapse.

"It wasn't you." Gabi pulled open the ice chest in her grandmother's tent in search of something cold to put on his jaw.

"You don't have to sound relieved."

Not dignifying that with an answer, Gabi whipped a bag of semi-frozen peas across the tent.

Jerkface — he was back to Jerkface because he apologized for making her cry and it had nothing to do with him — caught them one-handed.

"He was a nice guy for a male chauvinist pig of a dybbuk." And Israeli, unlike Jerkface.

"Who threw your grandmother down an embankment." Jerkface winced as he pressed the peas against his jaw. "What was he even doing in Turkey anyhow?"

Gabi shrugged as she sat at the small table where *Avó* did her notes. "Dybukkim aren't long on logic. He probably attached himself to the jacket of the first Syrian he found or something and ended up here when it got passed to one of the refugees."

"So why me?"

Another shrug. "You knew the incantations for summoning mazzikim."

"So does your grandmother."

Instead of asking how he knew that — it was probably an article she'd written — Gabi pulled out the glowing red flask Eitan inhabited. "Male chauvinist," she muttered, but the strength of her voice had fallen away and the flask had taken her heart with it. Its match rested more than a thousand miles away in a locked desk drawer, where it would stay until she found enough forgiveness to deal with it.

"It's not your fault." An ice-chilled hand squeezed her shoulder.

Startled from her reverie, Gabi glared up at him.

He stood his ground. "You did what you had to do."

"What would you know about it?"

"I was there, remember?"

You did the right thing, Gab.

How would you know?

I was there, remember?

Lips pressed tightly together trembled against the onslaught of the grief that had sent her on compassionate leave. "She shot him."

Jerkface crouched beside her but didn't ask any stupid questions.

So, slowly, haltingly, Gabi told him the whole story, the real story that wasn't anywhere in the files.

Shiri had been killed in a drunk driving accident she'd caused after her boyfriend confessed to having a gay affair. She'd come back to "avenge" herself. Smart, driven, and in the body of a Parisian police officer, she'd proven near impossible to track down until Piotr had gotten the bright idea to pose as the ex's lover. The meeting took a bad turn, and Gabi knifed Shiri's host just as she shot Piotr. Gabi had cast the dybbuk from the fallen officer and called for an ambulance. Anne-Marie survived, but Piotr bled out in her lap, his last words that it wasn't her fault.

"No wonder you punched me," he said quietly.

Gabi summoned up a pained smile. "It wasn't you, Ital."

She'd been asleep maybe ten minutes when the wind bellowed and the tent did its best impression of Auntie Em's house.

Gabi pulled on her boots and a sweater to ward off the wind and overnight chill. "Ital?"

No answer.

Apparently, he'd ignored her suggestion to spend the night in her grandmother's tent with her in case there were more mazzikim.

Brilliant.

A flashlight in one hand and her kit slung over her shoulder, Gabi emerged into Tent Hell and promptly ate a mouthful of hair. *Tent Gehenna, meu bem,* her grandmother's voice sounded in her head.

"Ital?"

The wind swallowed her voice.

Ignoring the creeping dread and deja vu, Gabi moved methodically from one partial windbreak to the next. Each time she stopped, she swept the light in an arc ahead of her to look for debris or worse.

Seeing nothing and no one, Gabi kept to her search, one meter at a time. Eventually the cause would reveal itself. The imprint of a cock's feet in the dirt, untouched by the wind. A spirit force grabbing her —

An ox-headed storm-demon plowed through a half-downed tent bawling furiously and followed by Ital, who was carrying a two-handed axe.

Combat archaeology.

Gabi suppressed the urge to smile, raced to his side, and snarled, "You couldn't have mentioned the shedim you summoned?" instead.

"It wasn't me, remember?" he yelled as he swung the weapon at the demon's ... flank?

Now she did smile, choked on a laugh when the end of her ponytail filled her mouth again. "How did you even hear that?"

"What?" He grinned at her, his teeth white and gleaming even in the beiged-out night.

Rolling her eyes, she gestured that she needed to get out in front of the shedim. Like bodybuilders in a roid-rage, shedim tended to forget they could fly, or really do anything other than run and make wind.

Ital didn't bother trying to make himself heard, just slammed the flat side of the axe into the demon. It spun to face him. The demon raked its clawed wing across Ital's chest.

Storm-wind threw her howl of denial back in her face.

It whipped a cyclone of sand around the demon and Ital and they disappeared from sight.

Don't get attached. Most of you won't survive six months in the field.

"Fuck that noise," Gabi growled into the dark-beige night.

She crouched low beneath the major gusts where the sand only eddied in swirls around her feet and didn't cut her face. Quickly, she wrapped her head and shoulders in a sky-blue cashmere pashmina from her kit, then prostrated herself in the dirt.

"Tell me your name, great shedim," she whispered reverently into the wind and put every ounce of her will into it. It was a risk, one that opened her to spiritual attack, but once upon a time, the shedim had been gods. "Tell me who you are. Please, lord." Lowercase, but it wouldn't hear that, if it heard her at all.

Nothing happened.

"Please," she begged. "Please, great lord."

The wind slowed and seemed almost to pause and consider. Her light, on the ground but aimed out ahead of her, revealed Ital curled over his knees, clutching his torso.

"Please, storm lord. My people worshipped you once," Gabi murmured.

The ox-headed demon turned toward her, leaving Ital to his fate as its rage seemed to die away. Its wings folded down. "Very well, young one. If you will know, I am Pazuzu, god of the South-West wind and son of Hanbi."

Demon of the South-West wind. Even in its own mythology, Pazuzu had never been a god, and arrogance had always been its besetting sin.

"Pazuzu." As though a sculpture made of sand, the demon's form shuddered and shivered. It tried to bellow up a proper wind but it could only bawl. "Zuzu." The edges of its wings and horns and hooves eroded and its substance began to trickle away. "Zu."

Before the demon lost its battle with being, Gabi was up on her feet and racing across the now quiet Tent Gehenna. She dropped at Ital's side and caught his face in her hands.

"Nice work with Paz," he coughed.

She winced and pushed him back to see how bad the damage was — and found nothing but torn clothes and a few minor scratches across an inked hamsa on his left pectoral muscle. A hamsa inscribed with a Star of David and the Aleph-Lamet-Dalet on the chest of an interesting, compassionate, intelligent, sexy scholar saying, "Hamsa, hamsa, hamsa, tfu, tfu, tfu," to ward off the demon he'd almost invoked again.

"You're *Jewish*?" Gabi demanded, unable to tear her gaze from his perfectly intact chest.

"One second you look like an avenging angel and the next you want to know my faith?" Ital looked ... adorably confused.

Gabi took a note from her grandmother and declined to clarify. "Why didn't you tell me?"

"When did you want me to do that? When you were punching not-me? When you were grieving for your boyfriend? Or maybe in the middle of battle with a storm-demon?" He shook his head and climbed to his feet. "I knew you had issues, Gabriela, but I didn't think you were a bigot."

"What?" Now Gabi wanted to clarify. "He wasn't my boyfriend."

"That's not really the point."

"Yes, it is. If I'd known you were Jewish, I would've at least kissed you good-night."

"From bigotry to fetishization in under sixty seconds."

"Oh, for fuck's sake."

Gabi pulled out her cell phone and, heedless of the hour, texted Avó. *Why didn't you tell me he was Jewish?*

As though she'd been waiting for the question, her grandmother responded immediately. *You would have suspected my motives.*

Gabi snorted back a laugh. *Would I have been wrong?*

No answer. Shrugging, she tucked her phone back in her jeans pocket.

"What was that about?" Ital looked as prickly as he sounded.

For an answer, Gabi hauled herself up along his arms, hooked her hand behind his neck, and released a half-dozen emotions into a hard, edgy kiss. Eventually, he relented and wound his arm around her, which steadied her knees gone weak from the adrenaline draining out of her.

"I'm Jewish, too, jerkface," she whispered. For a long moment, eyes closed and tension fading with the warmth of physical contact, Gabi silently gave thanks she wouldn't be burying her impromptu partner. "My dad's a rabbi. He'd kill me if I brought home anyone but a nice, Jewish boy."

"Oh." Smiling, Ital pulled a sandy lock of her hair from her lips and then erased the memory of the dybbuk's kiss with one of his own. "You know, we did this backwards. I've already met your grandmother."

Rati Mehrotra

REAL WOMEN ARE DANGEROUS

THE TROUBLE STARTED WHEN Jai found out where the women were hiding. I didn't believe him at first — there were so few left on the planet. Especially *our* part of the planet, which already had millions more men than women even before the Femonza outbreak. But Jai was utterly convinced.

"My sensor picked her up," he told me at the New Year's Eve office party in the Tej Hotel. "Walking into an electronics store as cool as you please, just as if she was a man. She was dressed like one, of course, but I got the genetic readout, clear as anything. I followed her out and saw her go into ..."

"Quiet," I hissed. I glanced around the crowded room, but no one seemed to have heard. "You and your stupid sensors. You'll land us both in jail."

"More snacks, sir?" the house robot trilled in my ear, nearly giving me a heart attack. Jai helped himself to a chicken seekh kebab, and the robot glided away to a group of our colleagues nearby.

Jai jabbed a finger in its direction. "Once those were real. Imagine? Real women serving you. Real women giving you a massage. Real women ..."

"... being doctors and engineers and scientists," I said. "I know. What's your point?" Not that I was interested. Jai was always going off on these tangents.

Lights flashed and someone began to sing *Auld Lang Syne*. The countdown would begin soon. Another year, another missed promotion, another 'informal' chat with the company head about how I wasn't living up to my potential. Top student at the Bioengineering Institute of Pune, and what did I have to show for it? A lousy fifty thousand a week job at a second-rate organ manufacturer. My mother would have died of shame if she hadn't died of the Female-Only-Influenza pandemic twenty years ago. Of course, if she'd known of the clandestine little research project that was taking up all my time and energy, she'd have disowned me *before* dying of shame.

I wrenched my mind back from the unproductive turn it had taken.

"... knew that modified sensor would come in handy. I've been looking for them for years. Stands to reason the government would hide the survivors. Can you imagine the chaos if it came out? Men would just fling themselves on that building and tear each other apart. It would be like the Emergency all over again."

I winced. The Emergency in Delhi had lasted almost four years before the government took control of the situation. I could still remember the news feeds, the undistilled horror of it.

"Not everyone is as idiotic as you," I said. "Real women are dangerous. I wouldn't go near one, not if you paid me. The ones who've survived might be carriers. That woman had no business walking into an electronics store and exposing everyone to her germs. I suggest you go in for a Complete Clean."

I couldn't help grinning as I said that. Jai had to endure a Complete Clean — physical and mental — a couple of months ago when he was bitten by a stray dog he'd adopted. The physical part of the Clean is easy. It's the mental re-training that's agony. But there's no getting out of it. They don't want you indulging in deviant behaviors, after all. Strays are supposed to be euthanized, not brought into your apartment and fed milk-soaked bread.

Jai stiffened and glared at me. "You don't get it, Shyam. There are actual women living in Delhi. Today, in the year 2048!"

The lights dimmed and one of the walls turned into a firework display. A DJ began the countdown. "The year 2049," I said. "And that's Dr. Shyam, if you please."

Jai snorted. "Fat lot of good your doctorate has been. You'd have been better off trying to find a cure for Femonza rather than trying to replicate hearts and livers. Who *cares* about hearts and livers?"

Infected men who would die without replacement surgery, I could have said, but didn't. There wasn't any cure for Femonza; Jai knew that.

The countdown finished and the room erupted in cheers. The lights came on. My colleagues lined up at the elevators to the private pods up on the fortieth floor. Once a year, after the New Year's Eve party, we could avail of the services of Ayesha models, all at company expense. The latest Ayeshas were the best, almost indistinguishable from the 2017 beauty queen they were modeled after. Without her germs, of course. Not that I knew. Thirty minutes with an Ayesha cost more than six weeks of my salary, and I had never been able to make myself push through the lines at the office party. It just seemed pointless when I could get what I needed easily enough at home with my vag-sim.

Jai tugged my shirtsleeve. "Come on. Let's get out of here."

"And go where?"

Jai didn't bother to respond. He always knew where to go and have the most miserable time possible. Last year he'd dragged me to the Lotus temple for the ringing of the bells — 108 times, one for each human defilement. I hoped we weren't going there again.

Outside it was raining — cold winter rain, the kind that sneaks into your lungs and gives you pneumonia. I shivered and thought of my warm bed.

"Jai, I need to go home."

"Shut up, Shyam. What you need is a drink and a fuck, in that order."

I rolled my eyes. "Not the red light district. Please."

Jai hailed a cab. "You know your problem? You lack human contact. You need a little love to get your creative juices flowing, get that promotion that's been eluding you for the last three years."

"Jai, you're a fool." I followed him into the cab, glad of the darkness so he couldn't see my face. Okay, so I hadn't had a promotion in three years. This was also how long I had been working on my personal project. Even Jai didn't know about it. But the day I succeeded — if I ever succeeded — the whole world would know.

Jai gave the cabbie the name of the street and the cab jerked ahead. I could've sworn the driver smirked. Another pair of losers looking to get laid on the last night of the year.

It took almost an hour to get to Chandini market. Yellow streetlights, dim red bars, and the goods preening themselves in windows and strutting down the street, waggling their butts in front of cars cruising by with open windows. Chandini market was the home of the genetically modified and the factory discards. Much, much cheaper than the Ayeshas. The authorities turned a blind eye. Heck, the authorities probably came here, too.

We got out of the cab and went into a smoky bar, paying twenty thousand each at the door. There was a free drink — Scotch on the rocks — and a strip show, followed by a 3D simulated porn movie. When the movie started, some of the customers embraced each other. A little later, fights broke out and curses drowned out the moans, on-screen and off. Half-way through, right on cue, the depression hit. We pushed our way out of the bar.

Outside I breathed the cold, foggy air, trying to clear my head. Two in the morning and the crowd was beginning to thin. We leaned on the metal railings that separated the pavement from the street. I glanced at Jai. The rain had stopped, but his cheeks gleamed wet in the streetlight.

"I'm thirty-eight," he said. "What am I doing with my life and my education? What are you doing?"

"We're the lucky ones, remember?" I said, although my head was pounding and my mood was black. "The ones with the Y chromosome. The ones who don't have a trace of infection. Many men weren't so lucky."

Jai spat on the ground. "You call this luck?" he snarled. He shook his fist at the sky. "The gods have deserted us. Or maybe the goddesses have deserted the gods. This is our punishment for centuries of femicide. Shiva, where is your Shakti? Vishnu, where is your Lakshmi? Tell them we repent!"

People turned around to stare. Such outbursts are not uncommon in Chandini market, but I hailed a cab anyway. No point prolonging this night, which already felt way too long.

"I'm going to get ahold of a real woman," said Jai when I dropped him off at his building. "It's my resolution for the new year."

I didn't say anything. I thought he'd be fine after a good night's sleep, once the alcohol had worn off. And really, what could I have said that would have made any difference?

Jai didn't come in to work all week. He didn't pick up his phone either. I dropped in at Human Resources to ask after him, and the manager said he was on sick leave.

I waited until the weekend to visit him. I thought perhaps he'd adopted another stray, or maybe he was just sulking.

The building bot scanned my retina and relayed the information to Jai's apartment. Several minutes passed before I was granted entry. I wondered about that. Maybe he was really sick. I found my anxiety mounting as the elevator soared up to the thirtieth floor. By the time I reached his apartment, I had convinced myself that he had picked up a serious bug in Chandini market.

The door flew open and Jai stood in front of me, rumpled but healthy. There was an expression on his face, half-triumphant, half-defiant, that I hadn't seen before. Not since the night he peed in front of the dean's office, at any rate.

"Shyam. Just the man I wanted to see." He pulled me in and slammed the door shut.

"What's the matter? Why haven't you been coming in to work?" I demanded, walking in. His small flat looked the same as ever, scarlet cushions on a coffee-coloured divan, three walls lined with screens, the fourth leading to the hygiene cabinet.

"I have a visitor," he replied. "Sit down and you will see."

I sat on the divan, thinking that Jai would have real trouble with HR this time. You needed a medical certificate for sick leave longer than a day.

One of the screens slid back and a woman stepped through. I knew right away it was a woman and not a bot by how utterly *ordinary* she looked. Nothing like an Ayesha. No make-up, no style, no hour-glass figure. Just blue jeans and a loose white T-shirt and limp, straight hair tucked behind her ears. In her hands she held a tray, balancing a cup.

She walked right up to me. I was frozen, or I suppose I'd have done something. Run screaming to the hygiene cabinet, probably.

"Tea?" she asked and bent forward, the front of her shirt falling open. I couldn't help staring.

"I told you," crowed Jai. "Told you we'd have a real woman serving us one day." That was when she spilled the scalding tea on my lap.

"Shit!" I leaped up and hopped around. I must have looked ridiculous because she covered her mouth and laughed.

Jai hustled me into his closet and gave me a pair of dry trousers, and advised me not to make a fool of myself in front of Devyani again.

A little later I found myself sitting on the edge of the divan, across from the woman Jai had called Devyani. She perched on a stool opposite, smiling shyly at me. She was younger than I had expected — she must have been just a baby when Femonza hit. But even if she hadn't caught the infection, she could be a carrier. I began to sweat.

"Even being in the same room as her is dangerous," I blurted out.

Jai snorted. "Don't be silly. Devyani is not a carrier." He turned to her. "Don't mind him, please. He's not used to the company of women."

"That's okay," said Devyani. "He won't tell anyone, will he?"

"No way," said Jai. "He's my oldest buddy, way back from college. We can trust him."

"Trust me?" I said. "Sure. But you'll be found out anyway." I pointed to her. "She's gone missing from wherever she's supposed to be. People will be looking for her — people with guns and listeners. Maybe they're listening to us right now, working out how to extract her and dispose of the two of us with the minimum mess."

"I was very careful," said Devyani. "I made sure I wasn't followed. They don't guard us every minute, you know. They think the stories of rape and murder are enough to keep us in the facility. It works for most of the women."

"Obviously didn't work for you," I said, "or you wouldn't be here, endangering the life of my friend."

Jai stood up. "Now Shyam, don't take that tone. She didn't want to come here. But she needed a place to hide and I offered my apartment."

"Could be a government agent," I said. "They use women as bait sometimes to trace fools like you."

"Are you a government agent?" Jai asked Devyani.

"Of course not," she said.

"There you are," said Jai. "Satisfied?" He dropped a possessive hand on her shoulder. "Devyani ran away because she didn't want to become an industrial womb, like her sisters."

She covered her face with her hands. "I'm sorry if I land you in trouble," she said in a muffled voice, "but I didn't know where else to go."

Jai squeezed her shoulder. "Stay with us as long as you wish," he said. "Right, Shyam?"

"Right," I said. "What's this about an industrial womb?"

She raised a tear-stained face and I felt like a heel for doubting her. "You should know they haven't been able to replicate womb-like conditions for growing fetuses."

I made myself stay expressionless as I nodded. Of course, it was a major issue. The population had literally halved in one month and there was no way to sustain it. Cultured cell lines could be used to grow an endometrium; the problem lay in the interface and the composition of embryonic growth factors.

"They use us to reproduce," said Devyani. "The women who survived. Some of us are carriers but others are naturally resistant, and they hope to produce enough resistant females to one day bring the population growth rate back to zero. We're fertilized at the age of eighteen and it doesn't stop for years, not until we're fifty-five. Can you imagine what it's like, making babies year after year after year? What it does to your body, despite the best care?" She shuddered.

No, of course I couldn't. "Is the plan working?" I asked.

She shrugged. "I suppose. There were about one hundred and fifty girls and women in Delhi in 2028. Now there are over two thousand of us."

"Two thousand!" I stood up and began to pace. "Jai, you're in deeper shit than I thought. You've seen this place, haven't you? Where the women are being kept?"

He nodded. "I followed Devyani there a couple of times, although I didn't try to enter. It's just an ordinary-looking building in Gurgaon. We didn't even talk in the electronics store, just exchanged notes."

"Good," I said, my brain working overtime. "There's a small chance they actually don't know where she is. Unless they scan the security feeds from the store and detect the note-passing. Maybe we should try and scramble the feeds, just to be on the safe side."

"I already did," said Jai. "See, I'm a step ahead of you."

"Anyone for more tea?" said Devyani.

I declined the tea and left a little later, promising to stay in touch. I suppose I felt a bit jealous of the way she looked at him, the way she touched him. Over four hundred thousand males in Delhi, and she'd chosen him.

Not that I wanted her, of course. She was Jai's problem. But that night, after I had done a complete physical in the hygiene cabinet and slipped into bed with my vag-sim, it was Devyani's dusky face that floated in front of my sleepless eyes.

*

I kept myself busy the next week. I got a free check-up at e-health, just in case Devyani was a carrier. Then I hacked into Jai's company account and uploaded a forged medical certificate for him. Cost three weeks' pay — Jai's, not mine.

For the rest of it, I threw myself into my work. I felt like I was close, on the verge of a breakthrough in my project. But something fundamental about the stability of my model continued to elude me.

I tried not to think too much about the two of them — what they were doing, whether they had been traced, what Jai was planning. He was the closest I had to a friend, but Devyani's arrival had changed things. I guess I was hoping she'd just go away, back to the facility, and things could go back to the way they'd been. Or maybe I hoped for something else and just didn't want to admit it.

One night, about a week later, Devyani showed up at my place. I knew it was her because the building bot — not recognizing her retinal scan — sent me a picture of her face. I buzzed her in, trying to compose myself.

"What happened?" I said as soon as she was inside. "Is Jai okay?"

Instead of answering, she shrugged off her raincoat and flopped down on the sofa. "I'm so tired," she said. "I walked all the way here because I didn't want to risk the train. It must be over four kilometers."

"Have they taken Jai?" I demanded. "Where is he?"

She gave a mocking smile. "Very concerned about your friend, aren't you? Well, you don't have to worry. He's safe and sound in his apartment."

I didn't understand. "Then why are you here?"

"Don't have anywhere else to go. I found your address in his phone when he was sleeping."

I reached for my cell. "He'll be really worried about you. I'd better tell him you're here."

She leaned forward and grabbed my sleeve. "No. He kicked me out. We had a fight and he told me he never wanted to see my face again." She must have noticed my disbelieving expression because she snapped, "If you don't believe me, then go ahead and call him."

I sat down next to her and exhaled. Jai was okay. They'd had a fight, that was all. It must have been pretty serious for him to kick her out. That wasn't like him. I'd have to talk to him about it.

"Can I get you anything to eat or drink?" I asked.

She gave a grateful smile. "Please. I've had nothing since last night."

I hurried to the food-maker, glad of something to do. Her presence made me nervous, even though I'd established she wasn't a carrier.

Later, over cheese sandwiches and masala chai, she told me more about herself. Women at the facility were trained to be more than just wombs. Devyani was a teacher and philosophy was her passion. She talked of Fitch, Kant, and Aurobindo as if they were old friends.

"My version of the paradox of knowability," she said, draining the last of her tea. "Not everything that is true can be known, and not everything that is known is true. We are separate egos locked in bags of skin, thrown into a world we cannot understand, imprisoned by our history, enigmas even to ourselves."

"What is the solution?" I asked, fascinated.

"What is the question?" She got up and smiled. "Thanks for the tea and sandwiches. I'm going to use your hygiene cabinet, if that's all right."

"Sure." I rose and cleared the table, and folded it back against the wall. When I'd finished, I saw that the screen to my sleep pod was open. I walked over, hoping Devyani hadn't found my vag-sim.

She had. She was standing next to my bed holding it, turning it over in her hand. "What's this?" She sounded genuinely puzzled.

I swallowed my embarrassment. "A toy. Some version of which just about every straight male uses."

She inspected it with interest. "Cool. So you put your thing here and ... what're the wires for?"

"Fantasy overlay," I said, hoping the shortness of my answer would give her the hint to stop talking.

She tossed my vag-sim on the floor. "We can do better than that, can't we?" And she pulled her shirt off over her head.

I don't know what I expected. I'd never slept with a woman before, so I didn't have anything to compare it with. It was nothing like the vag-sim, nothing like my limited experience of Chandini market. It was both wonderful and terrifying. When it was over, I felt drained and exhilarated, as if I'd won a marathon. Had Jai felt like this, too?

Devyani slept, her face slack and open. I watched her for a while, then rose from the bed, carefully so as not to wake her. I padded to my closet and pulled on a pair of fresh shorts and a shirt. There was something I needed to do.

I opened a drawer stuffed with odds and ends and managed to find a blank sheet of paper, even an old charcoal pencil. Twenty years since I'd drawn anything. My fingers barely remembered how to hold the pencil.

I sat on the end of the bed and tried to sketch Devyani's sleeping face. But my skills were too rusty and after a while I gave up. And she was fundamentally unknowable to me; I couldn't capture her. I stuffed the paper back in the drawer and went to the living room. Perhaps seeing my old sketches would remind me how to draw. Remind me what I'd been.

I flipped open my work table and the computer screen sprang to life. I tapped in a password to gain entry into a restricted folder that I hadn't accessed in years.

A collage of sketches and photos popped onto the screen. A wheat field. A mother holding a baby. The pretty teacher I'd had a crush on in fourth grade. A farmer. A class picnic. My older sister, getting married to the man who would jump off the thirty-fifth floor of a building when Femonza hit. The pictures flew by too fast and I wanted to slow them down. No, I wanted them to stop, to go into reverse and take me with them. Back into time. Back when things were normal and I was a dreamy-eyed kid with a camera and a sketchbook.

A shadow fell over the screen and I snapped it closed. Devyani stood behind me. She put her hand on my shoulder. "Was that your family?"

I swung around to face her. She was wearing my shirt. She could have been my wife, my sister, my mother. But she wasn't.

"You're not really from the facility, are you?" I said.

Devyani only smiled.

My throat felt dry. "You're not a real woman."

Devyani removed her hand from my shoulder. "I'm virtually indistinguishable from one. Isn't that enough?"

"How did Jai figure it out?" I asked.

"He caught me in the hygiene cabinet, voiding the samosas he'd made me eat. How did you figure it out?"

"Logic," I said. "They'd never let an actual female out of sight. They'd have tracers, neural bugs." I paused. "What did Jai do?"

"I told you," said Devyani. "He kicked me out. It's too bad. Now he'll get a mindwipe."

I got up. I suppose I said something, pushed her away.

"You don't get it, do you?" said Devyani. "A mindwipe will give him a chance to start afresh. Would you rather he was euthanized?" She shook her head. "As it is, he is too full of bitterness to be happy, or do anything useful."

"Why did you come here?" I demanded. "Why pick us?"

"Jai was selected for the Delhi pilot program," said Devyani. "With his illegal sensors, he came to the attention of my boss years ago. So passionate, so determined. He was a prime candidate for the program, which seeks to reintroduce women into society."

"Not real women," I said.

"Real women are dangerous," said Devyani. "Isn't that what you said?"

"They planted listeners on us?" The bile rose in my throat. "I suppose your boss is listening to us right now."

"What does it matter?" said Devyani. "You and I, we can be a team. I'm not an Ayesha; I'm as close to an actual woman as you're ever likely to get. Jai couldn't accept me. But you're different from him." She stepped forward and grasped my hand, gazing intensely into my eyes.

I shivered. Her touch so warm, so right. "I can't," I said.

Her grip tightened. "Did I not meet your *expectations* of what a woman should do?"

I thought of Devyani bending down to serve me tea, of pulling the shirt off her head, and I cringed. "I'm sorry, I ..."

"You are as much a program as I am," said Devyani, "a set of responses tainted by your history. Why then this difference between us? Why deny my right to be?"

"You have as much right to be as I do. But it would always feel like a lie to me."

"And what you felt last night," she said softly. "Was that a lie? Am I just a vag-sim to you?"

"Of course not," I said, and stopped. I didn't know how to express myself without hurting her feelings. But I wasn't sure she even *had* them. Was there really such little difference between us?

"You should take what you can get," she said. "Life is only so long."

"That's exactly why you shouldn't take what you get," I said. "You only have so many years to make sense of it. You can't substitute what you have with what you need."

"But you can substitute what you need with what you have," she said.

It was at that moment, when she said those words, that the answer that had been eluding me for so long hit me.

Devyani continued to speak for a while, but I didn't hear her words. I was looking at the solution that would solve the dilemma that had stumped me for the last three years, and it was so beautiful, so amazing in its simplicity, that I felt like laughing and clapping my hands.

Devyani finally stopped speaking and asked me why I was grinning like a fool.

I bent down and kissed her bewildered face. "Tell you later," I said. "Got to do something in the lab first."

I rushed out of the apartment and down the elevator. I caught a late bus to the office district, almost tearing my hair off when the bus broke down midway. I finally got to the research lab at midnight, and then I worked uninterrupted until morning. When I had finished my notes, I emailed them to six different universities that I had been in touch with over the years. As I hit 'send', my phone buzzed.

It was Devyani. "Where've you been?" she complained. "Leaving me alone like that. I had a hard time convincing my boss you would be fine."

"I'm fine," I said, "and you can tell your boss to go screw himself."

There was a snort at the other end. "That will be a bit hard, seeing as my boss is a software program."

"What?" I digested this. "Okay. You can tell that piece of shitty software that soon there will be no need for it and its ilk, because I, Dr Shyam Arora, have discovered how to build a stable artificial uterine system for the growth of healthy embryos." *Drumroll please*, I thought.

Instead there was silence for so long that I thought Devyani had gone catatonic. Finally she said, "Congratulations, Dr Shyam. My mission is a success."

"What?" I said, confused. "What mission?"

But Devyani only laughed and put the phone down.

When I went back to my apartment that evening, it was clean and empty, as if she had never been there. The next few weeks were busy and I put Devyani out of my mind. Jai came back to work a month later, a bit subdued after a high-grade Complete Clean, but with more of his memories intact than I'd hoped. At least he remembered me. They'd only done a partial wipe.

News of my project spread quickly. I had been able to build a placenta 'naturally' on a layer of endometrial tissue, quite early in my research. But the problem had been making the placenta do what was needed — regulate nutrient delivery and hormones to mimic what nature does so well. Additionally, the fetus had to be stimulated — sung to, touched, walked, exposed to a 24-hour cycle of day and night, just like a human mother does.

My solution? Grow the uterus inside a specially designed robotic 'parent.' Substitute what you need with what you have.

All over the world, research labs got to work building prototypes and testing my results. Eggs frozen from the pre-Femonza years were fertilized, and the embryos' genomes edited for resistance to Femonza. A new generation would be brought into being, using my methods.

I got a promotion and a salary hike big enough to enjoy the services of an Ayesha whenever I wanted. I also got multiple job offers, all of which I turned down. There didn't seem to be any point; I'd already done the most important thing I would ever do — the rest of it was just a talk-show, a media merry-go-round that I longed to get off.

I put out anonymous advertisements in different outlets every week. *To the only real person in my life: please come back. We could be a team, you and I.* Months went by and no one responded. I was disheartened, but I didn't give up.

A year-and-a-half later, the media frenzy shifted from me to the first products of the artificial uterine systems, crawling on nursery floors, wetting diapers, and gurgling into cameras. The sex of the babies was withheld — it was assumed that half would be girls and half boys — but the intent was to allow them to grow in a gender-neutral environment for as long as possible. Perhaps, unlike us, they would be free of the taint of history.

One hot summer evening, I pushed open the door of my apartment and there she was, sitting on the sofa and smiling like she'd never left.

I crossed the room in two bounds and knelt before her. Devyani took my face in her hands and I tried not to shake, tried not to cry. *This is happiness*, I thought. *Remember it.*

"Shyam," she began, "I'm not really …"

"Shh," I said. "I don't care what you are and what you are not. All that matters is that you're here."

That night, when Devyani had fallen asleep, I got up and switched on the lamp so its light fell on her face. I dug out the paper I had shoved into the drawer months ago. It wasn't easy completing the sketch I had begun. My hands trembled and I was consumed by fear that it was no good, that there was no way I could portray her as she actually was.

But I did it. Because we are all fundamentally unknowable to each other, separate worlds that spin and dance on their own axes. But if you try hard enough, you can sometimes make a bridge from your own truth to another's.

When I had finished the sketch, I taped it to the wall where she could see it when she woke the next morning.

SECTION II:
DISCUSSING THE TROPES

PATRICK HESTER

I'M PRETTY SURE I'VE READ THIS BEFORE ...
The orphan kid is the hero ... But if anyone has sex, they're all gonna die

INTRODUCTION

Have you ever wondered why some stories sound familiar to you, even though you've never read them before? Isn't it annoying? You're sitting there thinking, "wait, have I started this book before?" Or, "I don't remember watching this movie, but it all seems familiar." Maybe you pick out the plot in the first couple sentences and wonder how you are doing this. Have you manifested your mutant powers at last? Or are you just losing it?

You're not going crazy. Well, I don't know that for sure. I mean, I'm not a trained mental health professional, nor do I play one on TV. And, let's face it — if your mutant powers haven't shown up by now, you're gonna need some sort of catalyst — but that's another essay for another time.

In all likelihood, you've started to notice these pesky little metaphorical elements in storytelling we authors use to shortcut our way into your brain and your heart.

Why?

Because they work. Really well, in fact. They speak to us and we identify with them on a very primal level. Almost like a racial memory. If I mention the orphan who learns they have a greater destiny, where did your brain go? A story popped into your head, right? Something you love? Something you hate?

Harry Potter, maybe? How about Annie? More recently, Rey from *The Force Awakens*? Or Luke Skywalker before her? Spider-Man and Superman? Let's go back further. Jane Eyre, Oliver Twist, heck — Moses. All are orphans with some sort of secret destiny just waiting to be unlocked.

We call this a trope, and the best authors don't simply use them in their storytelling, they flip them, twist them, and lure us into a false sense of security that we somehow know this story, know this character, and what's going to happen next — and then they surprise the hell out of us.

PART 1: RECOGNIZING TROPES

The problem with being a writer, aside from the lack of steady income, health insurance, and paid vacation days, plus the extreme introverted tendencies, is how you start to recognize tropes across all media. And can't turn it off. Not when you're reading, watching a movie or TV show, nothing. It's annoying for you and your friends and family alike, so at least it's a universal pain.

If you're a prolific reader, you may have experienced something very similar.

Follow along with me for a second. You're sitting on the comfy couch with the loved one of your choice, about to watch the new great show absolutely everyone is talking about. The commercial lead-in ends, you sit back to enjoy and roughly three to five minutes in, brow furrowed, know who the killer is, who is sleeping with who, and how the whole thing is gonna end. Which you, being you, blurt out in utter exasperation.

The first time this happens, your loved one laughs and says something like, "No way!" Then everything falls into place exactly (or near enough) as you described and they stare at you as if examining an odd bug that just crawled into the room. Now, somewhere around the third or fourth time you do this, the laughing stops. The loved one in question refuses to watch anything with you unless and until you can keep your trap shut without ruining everything.

Sound familiar or am I projecting too much?

While you may not have known this is called a trope, you did recognize something familiar, like a warm blanket you used to have as a child. Why? Because that's when we are all first exposed to common tropes about heroes and villains, good and bad (of a sort) — in fairy tales.

Think about it. Some of the first stories we're told as children often setup the tropes of the orphaned child with a destiny, the evil stepmother or crone/witch, and the handsome prince.

The Orphaned Child[1] is often a child born of kings and queens, who is spirited away and raised far from their homes only to return someday to right the wrongs done in their absence and bring balance to the world. The Evil Stepmother/Crone[2] or Witch[3] is more often than not responsible for the death of or displacement of the main character's mother. She is petty and cruel, interested

---

1 Trope: The Chosen One / Orphaned Child with a Destiny, TVTropes.org, http://tvtropes.org/pmwiki/pmwiki.php/Main/TheChosenOne
2 Trope: The Evil Stepmother, TVTropes.org, http://tvtropes.org/pmwiki/pmwiki.php/Main/WickedStepmother
3 Trope: The Wicked Witch / Old Crone, TVTropes.org, http://tvtropes.org/pmwiki/pmwiki.php/Main/WickedWitch

in power, and is more often than not setup as an obstacle for our hero or heroine to overcome. The Handsome Prince[4] will ride in on the brilliant white stallion to raise our orphaned child up out of the muck, be the romantic ideal, etc.

This is changing these days, as people reinterpret fairy tales for modern audiences, but the roots are still there. The orphan with the destiny — did anyone out there think Snow White? Isn't it a powerful image, the orphaned child doomed to a life of misery who discovers a destiny far beyond what they could've dreamed. Go back even further and you have Arthur and the Knights of the Round Table. A boy taken from his parents as a baby, raised in obscure poverty only to have a wizard come along and reveal his true identity and destiny once he is "of an age." Or perhaps I'm talking about Rand Al'Thor and The Wheel of Time series?

To an extent, we as readers and watchers allow the trope to work because we find it familiar and comforting. Remember that old blanket?

But is that a good thing? Should we be comfortable with our stories? Wouldn't it be better to be uncomfortable? Or surprised? Isn't that what science fiction does best? Makes us think and feel a little uncomfortable, pushing the bounds of what's acceptable so we, as the reader, grow?

More on that in a second.

Sometimes a trope becomes part of the culture. If I say "that guy is a red shirt,"[5] you will probably smile because you understand. I don't have to explain it, don't have to go any further than those words. The guy is gonna die like all those poor, defenseless Starfleet officers did on all those random planets. You know it and so do I. If we're watching a horror movie about a bunch of kids going off somewhere for the weekend to camp, drink, smoke pot, and have sex, we know something or someone is going to come along and start killing them. We have tropes, tropes, and more tropes including: Death by Sex[6], Drugs are Bad[7], and Don't Go into the Woods[8], and they're all handled in different ways by different storytellers. Knowing sex, drugs, and rock and roll mean certain death can be kind of a buzzkill, but there it is. Which has been more about imposing a certain set of moral certainties on an unsuspecting audience than anything else.

---

4 Trope: The Handsome Prince, TVTropes.org, http://tvtropes.org/pmwiki/pmwiki.php/Main/PrinceCharming

5 Trope: Red Shirt, TVTropes.org, http://tvtropes.org/pmwiki/pmwiki.php/Main/RedShirt

6 Trope: Death by Sex, TVTropes.org, http://tvtropes.org/pmwiki/pmwiki.php/Main/DeathBySex

7 Trope: Drugs are Bad, TVTropes.org, http://tvtropes.org/pmwiki/pmwiki.php/Main/DrugsAreBad

8 Trope: Don't Go into the Woods, TVTropes.org, http://tvtropes.org/pmwiki/pmwiki.php/Main/DontGoInTheWoods

Ever been asked, "What's the moral of the story?" Fairy tales and parables have been used to impart moral lessons for as long as there have been humans. And they use tropes at their core to connect with us on that primal level.

Joss Whedon handled the Death by Sex trope in *Buffy the Vampire Slayer* — and he took it to the extreme and tossed in the Evil Boyfriend[9] trope for good measure.

I am now going to spoil *Buffy the Vampire Slayer* for you. If you have not watched this amazing show yet, I give up. You're never gonna do it, are you? Sigh.

When Buffy and Angel have sex for the first time, it triggers a curse and removes Angel's soul and returns the vampire/demon Angelus's control over the body. Thus, having sex both resulted in the death of the "love of her life," and released the "ultimate evil boyfriend," who never called her back and then tried to eat and/or kill all her friends, as evil boyfriends are wont to do.

This is a great example of the familiar trope being flipped and taken off in a direction we didn't really expect. Or at least, I didn't expect.

And then there's probably the most popular and overused metaphorical element of all time — The Hero's Journey[10]. Buffy was on it from the start. But she's not the only one.

You see, how-to books have been written about it. Workshops are done every year where writers are shown how this particular trope will not only get you published, but will resonate with audiences and get people talking about your stories. Why? Again, it's foundational. Look at Rey from *The Force Awakens*. She has a destiny, and when she is scooped up and tossed into the galaxy, she only wants to return home and not get involved. When opportunity calls — Han Solo offering her a job, a way off her planet, and a life of her own — she refuses, and again, wants to go home. Ultimately, she accepts her calling and becomes the hero she was destined to become.

This is the quintessential hero's journey. We see it in stories all the time, which is why we recognize it on some level when we're reading and watching, and how it has become, through so much use, a trope in its own right. And also why I kinda think it needs to die.

And yes, I totally just spoiled *The Force Awakens*, too.

PART 2: BECOME SOMETHING BETTER

---

9 Trope: Evil Boyfriend, TVTropes.org, http://tvtropes.org/pmwiki/pmwiki.php/Main/BastardBoyfriend
10 Trope: The Hero's Journey, Wikipedia.org, https://en.wikipedia.org/wiki/Monomyth

Okay, calm down. Just because I say I want the hero's journey to die, doesn't mean that it will. Or even that it can. It's one of those tropes so ingrained in who we are as a species that I don't think it could ever die. Take nearly any story and you can point to elements of the hero's journey informing the characters and the narrative.

Joseph Campbell first broke it down in *The Hero with a Thousand Faces*, and it goes something like this:

> *"A hero ventures forth from the world of common day into a region of supernatural wonder: fabulous forces are there encountered and a decisive victory is won: the hero comes back from this mysterious adventure with the power to bestow boons on his fellow man."* (Joseph Campbell)

When I was a kid, there were several things I obsessed over, including but not limited to: comic books and wrestling. Comics are full of tropes, including and building upon the hero's journey and taking things off in different directions. The hero is almost always called to action, refuses the call, and eventually accepts their destiny. Beyond that, you have a plethora of tropes including: Temporal Paradox[11] involving time travel and shifting timelines ala Cable from the X-Men, who grows up in an alternate universe only to come back and be a contemporary of his own parents; Back from the Dead[12] like Batman, Superman, Spider-Man, and pretty much everyone else who has ever "died" in comics (and daytime soap operas); Alternate Universe[13] where history took a left instead of a right, Orphan with a Destiny/The Chosen One (Superman, Bruce Wayne/Batman, Peter Parker/Spider-Man, again); plus universal themes like revenge plots, mentors, etc. The stories are also episodic and high on drama and romance, elements that resonate with us on every level. Essentially, they're soap operas for kids. The characters are archetypes, these massive, over-the-top heroes and villains who are constantly saving (or threatening) the world.

Switch to wrestling, specifically the WWF before they became the WWE, and you had the same kinds of archetypes and stories playing out week after week on television screens across the fifty states, Canada, and Mexico (Luchadors!). Larger than life heroes battling sinister villains and you'd think the fate of the whole world rested on the shoulders of whoever wore that shiny gold belt.

---

11 Trope: Temporal Paradox, TVTropes.org, http://tvtropes.org/pmwiki/pmwiki.php/Main/TemporalParadox
12 Trope: Back from the Dead, TVTropes.org, http://tvtropes.org/pmwiki/pmwiki.php/Main/BackFromTheDead
13 Trope: Alternate Universe, TVTropes.org, http://tvtropes.org/pmwiki/pmwiki.php/Main/AlternateUniverse

Spoiler: It didn't. But how much fun was it to pretend that it did?

Is it any wonder I imprinted these tropes early on and recognize them so readily today? I bet you do, too, even if you didn't know it until this very moment.

But I want to get back to the hero's journey for a second. The best stories, the ones that really, truly make us sit back in stunned silence, turn this trope on its head. Case in point, the books in the Memory, Sorrow, and Thorn series by Tad Williams. Epic fantasy has a well-known set of tropes[14] that tend to follow along with the hero's journey quite well. However, Williams took them and masterfully flipped them on their head — and brought this reader along for the ride.

Not only did the characters not do what I knew they were going to do, they made bad decisions. Very bad. Repeatedly. They went left when I thought for sure they would go right. It was the first time I ever found myself pausing while reading a book to actively yell at the characters. Seoman Snowlock aka Simon Mooncalf, is that hero right out of destiny. Orphaned and working a shit job and looking for a break, he refuses the call only to find he can't escape his destiny, and then he runs off with elves and has adventures. And he's in love with the princess, Miriamele. And everything is setup to make you believe they are going to be together and save the land from the big bad evil. And then a series of seriously left turns occurs — I'm actually getting pissed off just writing about this! *I am still angry at the decisions these characters made*, and it's been years since I read the books.

Williams brought the characters together in an unconventional way. He made them real, allowing them to make stupid decisions like we would make here in the real world, and in doing so, inverted the tropes and surprised us. Or me.

I wish I could tell you that this was the only time I've ever shouted at characters in a book. Sadly, I can't.

Kate Elliott is also responsible for such an incident. Her Crown of Stars series made me question everything I thought I knew about epic fantasy. She tore it all down and built it back up again, adding in so many rich details and so much political intrigue, my head was spinning. I read these books before George R. R. Martin's *A Game of Thrones*, by the way. And the trials and tribulations of Alain and Liath had me hooked, exasperated, and, yes, yelling at the characters.

But I kept reading. Because she flipped things on me, and I loved it.

And years later, I had the opportunity to tell each of these authors in person exactly how I reacted to their books, and they were quite pleased about the

---

14 Trope: Fantasy Tropes, Wikipedia.org, https://en.wikipedia.org/wiki/Fantasy_tropes

whole thing. They loved the idea that their words had made me so upset I had to take a moment to yell at *fictional characters* just to get it out of my system.

That's powerful writing.

Williams and Elliott — and Martin, of course — took the familiar elements of the hero's journey, of the epic fantasy tropes we've come to know thanks to authors like J.R.R. Tolkien who laid the foundations with *The Lord of the Rings*, and shifted them just enough to make us uncomfortable. They broke the mold and the cycle. They stood out from the pack, as it were, and all are still writing epics today, and making audiences and readers, new and old, continue to be uncomfortable — and keep reading.

I asked before if that was a good thing or not, and I fall squarely on the side of yes — that is a very good thing. I would rather be challenged and surprised by uncomfortable ideas than fed the same old thing over and over. And when I talk about the death of the hero's journey, really what I mean is I want to see it evolve and change.

Become something better.

PART 3: FINDING THE BALANCE

And just when you think it's all good, someone comes along and tears up a city full of innocent people to make a point about superheroes.

There's been a recent debate over the proliferation of movies based on comic book characters. Well, several, actually. But I am specifically thinking of the whole Marvel vs. DC thing. Marvel has been pumping out movie after movie following the hero's journey quite closely — Tony Stark, Steve Rogers, Thor — delivering to audiences archetypal heroes who refuse the call, but end up battling over the top villains while mixing in a few one liners, jokes, and amazing music soundtracks, and it works.

Let's not talk about the Hulk movies, okay?

To my point about wanting to change things up, DC gave us *Man of Steel* in 2013. In doing so, they shook the foundations of the tropes we associate with an iconic character like Superman, and the reaction was a mixed bag with fans and critics alike. Criticized for decades for being a "boy scout," audiences did not appreciate seeing the man of steel killing his enemy and ignoring the innocent people hurt and killed in the wake of his battle. DC and Warner Brothers followed it up with *Batman Vs. Superman: Dawn of Justice*, which, again, shook things up and delivered a very dark take on the entire DC catalog of A-list heroes that did not resonate well with many audience members.

DC wanted to counterpoint Marvel, which they did in spades. They surprised people. Surprised me. And made a lot of people very uncomfortable. Including me. And they managed to tick off the check boxes I just asked for, and a slew of fans and critics in the process, who walked away shaking their heads and wondering where their beloved heroes had gone.

The question is — did they go too far? Or are we just so hung up on the trees we can't see the forest?

I believe the answer is yes — they went too far. It's all well and fine to push the boundaries and change things up, but if you go so far the reader — or in this case, movie watcher — can't follow you, you've gone too far.

There has to be a balance. And DC, unfortunately, hasn't found that balance yet.

Let's return to *Game of Thrones*.

George R. R. Martin continues to push comfort levels just a little farther with each subsequent book in his Song of Fire and Ice series (and the HBO television show based upon it). Just when you think he can't possibly surprise or shock you, there's a red wedding, and you find yourself thinking you should never accept a wedding invitation from Mr. Martin. Nope. Not ever. And people lap it up like milk from a saucer. And in that analogy, people are cats because otherwise that would be kinda weird and creepy.

Anyway.

Mr. Martin finds that balance. He doesn't go so far that he loses you. And sure, you might have to take a moment (or three, or ten) after reading (or watching) one of those scenes before you can go on, but you do go on.

On the other side of the spectrum, *The Force Awakens* didn't seek to be balanced or do anything at all other than to follow the hero's journey to the letter, yet it worked. Worked damned well. Why?

Rey is the reluctant hero we can identify with. We care about her from the beginning. We cheer when she succeeds, feel the same disappointment she does when she fails. And we get it, leaving home is difficult, but once you do, all the adventures begin.

And that works for us, too.

CONCLUSION

For an author, tropes are part of the toolbox. They make it easier to connect readers and watchers with the story they have crafted — as long as the tropes are not overused.

For a reader, tropes help us get into the story quicker and become comfortable with the characters, plot, and setting. They call to mind the things we've read or seen before in a good way. It's almost like a secret between us and the author. We can think to ourselves, "Oh, I see what you're doing there ... and I like it!"

Sometimes, not all the time, we recognize these things for what they are — a trope. And that can break us out of the story, ruin the fun of discovery, which is bad.

What's better?

When an author takes a trope and gives it just a little spin, not so much that we can't still feel that warm sense of familiarity, but just far enough that we're pleasantly surprised, even shocked and a little uncomfortable. Where we sit back and say, "Whoa!"[15] in our best Keanu impression.

Look at the books you've read over the past year, or the past five years, or ten and beyond. Thumb through the older titles and compare them to the newer ones. How have your tastes changed? What do you find redundant or derivative, and what really grabs ahold of you and won't let go?

Do they include some version of the hero's journey? Is there an orphan with a destiny?

Those are the kinds of stories we want. That we crave. Because they challenge us, but not so far we can't follow.

They evoke emotions inside of us, and that is the very best kind of writing.

---

15 Trope: Whoa!, Keanu Reeves, TVTropes.org, http://tvtropes.org/pmwiki/pmwiki.php/Creator/KeanuReeves

WORKS CITED

The Amazing Spider-Man. Stan Lee, Steve Ditko, Creators. Ongoing comic book character, debuted in *Amazing Fantasy* #15, 1962.

Batman v Superman: Dawn of Justice. Zach Snyder, Director. DC Comics, Legendary Pictures and Syncopy Films, and distributed by Warner Bros. Pictures, 2016.

Brontë, Charlotte. *Jane Eyre: An Autobiography*. Smith, Elder & Co. of London, 1847.

Buffy the Vampire Slayer. Joss Whedon, Creator. The WB, 1997.

Cable, aka Nathan Summers, 1st appearance in *Uncanny X-Men* #201, Chris Claremont, Louise Simonson & Rob Liefeld, Creator(s), Marvel Comics, 1986.

Campbell, Joseph. *The Hero with a Thousand Faces*, Pantheon Books, 1949.

Collins, Suzanne. *The Hunger Games*. Scholastic Press, 2008.

Dickens, Charles. *Oliver Twist*. Penguin Classics; Reissue edition, 2003.

Elliott, Kate. *Crown of Stars* (series). DAW Books, 1998.

Grimm, Brothers. *Grimms' Fairy Tales, Snow White and the Seven Dwarfs*, 1812.

Jordan, Robert. *The Eye of the World*. Tor Fantasy, 1990.

Mallory, Thomas. *Le Morte D'Arthur*. Oxford University Press, 1998.

Man of Steel. Zach Snyder, Director. DC Comics, Legendary Pictures and Syncopy Films, and distributed by Warner Bros. Pictures, 2013.

Martin, George R.R. *A Game of Thrones*. Bantam, 1996.

Marvel Comics Cinematic Universe (MCU). Marvel Studios, 2008.

Rowling, JK. *Harry Potter and the Sorcerer's Stone* New York: Scholastic, 1998.

Star Trek: The Original Series. Gene Roddenberry, Creator. NBC Television, 1966.

Star Wars: A New Hope. George Lucas, Writer/Director. Feature Film, 1977.

Star Wars: The Force Awakens. JJ Abrams, Producer/Director. Feature film, 2015.

Superman. Jerry Siegal, Joe Shuster, Creators. Ongoing comic book character, debuted in *Action Comics #1*, 1938.

Tolkien, J.R.R. *The Lord of the Rings* (series). Del Rey (Collection, *The Hobbit, The Fellowship of the Ring, The Two Towers & The Return of the King*), 2012.

Various. *The King James Bible*. Oxford University Press, 2005.

Williams, Tad. *Memory, Sorrow, and Thorn* (series). DAW Books, 1988.

Lucy A. Snyder

FRACTURED SOULS: THE EVOLUTION OF THE GOTHIC DOUBLE FROM STEVENSON TO KING

The "Gothic double" is a literary character trope most readers are familiar with, even if the term itself is unfamiliar: it embodies the idea of a personality divided between good and evil. Robert Louis Stevenson's Dr. Jekyll and Mr. Hyde are not the first examples of the Gothic double (Strengell), but they're one of the most enduring and influential examples in literature. Consequently, Mr. Hyde has become firmly embedded in literature and pop culture as a classic fiend as recognizable as Count Dracula or Frankenstein's monster. But without the upstanding Dr. Jekyll as his alter ego and tragic foil, Hyde as a character would lack impact. Much of what fascinates readers about these dual characters is the tension between good and evil, sanity and sociopathy, gentility and debasement.

The tension of that duality goes deeper and is more complex than good versus evil: it intersects with issues of class, race, ability, and gender. Hyde revels in underclass debaucheries that are far beneath the upstanding Dr. Jekyll. Further, he is repeatedly described as "ape-like," a loaded description with negative connotations towards nonwhite races. The 1931 movie adaptation directed by Rouben Mamoulian deliberately gave Hyde African features, clearly playing on his white audience's fear of blacks (Eaton 143). American feminist literary critic Elaine Showalter argues that *The Strange Case of Dr. Jekyll and Mr. Hyde* is "a story about communities of men" in which "*the romance of Jekyll and Hyde is conveyed instead through men's names, men's bodies, and men's psyches.*" (Showalter 108)

The classist, racist, and patriarchal subtext of Stevenson's novella cried out to be subverted and updated by modern authors. Author Steven King accomplished just such a subversion and modernization of Jekyll and Hyde with his characters Odetta Holmes and Detta Walker in his second volume of The Dark Tower series, *The Drawing of the Three*, and in doing so he added new complexities to the fractured soul trope that the Jekyll/Hyde characters have come to represent. Because King's novel series is considered to be a modern classic, his evolution of this character trope can therefore serve as a craft model to other writers who are seeking to accomplish similar evolutions in their own creative work. But to understand why King's characters represent such an interesting modernization and subversion of Jekyll and Hyde, we first have to dig deeper into Stevenson's original characters.

MR. HYDE: ID MADE FLESH

Portrayals of Mr. Hyde evolved considerably in 20th and 21st centuries. To most modern moviegoers, Mr. Hyde is the Victorian progenitor of The Hulk: a powerful, violent, unrestrained incarnation of pure id. To fans of Steven Moffat's BBC miniseries *Jekyll*, Hyde is a sexy, sociopathic Superman. The modern Hyde is a fiend of monstrous proportion, perhaps not physically, but he's certainly no diminutive, Gollum-like creature.

Except, in the original text, he's exactly that:

"Mr. Hyde was pale and dwarfish, he gave an impression of deformity without any nameable malformation, he had a displeasing smile, he had borne himself to the lawyer with a sort of murderous mixture of timidity and boldness, and he spoke with a husky, whispering and somewhat broken voice ..." (Stevenson 16)

Hyde's youth and tiny physical stature — he's so small he's swimming in Jekyll's clothes after his transformation — is a surprise to many modern readers. And so is Hyde's demeanor, since he has none of the wicked charisma that Moffat and other filmmakers have imbued him with on screen. The other characters in Stevenson's novella find Hyde utterly repellent; he's as dangerous as a rabid sewer rat, and the only person in the whole of London he seems capable of seducing is Dr. Jekyll.

Hyde's characterization makes perfect sense from a metaphoric standpoint, and many readers will intuit it well before Stevenson offers an explanation late in the story. Hyde is small because the evil in Dr. Jekyll is initially just a small part of his personality, and he's young because the exploration of wickedness that he represents is a new experience to the handsome, upstanding doctor.

However, Hyde unfortunately represents a distasteful trope: the use of physical deformity and ugliness to signify evil and moral turpitude. That particular trope is both creakingly ancient and presents a toxic mix of ableism, classism, and victim-blaming and posits that if a person is disfigured, he or she must have done something bad to deserve it; this notion ignores the reality that the possessors of unattractive faces often got their scars from a life of having been forced to work dangerous, body-breaking jobs that (despite the societal necessity of the work) don't pay enough for niceties such as plastic surgery and tooth repair. The idea that upstanding citizens could somehow recognize the rapists, thieves, and murderers among them because miscreants all have misshapen features is a comforting lie. The people who've done the most harm to the rest of humanity have often had great hair and million-dollar smiles.

DR. JEKYLL: TALL, HANDSOME, AND COMPLICIT

Stevenson's Henry Jekyll was born into wealth and good health, and as his career as a physician of good repute progressed, he found it harder and harder to reconcile his public face with his private desires:

> "It was thus rather the exacting nature of my aspirations than any particular degradation in my faults that made me what I was, and, with even a deeper trench than in the majority of men, severed in me those provinces of good and ill which divide and compound man's dual nature. ...
> With every day, and from both sides of my intelligence, the moral and the intellectual, I thus drew steadily nearer to that truth, by whose partial discovery I have been doomed to such a dreadful shipwreck: that man is not truly one, but truly two." (Stevenson 77-78)

His interest in exploring that dual nature soon became an obsession and he began to conduct laboratory experiments to compound a drug that would let him fully experience his suppressed side. He takes the draught, and despite a physically arduous transformation, is thrilled when he becomes Hyde:

> "I knew myself, at the first breath of this new life, to be more wicked, tenfold more wicked, sold a slave to my original evil; and the thought, in that moment, braced and delighted me like wine." (Stevenson 79)

And like an alcoholic, Jekyll becomes addicted to turning into Hyde despite the crimes he commits:

> "Henry Jekyll stood at times aghast before the acts of Edward Hyde; but the situation was apart from ordinary laws, and insidiously relaxed the grasp of conscience. It was Hyde, after all, and Hyde alone, that was guilty. Jekyll was no worse; he woke again to his good qualities seemingly unimpaired; he would even make haste, where it was possible, to undo the evil done by Hyde. And thus his conscience slumbered." (Stevenson 82)

As time passes, Jekyll no longer needs to take the drug to become Hyde, but instead to keep from spontaneously turning into him. Final disaster strikes when he runs out of the ingredients he needs to make his draught, and, faced with becoming Hyde permanently and living as a hunted sociopath, Jekyll chooses to commit suicide.

The story of Dr. Jekyll is a clear morality tale: if a man chooses to indulge his baser desires, eventually he will become a slave to them. "Eventually" is key here, though; Dr. Jekyll is a man of great wealth and privilege and he's able to leverage his power to successfully dodge responsibility for the crimes he commits under Hyde's disguise for quite some time. A man of lesser means would not have had the resources to come up with the transformational drug nor stage the many cover-ups and cleanups that Hyde's behavior demanded. Socially, Dr. Jekyll is largely immune to comeuppance from external forces; he is driven largely by his own conscience and fears.

The events of the novella imply that despite his written confession, his male peers will discreetly cover for him, thus preserving his public reputation as a gentleman after his death: *"I would say nothing of this paper. If your master has fled or is dead, we may at least save his credit"* (Stevenson 63). Upper-class white male privilege has lasting rewards in Jekyll's world.

ODETTA HOLMES: A MODEL MINORITY

Readers of Stephen King's *The Drawing of the Three* encounter a pair of fractured souls reminiscent of Jekyll and Hyde: Odetta Holmes and Detta Walker. Much of the narrative of the book focuses on the other protagonists' efforts to cope with and subdue dangerous, profane Detta while they try to save polite, loveable Odetta.

Odetta shares some traits with Dr. Jekyll but is a departure from and subversion of his character in other ways. She is the daughter of an African-American dentist who makes a small fortune after patenting a capping process that became popular and makes an even greater fortune by founding Holmes Dental Industries with his newfound capital (King 196). Odetta has only known her family as wealthy and privileged (or at least as far as their skin color will allow them to experience privilege in America). She knows that before her father earned his fortune, her parents suffered and witnessed terrible racial violence, but he steadfastly refuses to speak of it:

"(T)o him, she realized, the past – those relatives, those red dirt roads, those stores, those dirt floor cabins with glassless windows ungraced by a single simple curtsey of a cur-

tain, those incidents of hurt and harassment, those neighbor children who went dressed in smocks which had begun life as flour sacks – all of that was for him buried away like dead teeth beneath perfect blinding white caps. He would not speak, perhaps could not, had perhaps willingly afflicted himself with a selective amnesia; the capped teeth was their life in the Greymarl Apartments on Central Park South." (King 197)

Odetta's father clearly expects her to be a good daughter, and she serves that role as best she can. She is educated and well-mannered; because of her poise and reserve she is often judged as uppity and a bit bitchy by white men such as her future lover Eddie Dean (King 199). She wears tasteful, expensive clothes. And she tries to further the welfare of less fortunate African Americans by working as a civil rights activist.

In a fundamental way, Odetta embodies the behavioral and social pressures many upper- and middle-class African Americans experience. In his essay "The Rise of Respectability Politics," political scientist Fredrick C. Harris writes:

"(It) started as a philosophy promulgated by black elites to "uplift the race" by correcting the "bad" traits of the black poor ... Even though respectability evolved as an elite ideology, it operates as common sense in most quarters of black America. Indeed, it even has its own lexicon. The word "ghetto," for instance, which a generation ago was used to describe poor, segregated neighborhoods, is now used to characterize the "unacceptable" behavior of black people who live anywhere from a housing project to an affluent suburb. Economic power is a needed development, of course, and one that can be used to leverage political power. But the politics of respectability has been portrayed as an emancipatory strategy to the neglect of discussions about structural forces that hinder the mobility of the black poor and working class."

The cost of being black and ambitious in America is to always be concerned about respectability and restricted by the need to attain it. But because of Mr. Holmes' rags-to-riches story, it initially seems that Odetta and her family have nonetheless attained the American Dream that eludes so many blacks born into an era of supposed freedom. And for a time, Mr. Holmes is able to maintain the illusion that his money trumps his family's race.

However, when Odetta is five years old, disaster strikes in the twin forms of a racist white taxi driver who refuses to let the family into his cab, forcing them to walk through a bad neighborhood (King 233), and Jack Mort, a white serial killer who works for the evil forces the gunslinger and his companions battle throughout the Dark Tower series. Mort drops a brick out of the fourth floor window of an abandoned building onto Odetta's head, knocking her into a life-threatening coma (King 234). Her mind is literally and figuratively shattered. During the coma, Odetta dreams of Detta, and when she finally regains consciousness, Detta begins to take over Odetta's body every now and again.

Unlike the shift between Jekyll and Hyde, there is no overt physical change associated with Odetta Holmes's shift to Detta Walker; it's all an alteration of spirit and psychology heralded by Odetta getting a headache. Neither Odetta nor Detta are consciously aware of each other, and they build separate false memories to seal the gaps for themselves. The few characters in the book who are aware of the divided soul sharing her body refer to her condition as a kind of schizophrenia (King 181), whereas a more modern, accurate description of a woman suffering from a similar (though less supernaturally freighted) condition would be dissociative identity disorder instead.

Regardless of the proper name for Odetta's condition, it's fundamentally different from Jekyll's situation in that she never sought out or asked to become Detta. Her split personality is thrust upon her by the evil of Jack Mort, who attacks her again when she's a young woman. He sneaks up behind her and shoves her in front of a subway train (King 211). The train cuts off her legs at the knees and Detta Walker comes strongly to the fore as a reaction to the trauma. After that second attack, Detta takes control of Odetta's body more and more frequently, and these takeovers drive a large portion of the plot of the novel since Detta actively works as an antagonist towards Eddie Dean and Roland the Gunslinger.

DETTA WALKER: JEZEBEL OR JUSTIFIABLE?

Detta Walker, of course, acts as Hyde to Odetta Holmes's Jekyll. On the negative side, it's possible to read Detta Walker as an embodiment of the Jezebel subtype of the Angry Black Woman stereotype, which history professor Blair L.M. Kelley describes in an article for *The Root*:

> *"Jezebel characters ... were fair-skinned, disloyal, greedy and hypersexual but not portrayed as beautiful. These blustering women yelled at their spouses and acted loud and inappropriately in otherwise genteel, public spaces to demonstrate all the ways that they were different from white women. ... These stereotypes served (to) justify the sexual exploitation of enslaved women by painting them as Jezebels, like the biblical wanton woman whose promiscuity and controlling nature was her supposed undoing. The rapes of enslaved women could be laughed away on a minstrel stage that showed black women as temptresses who wanted nothing but money and sexual attention."*

Given the historical ramifications, the Jezebel stereotype is a painful one; many people criticize it with appropriate harshness when they encounter it. Is King's portrayal of Detta relying on this kind of pernicious, lazy stereotyping? In her essay on the role of the Gothic double in King's fiction, Heidi Strengell describes Detta Walker as "sexually insatiable." However, it's possible that Strengell is conflating trauma-induced acting out with insatiability. Detta does get a charge from sexually taunting white boys (King 192, 398), talks of sex constantly, and occasionally masturbates, but she's not shown to actually have sex with anyone. She is pointedly and deliberately not a lady in manner or mind, and takes charge of her sexuality and her own sexual pleasure in a way that inevitably alarms people who expect women — especially women in wheelchairs — to be passive and sexually naïve. But there's not much evidence in the novel that Detta is particularly promiscuous (she certainly isn't shown to have slept with as many people as the hero, Roland Deschain).

Sexuality aside, Detta displays other Jezebel traits. She uses the most inappropriate, most cartoonishly clichéd language possible, and wields profanity like a verbal brickbat against anyone she sees as an enemy (the capitalization below is King's):

"YOU AIN'T NUTHIN BUT A BUNCHA HONKY SONSA BITCHES!" she screamed. Her face was monstrous, her eyes full of hell's own light. It wasn't even the face of a human being. "GOAN KILL EVERY MAHFAHIN HONKY I SEE! GOAN GELD EM FUST! GOAN CUT OFF THEIR BALLS AND SPIT EM IN THEY FACES!" (King 215)

Further, she compulsively shoplifts from the upscale department stores that Odetta visits, stealing handfuls of cheap costume jewelry and hiding them in her purse:

"In the time since the accident it was, for the most part, still Odetta Holmes who was in control, but Detta Walker had come forward more and more, the thing Detta liked to do best was steal. It didn't matter that her booty was always little more than junk, no more than it mattered that she often threw it away later.

The taking was what mattered." (King 217)

Why does the taking matter to Detta? On a superficial level, it pleases her to stick it to The Man she sees in the form of the wealthy stores' white male managers and security guards. But her actions are also driven by a deep emotional pain and sense of loss:

"I took the blue plate because that woman landed me in the hospital and besides I didn't get no forspecial plate an I bust it cause it needed bustin an when I saw a white boy I could bust why I bust him too I hurt the white boys because they needed hurtin I stole from the stores that only sell things that are forspecial to whitefolks while the brothers and sisters go hungry in Harlem and the rats eat their babies, I'm the one, you bitch, I'm the one, I ... I ... I!" (King 398)

Detta is certainly behaving in some wildly stereotypical ways in the novel. But systemic bigotry, whether it's racism or sexism or classism, is insidious: victims and perpetrators alike are exposed to bigotry's pervasive memes. And, unless an individual takes pains to examine and reject tainted beliefs passed off as universal truths, victims of racism and sexism are likely to internalize that bigotry and believe it to be true, emotionally if not intellectually.

Detta is Odetta's reaction to the trauma of Jack Mort's attacks. She's the embodiment of all the justified anger Odetta feels in a world where a white man can put a little black girl in a coma for a sadistic laugh and suffer no swift justice. Detta is her living, surviving rage at being pushed onto the tracks and losing her legs. She is everything that Odetta wants to feel and do but cannot because she needs to maintain her social status as a respectable upper-class black woman to be an effective civil rights activist. But as that civil rights activist, Odetta is jailed and humiliated by representatives of the Southern patriarchy:

"But I think most of them – even the dumb ones and they are by all means not all dumb – know the change will come in the end no matter what they do, and so they take the chance to degrade you while they still can. To teach you you can be degraded. You can swear before God, Christ, and the whole company of Saints that you will not, will not, will not soil yourself, but if they hold onto you long enough of course you do. The lesson is that you're just an animal in a cage, no more than that, no better than that. Just an animal in a cage. So I wet myself. I can still smell dried urine and that damned holding cell. They think we are descended from the monkeys, you know. And that's exactly what I smell like to myself right now.
"A monkey." (King 184)

Because of her social role, Odetta can't act out or take vengeance on the men who forced her to soil herself. She has to be respectable above all else. All she can do is take a bath and try to forget her mistreatment, but she can't, and she ponders whether her upper-crust Northern white neighbors secretly think of her in the same negative ways as her Southern captors:

"(I)t must have galled some of them mightily, knowing there was a nigger living in the penthouse apartment of this fine staid old building ... She hoped it did gall them mightily, and scolded herself for being mean, for being unchristian, but she did wish it, she hadn't been able to stop the piss pouring into the crotch of her fine silk imported underwear and she didn't seem to be able to stop this other flood of piss, either. It was mean, it was unchristian, and almost as bad — no, worse, at least as far as the Movement was concerned, it was counterproductive. ... There was more work to be done. Hate would not help do that work. Hate would, in fact, hinder it. But sometimes you went on hating just the same." (King 185-186)

Odetta can only stew and chastise herself for stewing ... but Detta can vent that anger. Through that socially unacceptable and therefore wicked rage, Detta represents Odetta's core strength and drive to fight and survive.

But Detta is also holding all of Odetta's darkest fears like a bag of squirming eels, and they have driven her more than half mad with paranoia. She's been through so many traumas that she is in a state of constant vigilance, constantly expecting more abuse, and Detta's deranged mind misinterprets and misremembers the other characters' well-intended attempts at kindness as debasing assaults and insults:

"She remembered everything: how she had fought them, how they had tied her into her chair, how they had taunted her, calling her niggerbitch, niggerbitch." (King 244)

Detta puts up a fearless front with her profanity and feigned wantonness. After all, what does Odetta, who's got decent, law-abiding, upstanding parents and lives in a more than merely nice neighborhood, know about becoming a wicked woman? She knows the stereotypes she grew up with. Just like everyone else in her America, she's been to the movies and theatre and has seen the Jezebel character played over and over and presented as a kind of universal truth about the dark side of black womanhood.

And so Detta deliberately wears the Jezebel costume because that's who she thinks she needs to be. Her playing Jezebel is partly a ruse to hide her considerable intelligence and cunning from people who would try to hurt her, partly a rejection of and rebellion against the respectability politics foisted on upper-class blacks that constantly constrict Odetta, and partly an adoption of the closest thing the mainstream media has ever offered her in the way of a strong countercultural female persona. The reaction of the other characters to her over-the-top speech and behavior supports this interpretation:

"It was crazy. She talked like a cartoon black woman, Butterfly McQueen gone Loony Tunes." (King 215).

"Eddie nodded. "That was an act, and she knew it was an act. But she's a pretty good actress and she fooled both of us for a few seconds. The way she's talking is an act, too. But it's not as good. It's so stupid, so goddamn hokey ... she talks like a cliché"" (King 264)

Even if a reader is inclined to think that King is simply dealing in unexamined, unmitigated racial stereotyping in Detta's characterization, she still represents a subversion of Hyde. Why? Because Odetta, literally and figuratively, needs Detta in order to survive. Detta isn't slowly killing Odetta as Hyde slowly destroys Jekyll. She has been saving her, over and over; she doesn't intend to, largely because she doesn't even consciously know Odetta exists, but by saving herself she also saves her proper, upstanding alter ego. Detta mostly fights against all the wrong things and makes terrible choices, but she keeps fighting and doesn't give up. Odetta would not have survived losing her legs on the track had Detta not come forward to fight against death:

"She – or it – also seemed superhuman. This screaming, writhing thing could not have just undergone impromptu surgery by subway train half an hour ago. She bit. She clawed out at him again and again." (King 215)

Hyde is the deliberate indulgence of a man who uses his privileged status within the patriarchy to avoid the legal and social consequences of his misdeeds. Conversely, Detta is the survival reaction of a black woman struggling to stay alive in the face of the traumas inflicted upon her by a more modern version of that same patriarchy. And that theme of indulgence versus survival is a fundamental and critical difference between the two characters.

Another critical difference between Detta and Hyde lies in their respective physical ability. Hyde is small and weak compared to Dr. Jekyll but is essentially able-bodied, although he's clearly an early incarnation of what TVTropes.org refers to as the "Depraved Dwarf" character. Detta, however, is a classic example of the "Handicapped Badass" character type: she's become a far deadlier opponent since she lost her legs, and the other characters in the novel fear and respect her skills and cunning.

SUSANNAH DEAN: THE DRAWING OF THE THIRD

At the end of Stevenson's novella, Jekyll, who deliberately sought out Hyde and has always been the aware architect of his existence, gives up all hope once he realizes he cannot stop from turning into Hyde:

> *"Will Hyde die upon the scaffold? Or will he find courage to release himself at the last moment? God knows; I am careless; this is my true hour of death, and what is to follow concerns another than myself."* (Stevenson 92)

The result of Jekyll's giving up is that Hyde takes poison and kills them both. There's a very traditional Christian morality at work there, namely in the idea that man's dark impulses cannot be a necessary force and must be purged at all costs. In this view, humanity is innately sinful, but it is only through the vigilant rejection of that sin that a man can succeed and thrive. There's never any room in that kind of morality for Jekyll and Hyde to reconcile and join forces.

The situation is critically different for Detta and Odetta. They have lived their separate lives with no conscious awareness of each other's existence until the gunslinger, Roland, forces them to see each other as they stand in a dimensional portal between worlds (King 397). At first, the two are just as hostile to each other as Jekyll and Hyde might be were they to confront one another directly: *"The two women lay face to face, bodies raised like snakes about to strike, fingers with identical prints locked around throats marked with identical lines."* (King 397). But Odetta, remembering her work as an activist and Eddie Dean's love for her, realizes that hatred is counterproductive, surrenders herself, and embraces her dark half:

> *"She could no more kill the hag and survive than the hag could kill her and walk away. ...*
> *Odetta let go of Detta's throat, ignored the fierce hands throttling her, crushing her windpipe. Instead of using her own hands to choke, she used them to embrace the other.*
> *(S)he could only whisper in the witch-woman's ear: "I love you."*
> *For a moment the hands tightened into a killing noose . . . and then loosened.*
> *Were gone.*
> *She was being turned inside out again ... and then, suddenly, blessedly, she was whole. ... She had been one; she had been two; now the gunslinger had drawn a third from her."* (King 398-399)

This scene is reminiscent of the climactic final confrontation between the wizard Ged and his shadow in Ursula K. Le Guin's *A Wizard of Earthsea*, and it's got the same kind of epic feel. In the context of everything Detta and Odetta have been through in the novel, the scene of Odetta's love and forgiveness and faith (reflective of modern, less judgmental Christianity than the strain portrayed in Stevenson's novella) and their merging into a new, whole person is one of the most exhilarating in the book. The gunslinger acts as midwife to the birth of Susannah Dean (as the new woman chooses to call herself, partly to signal her love for Eddie Dean), but she is a self-made woman through and through.

CONCLUSION

King's portrayal of Detta Walker and Odetta Holmes represents an interesting, modern update of the trope of the fractured soul as established by Stevenson in his original portrayal of Jekyll and Hyde. King moves past Stevenson's focus on class and physical appearance and explores more of the complexities of race, gender, and ability in his portrayals. In doing so, King presents a far more evolved, interesting set of characters. Even if King's characterization can be interpreted as racially flawed due to Detta's stereotypical behavior, a study of how King accomplished his characterization in contrast with Stevenson's would be fruitful for authors who are looking for ways of using and modernizing classic character tropes in their own work.

WORKS CITED

Eaton, Lance. "The Hulking Hyde: How the Incredible Hulk Reinvented the Modern Jekyll and Hyde Monster." *Fear and Learning: Essays on the Pedagogy of Horror*. Jefferson, NC: McFarland, 2013. p. 138-155. Print.

"Handicapped Badass." *TV Tropes*. TVTropes.org. Web. 18 Apr. 2016.

Harris, Fredrick C. "The Rise of Respectability Politics." *Dissent Magazine*, Winter 2014. Web. 23 Oct. 2015.

Jekyll. By Steven Moffat. Perf. James Nesbitt. BBC America, 2007. DVD.

Kelley, Blair L.M. "Here's Some History Behind That 'Angry Black Woman' Riff the NY Times Tossed Around." *The Root*, 25 Sept. 2014. Web. 24 Oct. 2015.

King, Stephen. *The Dark Tower II: The Drawing of the Three*. New York: Penguin Group, 2003. Kindle.

Le Guin, Ursula K. *A Wizard of Earthsea*. Berkeley: Parnassus, 1968. Print.

Showalter, Elaine. *Sexual Anarchy: Gender and Culture at the Fin De Siècle*. New York, NY, U.S.A.: Viking, 1990. Print.

Stevenson, Robert Louis. *The Strange Case of Dr. Jekyll and Mr. Hyde*. Amazon Digital Services, Inc., 2012. Kindle.

Strengell, Heidi. "'The Monster Never Dies': An Analysis Of The Gothic Double In Stephen King's Oeuvre." *Americana: The Journal of American Popular Culture (1900-Present)*, 2003. Web. 15 Oct. 2015.

A.C. WISE

INTO THE LABYRINTH: THE HEROINE'S JOURNEY

SINCE ITS RELEASE IN 1986, *Labyrinth*, starring David Bowie and Jennifer Connelly, has grown to be a cult classic. Like the fairy tales it draws inspiration from, there is a core, archetypal plot to *Labyrinth* that has helped make it such an enduring film. Even though the movie was released four years before Maureen Murdock published her book *The Heroine's Journey*, which proposed an alternative to Joseph Campbell's monomyth of the Hero's Journey laid out in *The Hero with a Thousand Faces*, *Labyrinth* still provides an excellent example of Murdock's basic structure. *Labyrinth* is a particularly interesting example of the Heroine's Journey model, as it can be seen as a front-runner of a new wave of interest in fantasy and science fiction films centering around women. Among classic 80s fantasy movies, *Labyrinth* is one of the few to put a young woman's journey front and center, and have her be active in her own tale.

This essay will explore *Labyrinth* as it maps to the Heroine's Journey, along with other examples of works following the Hero/Heroine's Journey model, with a brief discussion of the uses and limitations of tropes as a whole. Examples of written work will be touched on, however, the primary focus in this essay is on film and television. As a visual medium, there is an immediacy to film and television that allows it to be easily processed. As such, it is the first place many of us learn to recognize the language of tropes and understand the ways they can be used as building blocks to tell a story.

THE HERO'S JOURNEY: JOSEPH CAMPBELL'S MONOMYTH

In his 1949 book, *The Hero with a Thousand Faces*, Joseph Campbell introduced the concept of The Hero's Journey, an archetypal plot or monomyth he developed by looking at stories across history and from around the world.

> *"There are of course differences between the numerous mythologies and religions of mankind, but this is a book about the similarities; and once these are understood the differences will be found to be much less great than is popularly (and politically) supposed."* (Campbell, xiii)

Readers of epic fantasy and consumers of speculative fiction-related media will likely recognize the basic Hero's Journey plot structure. George Lucas, for example, was heavily influenced by *The Hero with a Thousand Faces* in his creation of the original *Star Wars*[1]. Reduced to its most basic components, a hero such as Luke Skywalker, King Arthur, or Frodo Baggins leaves the ordinary world to go on an adventure, faces self-doubt and enemies along the way, receives guidance from a wise old wizard, makes new friends, is gifted with a magical item, and eventually returns home triumphant.

There are variations and subplots, but as he stated in his introduction to *The Hero With a Thousand Faces*, Campbell believed this structure to be more or less universal, expressing a common experience that would be instantly recognizable and relatable, regardless of a person's individual culture, background, or beliefs.

Especially today, with the increasing awareness of the need for the stories we consume to reflect the full diversity of the world around us, the universal nature of Campbell's monomyth is questionable. To demonstrate just one facet that is not fully captured by the Hero's Journey, we can look to the overall absence of women. While *The Hero With a Thousand Faces* does offer up examples of women on journeys, such as the descent of Inanna into the underworld (Campbell, 87-89), the primary focus is on male heroes. Although Campbell may have intended to convey a universal experience, his model disregards the potential for the lived experiences of women to be different from those of men.

In his article *Joseph Campbell's Hero's Journey — The Twin Heroes*, Dr. Howard Teich lays out the framework Campbell uses to define his concept of a hero. Campbell's hero, as explored in his works (primarily his commentary on the Navajo myth Where the Two Came to Their Father published in 1943) is a twin hero, literally and figuratively. The twin heroes of *Where the Two Came to Their Father* encompass both traditionally masculine and feminine qualities. This dual understanding of the hero, Teich claims, carries over to the monomyth of the hero as a whole:

> "With its emphasis on an eventual transcendence of restrictive dualities, Campbell's monomythic hero's journey is analogous to nearly all psycho-spiritual systems. Whether the initiate be a mythic hero or heroine, yogi, shaman, or an individual seeking spiritual truth, a preliminary stage along the path involves recognizing the coexistence of polarized forces and working toward reconciling them."[2] (Teich)

---

1 http://www.starwars.com/news/mythic-discovery-within-the-inner-reaches-of-outer-space-joseph-campbell-meets-george-lucas-part-i

2 http://solarlunar.com/articles/twin-heroes/joseph-campbell-heros-journey/

However, even if Campbell did intend to be truly inclusive and have his hero represent an "everyperson" regardless of gender or background, the very idea of a universal story tends to flatten experiences into a one-size-fits-all framework, rather than expanding the archetypal model to recognize unique experiences. This can be seen in many examples of stories that follow the Hero's Journey model, which tend to focus primarily on men and male experiences. George Lucas's *Star Wars*, and J.R.R. Tolkien's *Lord of the Rings* both offer up examples of male heroes undertaking their journeys in worlds nearly devoid of women, with a few notable exceptions.

Even within *The Hero With a Thousand Faces* itself, the majority of the myths used as examples to illustrate the stages of the Hero's Journey use male heroes and male pronouns. Women appear primarily as Goddess and Temptress in the Initiation stage (Campbell, 91-104), which places them in the role of help or hindrance to the male hero, giving them no journey or agency of their own.

MAUREEN MURDOCK AND THE FEMININE ALTERNATIVE

In 1990, drawing on her background in psychology, Maureen Murdock proposed an alternate model with her book *The Heroine's Journey*, in direct response to Campbell's work. A prime example of the limitations of Campbell's model that Murdock sought to address comes from an interaction between Campbell and Murdock. A student of Campbell's, Murdock approached Campbell regarding the question of women's unique experiences and journeys, and his response was dismissive. "Women don't need to make the journey [...] All [she] has to do is realize she's the place people are trying to get to."[3] Murdock, understandably, was not pleased with this response.

> *"The answer stunned me; I found it deeply unsatisfying. The women I know and work with do not want to be there, the place that people are trying to get to. They do not want to embody Penelope, waiting patiently, endlessly weaving and unweaving. They do not want to be handmaidens of the dominant male culture giving service to the gods. They do not want to follow the advice of fundamentalist preachers and return to the home. They need a new model that understands who and what a woman is."* (Murdock, 2)

Murdock's model of The Heroine's Journey proposes an alternative, one meant to center women's unique experiences. Following Campbell's structural model, Murdock divides her book into sections, each examining a stage of the journey (Murdock, vii-ix):

---

3 http://www.maureenmurdock.com/heroine.html

1. Separation from the Feminine
2. Identification with the Masculine
3. The Road of Trials
4. The Illusory Boon of Success
5. Strong Women Can Say No
6. The Initiation and Descent to the Goddess
7. Urgent Yearning to Reconnect with the Feminine
8. Healing the Mother/Daughter Split
9. Finding the Inner Man with Heart
10. Beyond Duality

Since the publication of *The Heroine's Journey*, many creators have produced works featuring female protagonists and have centered the unique experiences of women as Murdock set out to do with her model. Examples include Buffy of *Buffy the Vampire Slayer*; Beatrix Kiddo aka Black Mamba of *Kill Bill* (based on The Bride); Sarah Connor of the *Terminator* franchise; Elsa and Anna of *Frozen*; and Katniss Everdeen of the *Hunger Games*.

A common thread in many of these examples is the importance of family, friendship, and the women striving for a return to some kind of normalcy or balance at the end of their tales. There are, of course, also differences that speak to the uniqueness of each woman's journey.

Buffy's series ends with a sense of continuing adventures to come, which is more in line with the Hero's Journey model, as will be shown later. Childcare is not a factor in Elsa and Anna's journey in *Frozen* (unless you count Olaf the snowman), though their bond as sisters is at the heart of the story. Similarly, Katniss's desire to protect her younger sister prompts her initial journey in the Hunger Games series. Teamwork, friendship, and the importance of family as seen in these stories are values traditionally associated with the feminine.

Although *Labyrinth* was released in 1986, prior to the publication of *The Heroine's Journey*, it encompasses many of the feminine qualities Murdock set out to highlight — an inward-facing journey that teaches the heroine about herself, a focus on family, and the importance of friendships. It remains an excellent example of the Heroine's Journey model; as stated earlier, it is one of the few movies among the pantheon of 1980s fantasy movies to put a female character front and center, and allows her to be an active participant in her own story.

ENTERING THE LABYRINTH

Labyrinth draws upon fairy tales for its overall aesthetic, as well as elements of its plot. Fairy tales themselves frequently offer examples of the Heroine's Journey model. Shortly before the inciting incident that begins her journey – the fateful wish that causes her step-brother Toby to be stolen by the Goblin King – Sarah invokes fairy tales directly as she bemoans her situation.

> *"Once upon a time, there was a beautiful young girl whose stepmother always made her stay home with the baby. And the baby was a spoiled child, and wanted everything to himself and the young girl was practically a slave. But what no one knew is that the king of the goblins had fallen in love with the girl, and he had given her certain powers. So one night, when the baby had been particularly cruel to her, she called on the goblins for help!"* (Labyrinth)

With this invocation of fairy tales, Sarah embarks on the first stage in the Heroine's Journey. She rejects the traditionally feminine activity of childcare, while also rejecting and separating herself from her step-mother – Murdock's The Terrible Mother/the Negative Feminine (Murdock, 18).

Sarah's association with the masculine, the second stage of the Heroine's Journey, takes two forms – in her embrace of the typically masculine activity of setting off on an adventure/rescue mission, and the allies she chooses along the way. Hoggle, Ludo, and Didymus are all male. As Murdock describes it:

> *"During the second stage of the heroine's journey a woman wishes to identify with the masculine or to be rescued by the masculine. When a woman decides to break with established images of the feminine she inevitably brings the traditional hero's journey. She puts on her armor, mounts her modern-day steed, leaves loved ones behind, and goes in search of the golden treasure."* (Murdock, 36).

The guides and allies the heroine looks to in this stage of the journey are inevitably masculine, or aligned with traditionally male characteristics, for example, an older, or childless, woman who fits the lone hero archetype.

With her male allies in place, and her traditionally feminine responsibilities left behind, Sarah embarks on the third phase of the Heroine's Journey, The Road of Trials. This is the Labyrinth itself, which also encompasses the Illusion of Success. After making initial progress, Sarah gets cocky and tells Jareth, the Goblin King, that his Labyrinth is "a piece of cake." He accordingly ups the difficulty, setting new and more terrifying obstacles in her path, which in turn causes Hoggle to temporarily abandon her out of fear.

The next phase of the Heroine's Journey is Strong Women Can Say No.

After biting into a drugged peach, Sarah falls into a crystal ball given to her by Jareth. Inside the ball, she sees what her life could be like, dancing with him, wearing beautiful clothing, and having her every wish fulfilled. As Jareth tells her when he first gives her the crystal, all she has to do is give up on Toby to have her dreams come true:

> *"It's a crystal. Nothing more. But if you turn it this way and look into it, it will show you your dreams. But this is not a gift for an ordinary girl who takes care of a screaming baby."* (Labyrinth)

Sarah is tempted by Jareth's offer. It is exactly what she wanted at the beginning of the movie; however, her journey has changed her. She refuses him, fleeing the illusion he's built for her, and breaks free from the crystal.

It is a step toward Sarah growing up, putting aside her fantasy, and putting Toby's needs ahead of her own. However, even though she wins free from Jareth's trap, she has another choice to face in the Initiation/Descent to the Goddess phase of the journey. Sarah breaks free from the crystal only to fall into the underworld of the junkyard where she meets the Junk Lady, a Goddess/Crone figure. Like Jareth, the Junk Lady tempts Sarah with a variation on her heart's desire. She shows Sarah a vision of her room back home, where she is surrounded by her toys, and offers Sarah the opportunity to stay a child forever, rather than being saddled with the adult responsibility of caring for her baby brother.

Murdock's Encounter with the Goddess describes a mature woman coming face to face with her sexuality, and her choice to embrace motherhood, or not, and her general relationship to her body and her femininity:

> *"During the descent, a woman faces a period of introversion or depression [...] She may feel homeless, orphaned, in a place of in-between. Like both Demeter and Inanna, she will bear no fruit... She may feel naked and exposed, arid, sexless, raw."* (Murdock, 105)

While Sarah is a younger protagonist, and her encounter with the Junk Lady does not map exactly to this stage of the Heroine's Journey as outlined by Murdock, the essential choice Sarah must make is the same. What is her relationship to the potentially nurturing/mothering side of her personality? Will she cut out and deny one part of her life (Toby) to dwell exclusively in a world of fantasy and dreams? This marks the beginning of Sarah's Reconnection with the Feminine, and the point where she must choose whether or not to care for her brother or abandon him.

Through her encounter with the Junk Lady, Sarah learns something about herself. She doesn't want to stay a child forever, and she's ready to take the adult action of placing someone else's needs above her own.

Sarah's completion of the last stages of the Heroine's Journey focuses primarily on Reconnecting with the Feminine, and living Beyond Duality. After facing down her temptations, and learning about herself, Sarah returns safely home with Toby, and ultimately finds a way to balance both sides of her personality. Even though she's growing up, the friends she made inside the Labyrinth appear to her in her mirror, assuring her that when she needs them, all she has to do is call. They are a part of her life, just as Toby is a part of her life. She can be a good big sister without having to give up everything she loves.

Thus, the Heroine's Journey is complete. Sarah has grown as a person, vanquished demons both real and metaphorical, carried out a rescue, and experienced a true adventure.

THE LIMITS OF THE HEROINE'S JOURNEY

When held up against Joseph Campbell's model of the Hero's Journey, Murdock's Heroine's Journey certainly expands the archetype by addressing uniquely feminine concerns. However, the model is still limited, taking for granted that certain questions or challenges will be universal to all women, and reinforcing a strong male/female binary that fails to account for the full spectrum of gender and sexuality.

In his essay "Essential Differences in the Gay Hero's Journey," Lloyd Meeker gives an example that illustrates the problematic nature of assuming any model of journey can convey a universal experience:

"When the gay hero's sexuality, or some other core aspect of his internal life, drives the story Separation from the World takes on deeper meaning, because a gay hero separates from the world before puberty. He discovers he's an outsider in the heteronormative world. The difference this makes to a gay hero's journey is massive..."[4]

Meeker's example is specific to gay men; however, the principle can be applied equally to any marginalized identity. Campbell's claim that his model is inclusive of all humanity ignores that there are very real lived experiences for marginalized individuals that are simply not shared — and sometimes simply not even seen — by someone like Campbell. The life experience of straight,

4 http://rainbowromancewriters.com/node/733

white, able-bodied, cis males is largely accepted as the default and the norm, even today. Someone living inside that framework may well see their experience as universal, and that view would largely be affirmed by the media available for them to consume.

This blind spot of Campbell's is one of the things Murdock set out to address in her work, showing there are some experiences that are unique to women which Campbell's model does not take into account. However, Murdock's model is not without blind spots as well. It also focuses on a particular segment of the female population and does not address all identities and intersectionalities within the subset of women.

Labyrinth shows some of these limitations to the Heroine's Journey model, as well as the strengths. Sarah's journey asks her to give up a world of fantasy and take care of a child. Even though Toby is her brother, this still places Sarah in a mothering role, positing the ultimate end point of a woman's journey as one of domesticity and child care.

While questions surrounding motherhood are reflective of many women's unique experiences, they are not universal. Not every woman wants to be a mother, and not every woman is physically capable of doing so. This comes with its own nasty set of clichés, for example, the notion that motherhood is the only way a woman can truly be fulfilled, or that a woman's sole value is her ability to give birth.

While Murdock's model does not convey a perfect universal experience for women, it does work as a response to Campbell's model by using his framework and expanding it to address the concerns of women and their desire for journeys of their own.

THE LIMITS OF THE HERO'S JOURNEY

There are also limitations to the structure of the Hero's Journey that do not necessarily link to gender, class, or background. The end point of the Heroine's Journey is the stability and balance achieved in the Beyond Duality stage. However, the final stage of Campbell's journey, the Freedom to Live, reads more as a state of suspended animation, a pause, waiting for the next adventure.

"The hero is the champion of things becoming, not of things become, because he is. [...] He does not mistake the apparent changelessness in time for permanence of Being, nor is he fearful of the next moment (or of the "other thing"), as destroying the permanent with its change." (Campbell, 209).

At the end of his journey, the hero lives in the moment, not regretting the past or looking forward to the future. It is a state that allows him to be forgiven for his past actions and not held responsible for his future actions, simply going where he is called.

In the applications of the Hero's Journey given as examples earlier - Luke Skywalker, King Arthur, and Frodo Baggins — this certainly seems to be the case. There is an undercurrent of loss to the end of each of their stories, but also a rejection of the domestic as well. Like Odysseus at the end of *The Odyssey*, these heroes do not find domestic bliss. They sever ties with their families (or those ties are severed for them), and they await the next adventure.

In these practical applications, the hero is never asked to grow up in that they are not asked to deal with the consequences of their heroism in the world. They do not stay to raise children, and if their wisdom benefits later generations, it is further down the line at a remove (see, again, Luke Skywalker). These heroes remain iconic, frozen in the moment of their heroism, ready to be called on again in the future, while the rest of the world moves on. The Hero's Journey is a circle; the Heroine's Journey is a straight line. Campbell's model, and many of the stories drawn from it, allow only for a limited understanding of heroism, and a limited model of masculinity — one that calls for a constant state of action, rather than domesticity and rest.

USING TROPES TO BUILD A BETTER STORY

As this essay has shown, *Labyrinth* can be mapped to the Heroine's Journey as laid out by Maureen Murdock. However, not every step is a one-to-one match. In its practical applications, The Hero/Heroine's Journey trope is malleable, like all tropes. Buffy can end her journey with the Freedom to Live. Elsa, Anna, and Katniss do not need to Encounter the Goddess or Reconnect with the Feminine in a way that requires them to consider whether they want to have children in order to make their journeys complete. Steps of the journey can be swapped out, rearranged, or dropped all together.

Tropes and archetypes are narrative building blocks, a jumping off point, not a set of hard and fast rules. Not every woman wants to settle down into motherhood, or return to the status quo at the end of her tale. Not every man wants to keep on adventuring. Some heroes might want to settle down and start a family, and some heroines might want to continue journeying and see what is beyond the horizon.

Just as Maureen Murdock took Joseph Campbell's model and expanded the conversation to include the unique experiences of women, we must recognize there are other stories to be told and other archetypal models for expressing them.

We need to recognize stories that flip the script. We need models that do not require heroines to reject femininity in order to begin their journey, or reclaim it at the end. We need models that allow for men to find domestic bliss and balance at the end of their tales. Even more importantly, we need models that recognize the unique journeys of non-binary characters, trans characters, characters of color, neuro-atypical characters, and characters representing a wide array of marginalized identities. Like the Heroine's Journey itself, Murdock's model is only a jumping off point. We need to keep the conversation going and continue to expand the models and tropes that form the building blocks of our stories in order to capture all the facets of our world.

WORKS CITED

Campbell, Joseph. *The Hero With a Thousand Faces* (The Collected Works of Joseph Campbell). Navato, CA USA: New World Library. Third Edition. 2008.

Labyrinth. Dir. Jim Henson. Lucasfilm/Jim Henson Company, 1986. Film.

Meeker, Lloyd. *Essential Differences in a Gay Hero's Journey — Starting on the Outside*. Rainbow Romance Writers. 7 April 2014. <http://rainbowromancewriters.com/node/733>

Murdock, Maureen. *The Heroine's Journey*. Boulder, CO USA: Shambhala, 1990.

Teich, Howard. *Joseph Campbell's Hero's Journey — The Twin Heroes*. SolarLunar., <http://solarlunar.com/articles/twin-heroes/joseph-campbell-heros-journey/>

VICTOR RAYMOND, PhD

ESCAPING THE HALL OF MIRRORS

NEW YORK AND SEATTLE are cosmopolitan cities, home to dozens of different ethnic communities, each city having a vibrant cultural life. But in both cities[1], attempts have been made recently to stage new productions of *The Mikado* — the Gilbert & Sullivan opera set in an imagined feudal Japan. In both cases, the productions were criticized for being examples of "yellowface" — casting white actors in Asian roles, when there are clearly lots of Asian actors available. That by itself wasn't the only problem. The deeper problem of *The Mikado* is that any traditional production is a racist relic of the 19th Century, and telling people to "lighten up already" doesn't fix that. There have been some very decent rewrites to update it for modern audiences, but more often than not, *The Mikado* gets staged in a traditional manner — racism and all.

Probably the biggest reason for this is that *The Mikado* is a reflection of British ideas about how the world looked at the height of empire, some 130 years ago. Between nostalgia and familiarity, there's enough of cultural resonance for many white Americans to not really notice how jarring it is for most Asians — especially Asians who grew up in the United States.

This cultural perspective — the world seen through Western (white) eyes — is pervasive in American and European media and literature. By placing a white — usually male — perspective as the viewpoint for seeing the world, it becomes easy to see everything else as "other" or "different" and often "inferior."

Consider for a moment the list of familiar archetypal characters easily found in books, movies, and other media:

* The Noble Savage: usually a "Red Indian" who is either a bloodthirsty warrior or living in harmony with Nature.
* The Happy Negro: from Stepin Fetchit to more recent depictions, a

---

1 "Why The Mikado is Still Problematic: Cultural Appropriation 101" Howlround.com, Desdemona Chiang, 10/5/2015, http://howlround.com/why-the-mikado-is-still-problematic-cultural-appropriation-101 and "It's Time to Reinvent "The Mikado" Without the Racism" ReAppropriate, 9/15/2015, http://reappropriate.co/2015/09/its-time-to-reinvent-the-mikado-without-the-racism/

character usually acting in ways to validate the social inequality of the status quo.

* The Yellow Peril: the stereotype of the mysterious and menacing Oriental, out to destroy the American way of life.
* The Shaman: somewhat more plastic in ethnicity, the Shaman is the holder of non-Western (and therefore suspect) knowledge. The Voodoo Priest is a variation on this theme.
* The Magical Negro — a Black character whose main job is to assist the (white) main character in succeeding, with the white main character getting the glory (and the girl) at the end of the story.

The list of clichés is practically endless. This suggests how wide-spread they are, as unquestioned elements of storytelling. The problem with the clichés already mentioned is that they presuppose a particular kind of unmarked state, that of a white, cisgender, heterosexual Christian male usually from an American or Western European cultural background. Anything that varies from this set of norms is therefore different or abnormal. It is particularly a problem for writers who are writing outside of their cultural background or frame of reference. In *Granta 92*, published in 2006, Binyavanga Wainaina dispassionately lists off Western cliché after Western cliché in "How To Write About Africa" — "The Loyal Servant always behaves like a seven-year-old and needs a firm hand; he is scared of snakes, good with children, and always involving you in his complex domestic dramas. The Ancient Wise Man always comes from a noble tribe (not the money-grubbing tribes like the Gikuyu, the Igbo, or the Shona). He has rheumy eyes and is close to the Earth...." — these are but two from a much longer list.

But if it happens in theatre and various genres of literature, does it happen in other forms of media? The answer is an unsurprising affirmative. TV Tropes, as a website (www.tvtropes.org), has many clichés, culled from television, movies, and related media. Yet movies get made and books get written which use these tired, outworn elements again and again:

* *Dances with Wolves* — a movie which suggests that the main character — who is white — is the only real savior of the native people he encounters. At least one friend of mine sardonically referred to it as "What These People Need is a Honky."
* *The Last Samurai* — this time with Tom Cruise, and set in early modern Japan. Seen as both an idealistic portrayal of an end of an era and also something of an outsider's view of the events around the Meiji Restoration.

* *Avatar* — which manages to repeat many of the themes from *Dances with Wolves* while also providing a look at a future human-alien conflict. The plot is centered on the perspective of a white male soldier from Earth, who "goes native" and becomes the savior of the Navi.

Each of these movies was successful, and each of them made a lot of money. As a result, there are clearly no barriers or disadvantages in terms of popularity for recycling tropes and clichés — indeed, there seems to be a clear market for what might be described as "comfort food" in terms of entertainment. Why should anyone be surprised? It's *safe* and it's a money-maker. What's not to like? It would be easy to cast this as a "popular work" versus "avant-garde work" but it's more complicated than that. The risks of movie-making are considerable, and often, films and television are willing to break new ground if there is some success elsewhere — often in published literature — to use as a guide for potentially successful projects.

Computer and video gaming is even more affected by the economics of production and sales. Lara Croft is a memorable character — but very much a cliché and stereotype. Beyond characters, the limitations of computer and video games end up embedding clichés into the very structure of many games: enemies are divided into "mooks" and "bosses" and problems are solved by fighting — over and over again. While there is some pressure to make adventures and storylines more varied, that doesn't often result in better games. In fact, there has been push-back from some gamers precisely when games try to break out of the mold and do things differently, notably in the *Dragon Age* series from Bioware. Fortunately, there is enough diversity amongst gamers for Bioware to continue dealing with issues of sexual orientation and gender identity — but this may be more of the exception than the rule.

At this point, it is worth suggesting that science fiction (perhaps more so than fantasy) has an internal responsibility to eschew clichés, if only because science fiction is based on the notion of speculation on the unknown, the improbable, and the yet-to-come. But this is where fantasy and science fiction literature are not as progressive as one might hope. "You need to maintain a connection with the reader" is one defense, usually with a set of assumptions about whom that reader might be. This seems based in the paradox that precisely because science fiction is so strange, it should avoid exploring that strangeness because it might be too strange. This "comfort food" approach means that at the very moment fantasy and science fiction are supposed to transform our perspective is exactly the moment when the opportunity is lost by playing it safe by providing the familiar and the comfortable. "Wait!" the concerned observer might respond. "What if the work itself is simply unintelligible to the reader because of that strangeness?" That particular frontier is much more shunned than crossed, and even when a work becomes a "difficult read," that doesn't mean it isn't rewarding and fulfilling, e.g. Iain M. Banks' *Excession* comes to mind (or really any of his Culture novels), or Anthony Burgess's *A Clockwork Orange*, or any of a number of works by authors such as Nalo Hopkinson, Nnedi Okorafor, Hiromi Goto, Ken Liu — the list is long and well worth reading.

It has also been suggested as another kind of defense that writers do not wish to burden their readers with *too many* unknowns, and instead prefer to use well-known (well-worn?) plot elements in order to avoid distraction from the *real* focus of the story, whatever that might be. Such a defense comes across as a justification for a "paint-by-the-numbers" approach to the edges of what are supposed to be original works. While more nuanced than the first approach I've mentioned, it also pre-supposes what the reader will find familiar and unfamiliar. But this is more treacherous territory than might otherwise be thought — simplifying your audience down to an archetypal "reader" or typical "gamer" is a vast oversimplification at the best of times. All that is happened is that the "reader" or "gamer" is substituted for the writer as the point of perspective — and with even less justification for what that perspective is, except some idea of who might be most likely to buy the book.

On a deeper level, it is difficult to avoid reaching the conclusion that fantasy literature has become more and more self-referential, with the implication that the clichés will themselves become part of the assumed background and the moorings connecting fantasy to the real world will be finally and completely cut. An illustrative example comes to mind: a number of years ago, I loaned a friend a copy of L. Sprague de Camp and Fletcher Pratt's *The Compleat Enchanter* — specifically the 1976 Del Rey edition — and later asked him what he had thought of it. "Oh, it wasn't all that bad..." he responded. My raised eyebrows must have given away my surprise at his relatively low assessment. "It was pretty good for one of those *Lord of the Rings* imitation stories..."

I pointed out the original publication dates for the stories — 1940 for "The Roaring Trumpet" and "The Mathematics of Magic" and 1941 for "The Castle of Iron" — "James, this was written **before** *The Lord of the Rings* was published."

"Oh! Well, then — it was really good!"

Considering that this conversation took place some twenty-five years ago, this problem has only gotten worse since then. In the case of fantasy fiction, Diana Wynne Jones' *The Tough Guide to Fantasyland* is a bitingly funny look at clichés in fantasy literature. In an immediate sense, *The Tough Guide to Fantasyland* highlights the shortcuts authors take when writing fantasy while adopting clichés, and how common — and obvious — those short-cuts have become. Science fiction — if considered as a separate genre (as Barry Malzberg suggested[2]) — may have a different set of recurrent clichés, but it doesn't take much to find them.

The price of fantasy and science fiction becoming self-referential involves two things: the loss of context and the risk of building barriers to entry through reliance on insider jargon and meaning. The loss of context is the more dangerous one, I would suggest, because of the lack of intended connection to *anyone's* world — the writer, the readers, really anybody. This is problematic in two ways. Because the connections made to the real world are still there, albeit inferential and not explicit, it makes it possible for people to claim that those connections are really in the eye of the beholder, and therefore a matter of subjective interpretation. It further creates a kind of echo chamber where different elements are combined without any sense of how they might or might not go well together. It is therefore possible for readers to encounter stories which careen back and forth between anachronisms and fantasy elements bereft of context — with the presumption that because it is supposed to be fantasy, it does not need to avoid these problems. It can even happen when an author is otherwise trying to have a coherent context for the story, e.g. the political discussions found in *Deryni Rising* by Katherine Kurtz, and critiqued by Ursula K. Le Guin in "From Elfland to Poughkeepsie" in *The Language of the Night*, which ring false precisely because there is no difference in the conversation between Prince Nigel of Gwynedd and his brother's liege Duke Morgan, and what a conversation in Washington, D.C. between two Beltway insiders might sound like.

So where do clichés fit into this?

Clichés are a kind of shorthand for an un-valued story element. Clichés are a shortcut for the lazy writer, and are a stand-in for actual creativity and reflection. All of this assumes that the use of clichés is not intended as some kind of ironic or meta-turn within the frame of the story itself, an increasingly favorite trick for some writers, so much so that it has become something of a meta-cliché itself.

There are a number of problems with uncritically accepting clichés: the first, and most obvious, is that it's lazy not just for the writer, but also for the reader. Further, it limits the range of possibilities in character viewpoint as well as audience identification with the characters and their story. The use of clichés is a set of clues towards who and what the author assumes is familiar to the reader, and the background of the reader in culture, language, class — everything. It presumes that a specific subset of the overall audience somehow has a greater

---

2 In his interesting but flawed examination of the evolution of science fiction and its relationship to fantasy, *Engines of the Night*, published in 1982.

claim of ownership to the viewpoints and perspectives of the main characters than anyone else.[3] The biggest assumption underlying all of this is one about the associations between the characters in the story, as well as the writers and readers — a set of assumptions about "us" and "them" and who belongs where and who is related to whom.

For science fiction and fantasy, drawing upon imagined contexts and created cultures, this set of associative assumptions is an extension of Benedict Anderson's argument in his book, *Imagined Communities*, that national identity is limited, sovereign, and constitutes a community — there is an "us" living within a set of boundaries "we" have defined and where people like "us" live. This is simultaneously in real and imaginary contexts. The real world context of writing provides one substrate of understanding which maps onto contemporary and historically-understood boundaries, while at the same moment, the imaginary context of the story provides a parallel substrate layered on top of the first, with connections between the imaginary and real world contexts as a set of guideposts for the reader; *e.g.* the Stewards of Gondor reign until a new King of the Dunedain returns — monarchy, mythic return, and a reference to the Matter of Britain. Clichés are an extension of this — but are not reliable markers of what to expect, save as much as the author is offhandedly (and possibly erroneously) implying. The entire notion of "Noble Savage" or "Yellow Peril" is grounded within a fairly specific Western and Euro-centric perspective, which creates them as the "Other" in opposition to the imagined writer and reader, as described by Edward Said in *Orientalism*, in which the definition of the Orient was done as a way to indirectly define the characteristics and qualities of the Occident — the West. In this sense, the continuation of clichés from the broader culture into the specific realm of science fiction and fantasy should not be unexpected — it is an entirely understandable result of the place of these genres as part of popular (Western) culture. "As above, so below" — a larger cultural pattern is reiterated within a smaller context.

So clichés such as the Magical Negro are themselves recognition of the subaltern status of the group such a character represents, as outlined in Gayatri Chakravorty Spivak's essay "Can the Subaltern Speak?" In this sense, "subaltern" status is a reference for the dominant-subordinate relationship between the characters and groups implied by the cliché used in writing. The cliché becomes a referent for that dominant-subordinate relationship — and the great potential within fantasy and science fiction for turning that relationship on its head. What is presumed to be difficult in other genres because of a need to re-

---

3 Whether or not this is merely an implied or explicit supposition of the author is outside the scope of this essay, however...

main grounded in a "real world" is where these genres have freedom to escape that stricture and say something new. With this in mind, the danger of using clichés is that they are reinforcing a presumed relationship which is both unequal and oversimplified. This doesn't just happen with nationality and race, but also gender — which famously has been the subject of considerable debate within the science fiction and fantasy community[4], as well as more recently within the realm of computer games — ask any female gamer about choice of characters and interactions in computer games, all as part of a larger social debate about who "owns" computer games as a hobby. Or sexual orientation — recent debates within the computer gaming hobby are themselves echoes of earlier debates about whether or not non-heterosexual characters in fantasy and science fiction could be anything more than clichés themselves. All of these issues provide frames of reference and meaning for those encountering stories and games — meaning derived from the experiences of the real world, and are therefore reinforced through what we read and what we play.

The danger lies in separating those frames of reference from the entire process of writing fantasy and science fiction, detaching context from the shape of the story and its background, justified with a wave of the hand and an airy "it's just fantasy, it doesn't have to be real." In so doing, the entire basis for truly understanding the connections between the story and the real world becomes obviated, and therefore there is no need to question clichés in any meaningful way. Clichés instead turn into touchstones of familiarity, without any real urgency to the deeper, more problematic issues raised by their appearance in the story. We end up being left with a sense of dissatisfaction with recycled tropes and ideas, as mentioned by Annelee Newitz, writing about the movie *Avatar*: "But it is nevertheless a story that revisits the same old tropes of colonization. Whites still get to be leaders of the natives — just in a kinder, gentler way than they would have in an old Flash Gordon flick or in Edgar Rice Burroughs' Mars novels."

The entire idea of subverting clichés into something new is a way to provide a perspective for whatever the cliché itself was oversimplifying. Subverting clichés in that sense becomes a radical act if done right. To stand a cliché on its head and to re-present it subversively creates an opportunity to give voice to something previously not heard. While this kind of writing does not automatically result in deeper meaning or a more nuanced perspective, it does suggest a difference in perspective which can represent something more. In the specific case of clichéd characters, the subversion of the cliché is recognition of their ex-

---

4 A more in-depth examination of the history of this can be found in Justine Larbalestier's *The Battle of the Sexes in Science Fiction*, published in 2002 from Wesleyan University Press.

istence as the "other" — with the implied suggestion of who the reader is supposed to identify with also similarly upended. And this particular re-connection is important, especially when considering the real-world context from which characters are drawn — frames such as class, race, gender, background, ability status, age, sexual orientation are not just *identifiers* but provide deeper meaning for the story as a whole. Nisi Shawl and Cynthia Ward provide excellent advice for writers on how to do this, in their slim volume *Writing the Other: A Practical Approach*. Rather than "writing what you know" Shawl and Ward suggest that there is a great deal to be gained from writing about those you might *not* know, and how to do this well. There is also a growing body of online writing addressing these issues, much of which is accessible and worth reading.

So where does this leave us? What should be done about clichés? If we get better at spotting them, it becomes easier to reward good storytelling and avoid bad storytelling. More importantly, this supports and encourages the very thing that science fiction and fantasy — and speculative writing in gaming of all sorts — says that it is about: using our imaginations to envision something truly different. This is good for readers, as we get literature and games and media that show the truly diverse world we *already* exist in, as well as taking the next step to show us worlds which are truly different and amazing.

WORKS CITED & FURTHER READING

Anderson, Benedict, 1991. *Imagined Communities*. Verso.

Chiang, Desdemona, October 5th 2015. "Why The Mikado is Still Problematic: Cultural Appropriation 101." Web. Date accessed here: month/year. <http://howlround.com/why-the-mikado-is-still-problematic-cultural-appropriation-101>.

Jones, Diana Wynne, 2006. *The Tough Guide to Fantasyland*, Firebird Travel, Penguin Books (USA) Inc.

Hines, Jim C., May 1st, 2014. "Diversity, Appropriation, and Writing the Other" <http://www.jimchines.com/2014/05/diversity-appropriation/>.

Labalestier, Justine, 2002. *The Battle of the Sexes in Science Fiction*. Wesleyan University Press.

Le Guin, Ursula K., 1973. "From Elfland to Poughkeepsie", *The Language of the Night*, G. P. Putnam's Sons, New York.

Malzberg, Barry N., 1982. *Engines of the Night*. Doubleday, New York.

Narayan, Uma, 1997. *Dislocating Cultures*. Routledge.

Newitz, Annalee, December 18th, 2009 "When Will White People Stop Making Movies Like 'Avatar'?" <www.Io9.com https://web.archive.org/web/20091230180018/http://io9.com/5422666/when-will-white-people-stop-making-movies-like-avatar>.

ReAppropriate, Spetember 15th 2015. "It's Time to Reinvent 'The Mikado' Without the Racism" <http://reappropriate.co/2015/09/its-time-to-reinvent-the-mikado-without-the-racism/>.

Said, Edward W., 1979. *Orientalism*. Vintage Books.

Shawl, Nisi and Cynthia Ward, 2009. *Writing the Other: A Practical Approach*. Aquaduct Press.

Wainaina, Binyavanga, 19th January 2006. "How To Write About Africa" *Granta* 92.

KEFFY R.M. KEHRLI

TROPES AS ERASERS:
A TRANSGENDER PERSPECTIVE

TW: *This essay includes frank discussion of anti-trans tropes, rapes, murders, and hate crimes. Additionally, if you Google "Tropes about Transgender people," you are likely to end up on a WordPress site named "TransgenderTropes101." This is a hate site and is best avoided.*

I GREW UP WITHOUT any transgender representation of any depth or value. To be fair, I also grew up with very little cisgender queer representation of any depth or value, either. There were oblique references, but typically not in the media that I was given to consume as a child. The references in adult media were filtered through daytime talk shows or the Rush Limbaugh-listening parents of friends. Or jokes. Or that one extremely pitiful-to-my-memory gay guy in *As Good As It Gets*. (My own parents are considerably more liberal, but left LGBTQ discussions for, "well, that's a thing that happens to other people's children.")

Until I was 20 and wandered away from my college campus to meet the locals who practically lived in an independent coffee shop a mile or so away, my experiences of trans people were limited to:

* Jokes and/or whispers I overheard about how so-and-so got a sex change. (Always trans women.)
* Maury Povich episodes. (Also always trans women.)

"But, Keffy," I can hear some of you say, having correctly done the math and knowing I'm not that old, "what about *Boys Don't Cry*? Wasn't that about a trans man?"

Well, yes. I didn't watch that because the film didn't sound interesting to me, just depressing. I had no idea that it was about a trans man because it was described to me as, "A movie about a girl who pretends to be a boy and gets murdered." Since Brandon Teena was played by Hilary Swank, that seemed like a likely description. I didn't know that *Boys Don't Cry* was about a trans man until after I had come out.

In any case, it had not even occurred to me that it was possible to be trans male — transgender people were exclusively trans feminine in my experience — until I was in a group of comic artists discussing gender, and one of them said, "Yeah, but you identify as female, right?"

Two things happened. First, I stammered out some "well, I don't know" answer because I had honestly never considered that I got a say in the matter of my own gender up until that point. And, second, after it sank in over a few days, I felt like I had crawled out of bed one morning to discover that I had no face. You see, I knew how to function as a gender defying young woman. I'd carved out an existence within the versions of womanhood opened up by feminism in which I felt it my duty to fight for any masculinity I wanted. I had models, though sometimes flawed, of women who had gone before me. Women who flipped the finger to the universe, picked up their beakers or strapped on their flight goggles and did what they needed to do.

I had no models for what a trans man was, except the vague unease that in order to be myself, I was going to have to betray feminism.

Thankfully, I found friends who were trans male, and in the grand tradition of being queer in a hostile world, they were my role models, flawed as they were. I've been continuously surprised since the mid-oughts, however, that the stereotype common within LGBTQ circles is that all trans men transitioned as children and are the most beloved in university campus queer communities. This was not my experience. When I visited the LGBTQ group at my university, I sat and talked to a couple of lesbians who could not wait to get rid of me. I didn't go back.

Feeling newly lost as I grew into my 20s had made representation of trans people outside the typical expectations a major issue to me. I was late in understanding myself because there was no room for me in the world. Trans people seemed to exist entirely within stereotypes and tropes: only trans women exist, trans women are jokes, trans women are liars, trans men aren't real, trans men all pass as cisgender men and have since they were children.

Tropes about groups of people (trans people, women, people of color, etc.) can affect the way others see us. They can also affect the way we see ourselves. Or, in my case, *if* we see ourselves. If the only models we have for the world are these tropes and stereotypes and we don't fit those, then what are we?

TRANSITION ISN'T MAGIC: SIMPLE, ONE-STEP TRANSITION AS A TROPE.

I was partly disappointed and partly relieved when I started to research transition and found out that it's an open-ended process rather than an event. Among the uneducated, transition is often discussed as a "sex change surgery." Transition can seem sudden if you're a cisgender person who isn't within the circle of trusted friends and family who hear about the impending transition ahead of time. There have been moments when I wished it was that simple, that it was a single surgery and you were just done, forever. Never needing to give myself another testosterone injection would be awesome.

The reality of transition is that it's a process that has different goals, outcomes, and time-frames depending on the person undergoing it. Physical transition of one's body is not an overnight event and is not desired by every trans person. When physical transition is required, the medical procedures chosen depend on the goals of the trans person and, unfortunately, their financial or medical means.

In fiction, however, the nuance is often lost. Gender Swap, Magical Sex Changes, replacement bodies, and the like have been a part of modern science fiction for decades. The magical Gender Swap frequently plays out in which someone magically wakes up in the "wrong" body. Magical Sex Changes involve a trans character being gifted the "right" body (meaning, indistinguishable from a cisgender body). Science fiction takes on these tropes usually by postulate replacement bodies, virtual reality existences, or "perfected" gender confirmation surgeries. There are similar tropes (although broken down differently than I do here) listed on the website TV Tropes as Easy Sex Change and Gender Bender.

Although the magical transition can be used to examine gender dysphoria, these are often stories written by and for cisgender people. The Gender Swap story is also typically about a cisgender character who has suddenly been shoved into a body with secondary sex characteristics of the "opposite" gender. The ensuing story is typically extremely binary and gender essentialist, with that little dash of fantasy or science fiction to make it interesting. Genitalia are typically obsessed over, almost to the exclusion of anything else.

This is also a trope that is often played for humorous purposes. For some reason, people don't seem to be able to get over the apparent hilarity of gender play, much as they still laugh at fart jokes. The joke here, of course, is something along the lines of cis men joking that if they suddenly woke up in a female body, they'd never stop playing with their breasts! Or cis women joking that if they woke up with a dick for a day, they'd write their names in the snow and jerk off for ten hours straight. Or, whatever.

This trope generally bears little resemblance to reality for most trans people and erases the real difficulties and decisions that we end up facing when we decide to transition, to whichever degree we decide to do so. Very few of us are able to pull off a rapid, let alone instantaneous, transition from one gender to another without a stage in which we don't "pass" as cis. Some of us never "pass" as cisgender no matter what we do. Not all of us want to. The instant shift from male to female (or female to male) in which nobody ever questions the gender of the person in question on either side of the magical transition feels extremely unlike the reality that myself and many of my trans or non-binary friends face. I'm not arguing here that every story featuring a transgender character needs to discuss that character's transition in detail. It's the trope in which these problems are actively waved away by the author that bothers me.

The magical/instant transition trope turns transgender people into a rhetorical device to examine the gender hang-ups of the cisgender author or readers. In this way, it takes our lived experiences, erases them from the most elementary framework of our lives (transition), and replaces those experiences with an exclusionary thought experiment or joke.

As a side-note, there are some pieces of science fiction and fantasy that deal with "hermaphrodite" characters, but those characters are usually aliens or other magical races. Regardless of whether the hermaphroditic characters are human or not, their lives and experiences seem to bear little to no resemblance to the lives of actual intersex people. The depiction of this character often focuses in lurid detail on their genitalia, typically with an overly simplified elementary school health class understanding of the biology involved in sex and gender. Although these characters are often non-human races, I have run across occasional depictions of human hermaphrodites, and these often postulate a being with Perfectly Functional Cis-Normative versions of "both" sets of genitalia. In reality, "hermaphrodites" are fictional as the term is no longer accepted for use when describing people with these conditions (ISNA). I've read a few depictions of intersex characters that I thought were interesting, for example, the protagonists in Kim Stanley Robinson's *2312* are well-written otherwise, and their lives don't revolve around their genders.

That said, I get extremely uncomfortable when I read about characters described as "hermaphrodites," especially if they're intended to be humans because I expect the depiction to be less than ideal.

TRANS PEOPLE DON'T NEED YOUR INCORRECT, FICTIONAL WARNINGS. SERIOUSLY.

When not imagining a world in which transition is painless and instant, tropes about transition focus on warning people away. Often the focus of these warnings is on transition's permanence, which is not always true depending on how one decides to transition. In the case of transgender children, the effects of transition are typically not permanent at all. Pre-pubescent transgender children, for example, will typically transition by telling others of their new name and pronouns and possibly changing their physical appearance via their chosen clothing and perhaps a haircut. That's hardly permanent. Older children are sometimes placed on puberty blockers so that when they begin to take hormones (typically starting between the ages of 16 and 18), they will only have to endure one puberty. The blockers are reversible. Nobody is rushing out and giving permanent surgery to young children.

While it is true that some of the effects of transition are permanent, trans people are not jumping into medical interventions without consideration of the effects. Trans people are typically well educated regarding our options, so much so that attending new doctors is disappointing because we often end up educating our doctors rather than vice versa. In the United States, the coverage for transgender treatments, especially surgeries, is often dependent on individual insurance companies. Worse, as I discovered a few years ago when researching options for top surgery, coverage is often dependent on the particular plan that your employer is offering. I was in the interesting position of working for a trans-friendly employer, with a plan from a company that covered transgender treatments in general, but the particular plan that I was offered through my employer did not have coverage. That has since changed, but unfortunately only did so a month before I got laid off.

Very recently — as in, while I was writing this essay — an episode of the Power Puff Girls reboot was released in which the tropes of instant, permanent, ignorant transition are played for body horror and an intensely ill-considered statement regarding trans issues.

The episode features a pony named Donny who wants to be a unicorn. Of course, The Professor has been working on a transmogrification ray that will do just that thing. The show depicts Donny ignoring a massive pile of potential side effects, and, of course, being punished for his desire to change his body by experiencing every horrible side effect that he blithely ignored (Jitterbug Jive).

The trope that transition will happen immediately and be completely permanent in every way was one of the things used to try and scare me away from making any changes to my body. My initial discussions with medical professionals about taking hormones essentially involved those professionals trying to talk me out of taking them. This will be permanent. You might not like all the changes. There are side effects when testosterone is taken by women. Etc. You will regret it. What if you regret it? Letting someone know the effects of the treatment is one thing, but trying to pressure us into not transitioning is something else entirely.

I still remember being told that when I started taking testosterone, it would turn me into a hulking, hairy, masculine rage monster. I did grow more body hair, that's normal. And I did have moments when my emotions were overwhelming. But ... as a transgender person who also suffers from depression and who has dealt with his share of PMS prior to taking testosterone, it wasn't anything that unusual.

The trope, however, is that testosterone is a horrific poison that is singularly responsible for all the evils in the world. Bullshit. Men don't act badly because of testosterone alone. Hormones aren't the only thing that controls our behavior. Testosterone is not the cause of toxic masculinity. Trans men don't take a shot of testosterone and then immediately go out to punch women in the street.

The irony, of course, is the number of people who would rail against gender essentialism in almost any other case who immediately became concerned that testosterone would send me into a massive "'roid rage." Starting hormone treatments can be a time of massive emotional upheaval for trans people, but the scaremongering is vastly overstated. I'm no angrier now than I was before I started testosterone.

This trope also showed up in a book I read a few years ago. *White Horse* by Alex Adams is about a magical plague wiping out most of humanity. The book takes place in the post-apocalyptic wasteland left behind. Besides the frustration that I felt in being served up yet another apocalypse story in which women are constantly dealing with rape and rape threats, the book had one of the most transphobic character depictions that I have read in a book. The villain, a terrible, violent man who had captured and wanted to rape the protagonist, was revealed to have been a woman before the magical transformation. The shift to a body that contained testosterone turned her (now him) into a horrifying monster who was willing to rape and murder everyone in revenge for having lost her (his) female body. The book somehow managed to hit both the anti-trans masculine trans trope of testosterone rage and the anti-trans feminine trope of the evil trans woman who is planning to rape and murder cis women to make up for her lack of a female body. Nice trick, that.

In retrospect, whether it was intentional or not, I'm rather impressed that the author managed to turn the "testosterone makes people violent" and "trans people are dangerous" tropes into a book that is wildly offensive against both trans men and trans women at the same time.

THE SCARY TRANS PERSON TROPE: WE'RE NOT MONSTERS, SERIOUSLY.

What's truly pernicious about anti-trans tropes is that they are often reiterated and kept alive by people who ought to know better. Several years ago, I was sitting in a room with a very good friend of mine when their boyfriend came into the room. "Hey, have you heard about the Black Widow?"

What followed was the regurgitation of an urban legend in which a large, black trans woman seeks out cisgender men to lure in with her femininity, and then rapes, kills, and/or otherwise assaults them. We let him finish, listening with a sense of growing horror, and then explained in no uncertain terms that he needed to never, ever, ever repeat that story again.

Ever.

The "scary trans woman" tends to be more of a societal trope rather than one in science fiction or fantasy (although, as I write this, I'm certain that someone, somewhere, is writing this trope into a story right now). This imaginary monster of a trans woman is overlaid on real trans women and creates a boogeyman that erases the very real dangers that trans women face. Worse, this imaginary threat puts trans women in even more danger.

Trans women, especially trans women of color, are the LGBTQ people most likely to be targeted in a hate crime. When we discuss people who have been murdered for being queer, most of these are trans women of color. Yet, because of the societal notion that the fragile masculinity of cis men must be protected at all costs from these women, the danger that trans women are in is upheld, protected, and justified.

We see this in the use (and success) of the "trans panic defense" when trans women are murdered. In this case, the murder of a woman whose transgender existence was a figurative assault on her murderer's masculinity. This was recently used in the defense of Jessica Laude's murderer, a U.S. Marine who killed her after discovering that she was a trans woman (Brydum).

Islan Nettles, a young black trans woman, was murdered in 2013 by a man who beat her to death in the street because he felt that his masculinity had been threatened by Islan's gender. The prevalence of the "trans panic" defense with respect to murdered trans women is so common that feelings tended toward relief when Nettles' murderer was charged with manslaughter (instead of murder) because at least he wouldn't be set free. (McKinley).

We also see this complete disregard given to the reasons why a trans woman being assaulted in the street would fight to defend herself. Look at the story of CeCe McDonald, who was sent to prison for two years because she killed a man in self-defense after he and his friends attacked her in the street (Erdely). The stats, the stories, these all led to the conclusion that a trans woman attacked by a man can expect to be a "Transgender woman murdered" headline (National

LGBTQ Task Force). As of 2015, the number of trans women murdered seems to be increasing yearly (Michaels).

The trope is that trans women are dangerous predators. The reality is that trans women are simply women trying to get by in a world that is determined to hate them.

As an aside, I felt torn writing this section of the essay. As a white, financially surviving trans man, the pain of trans women of color is decidedly not mine to write about. On the other hand, ignoring the very real harm done to trans women of color would be just another erasure. Please seek out the voices of trans women of color. Monica Roberts at *Transgriot* (Roberts) writes about these issues often.

IT'S ALL ABOUT CONTROL

Most of the tropes that have a negative impact on trans people are based in the ways in which a cissexist world tries to control our behavior and lives. If physical barriers to transition, body horror scares, and violence against us aren't enough to dissuade us, the next option is accusations of selfishness.

Cis people are used to viewing our lives through our own perspective. To many, we are, if not laughable or dangerous, simply incomprehensible. Unable to truly understand what a trans person is going through, it's easier for some people to only think about their own feelings. In this case, the idea that a trans person is doing what is necessary to live their own lives is taken as, if not openly hostile to the cis people in their life, selfish and inconsiderate. Pay attention next time you listen to an argument about whether or not a trans person should have been treated better by their family and community after coming out. Most likely, you will hear cisgender people trying to reframe the situation around their own feelings. Yes, they'll say, but how do you think I feel, finding out that this person was "really" a woman/man.

Trans people who have transitioned are portrayed as having made sacrifices that they shouldn't have (or that weren't theirs to make) in order to succeed. Frequently, this is also a method of blaming trans people for the bigotry that they face.

According to this trope, trans people transition without any thought or concern for the other people in our lives. This is, in fact, the direct opposite of my experience and that of many other trans people. So many of the people who have transitioned later in life (40+ years) considered transition much earlier in their lives but denied themselves out of concern for the world around them. Trans people often spend much of our lives trying to determine when and how we should tell our friends and family. That was one of the biggest hurdles for me. Changing my name was one thing, telling my parents that I had done so (and why) was much harder.

The trope that trans people are selfish about the decisions we make with respect to our own bodies and outwardly facing identities are based on a cisgender discomfort. We are saying that, having considered how the people around us will feel, we have still decided that transition is the best option.

The trope also ignores the fact that for many of us, transition (especially for those of us who are undergoing physical transition due to body dysphoria) is essential and life-saving.

"SHE'S STILL DEAD."

The tragically dying queer trope also applies to trans people. In many cases, the tragic death of the trans person doesn't even happen during the course of the story, and the depiction is limited to a dead sex worker found at the beginning of a detective story. This isn't the only way that trans people die in fiction. Sometimes we die during the course of the story, occasionally to forward the cause of the cisgender heroes.

I do sometimes wonder if one of the reasons that trans people die so often in fiction is that our lives are so devalued. It's as if, when writing about a trans character, in order to get an emotional response out of readers, authors feel that they need to push the feelings buttons harder. What better way to wring an emotion out of a reader than by killing the character?

Death is also an easy punishment or way of encouraging sorrow. A death can be divorced from the specific pains that marginalized people experience in their lives. You have to exercise empathy to understand a disappointment or punishment that would not unduly punish you. It doesn't take much more empathy beyond, "Wow, I don't want to be dead" to feel sad about someone having died.

Pay attention next time you read a book with a trans character (who is very rarely the protagonist anyway). Typically, this character will suffer, constantly, and probably die at the end. Or in the middle. Or even near the beginning.

I feel like I should have more to say about this trope, but it's also one of the tropes that has been discussed the most online. Think about a story that has a transgender character in it. Does she (or he, even more rarely) die before the end? Probably.

I was once on a panel that discussed LGBTQ characters in fiction, and we discussed the Dead Lesbian trope. Someone in the audience brought up Tara's death in *Buffy*, asking, "Well, but what about a character who is well developed and who dies because it's the right thing for the story?"

The answer I gave then was, "She's still dead."

This doesn't mean that no trans or other queer character may ever die in fiction. It does mean that creators should be aware that this trope exists and that no matter how well done the death is, there will always be people who are tired of seeing these characters die. The problem isn't that a single, individual character has died. Characters die in fiction all the time. The problem is that every one of these characters dies. A similar issue came up recently with the death of Abbie on *Sleepy Hollow*. Abbie was not a queer or trans character, but cisgender black women in media face some of the same treatments. In this case, the strong black woman character was called upon to sacrifice herself to save her white, male, co-lead. The problem was not that Abbie died — it was that Abbie died to forward the stories of the white characters and highlighted the problematic treatment of characters of color in *Sleepy Hollow* (Butler).

An example that comes to mind is Wanda from Neil Gaiman's *Sandman* comics, although I hesitate to bring her up because she is a contentious case. When I read the comic in 2004, she was actually the first transgender character I had read about in any science fiction or fantasy story who was dealt with in a sympathetic manner. While I was sad that her womanhood was denied in life and upset that she died, I read her story as, "It's dangerous to tell trans women that they aren't women because doing so literally kills them." This is a truth.

I've ended up talking about Wanda with many trans people. I've met trans women for whom Wanda was an important character, and who love her. I've also met trans people who say the same thing that I did on that panel regarding Tara, "Yes, but she's still dead."

This is true. Finding value in a work does not mean that it is no longer a part of a trope. It just means that we have either seen past a trope, accepted the trope in that case, seen that the trope is used for something greater, or, in the case of the stories in this book, decided to invert the trope.

The problem is not specifically that Wanda died. The problem is that Wanda died ... and so did nearly every other trans person in science fiction and fantasy stories.

By the way, don't be surprised if trans people disagree about the quality of any one depiction of a trans character. We are a very scattered group of people who are only loosely called a "community," and we come at these stories from extremely different backgrounds. It is for this reason that I also tend to use Wanda as an example of a problematic depiction. She's problematic because while she has meant a lot to some trans people, she is seen as harmful by others. How many of the problems come from Gaiman's writing, and how many come from the notion of womanhood that he was writing about and critiquing? Etc.

In any case, I am hesitant to write or publish stories in which trans people die tragically at the end, even though I, personally, tend to like tragedies.

On a similar note, it wasn't until I started editing reprints for my magazine *GlitterShip* that I realized just how many LGBTQ stories involve characters who have dead or dying lovers.

PITFALLS IN FLIPPING TROPES

One of the last terms that I want to hear regarding a work that contains transgender characters is "edgy." This isn't that I don't like fiction that pushes the boundaries of what is possible, or that seeks to shove the status quo off a cliff. It's that, so often, the types of things that get called edgy are status quo plus. Typically, these works show the seedy underbelly of cities, lives, worlds, but do so as a type of voyeurism. The intent is not to humanize people who are marginalized in our current status quo, but to be entertained watching them suffer.

What I expect from an "edgy" work featuring a trans character is that the character will be a trans woman, and probably a sex worker, and will somehow resemble none of the trans women or sex workers (or sex workers who are trans women) that I have met. Most likely she will suffer and be shown to be ridiculous, over the top, rude, and selfish. And then, she'll die so that the protagonists have a death to react to.

It's almost impossible to find media that avoids all of the anti-transgender tropes. Even when I'm not watching a comedy with raunchy humor, I always expect now that there will be a joke that's anti-trans somewhere in the story. The exception, of course, is in fiction written by my fellow transgender creators. In those cases, I might find things that make me uncomfortable (like I said, we don't all agree about everything!), but even those are at least thought through. What really makes most of the anti-trans tropes, stereotypes, and jokes burn is how casual and unnecessary they are.

It would be wonderful to be able to watch an episode of a new television series, or a new movie without feeling like I need to brace myself for the inevitable anti-trans joke. "Escapist" fiction gets a bad rap sometimes, but I feel like this is mostly due to the number of people for whom most of this fiction is escapist because they aren't the ones getting fed to the wolves for a cheap laugh. Fewer awful depictions of trans people, and more sensitive depictions — especially those that are #OwnVoices (Brinkley), would, if nothing else, reduce the stress that we feel as a result of being perpetually marginalized, even within genres that claim to welcome the unusual. (Yes, science fiction and fantasy, I'm looking at you.)

So, I ask for two things of the people reading this essay. First, seek out fiction by trans authors. We've been writing about our lives and experiences for decades and frequently ended up ignored. Thankfully, this is starting to shift, especially in short fiction. Some authors to start with are Nino Cipri, Caitlín R. Kiernan, Everett Maroon, and Pat Schmatz. You can also check out the sources listed below by John Hansen, Bogi Takács, and A.C. Wise for a longer list. (Bogi also writes #OwnVoices transgender and non-binary science fiction.) Second, if you're cis and planning to write or talk about trans people, consider these tropes. Are you supporting the way we are treated in the status quo? Are you accepting these tropes and stereotypes without consideration? Are you flipping them? Awareness is the first step toward creating a meaningful, respectful depiction of trans people, but awareness alone isn't enough.

WORKS CITED

Adams, Alex. *White Horse*. New York: Emily Bester/Atria Books. 2012. Print.

As Good As it Gets. Dir. James L. Brooks. Perf. Jack Nicholson, Helen Hunt, Greg Kinnear. TriStar Pictures, 1997. VHS.

Boys Don't Cry. Dir. Kimberly Peirce. Perf. Hilary Swank, Chloë Sevigny, Peter Sarsgaard. Fox Searchlight. 1999. Film.

Brinkley, Nicole. "#OwnVoices takes over Twitter." YA *Interrobang*. 11 Sept. 2015. Web. <http://www.yainterrobang.com/ownvoices/>.

Brydum, Sunnivie. "U.S. Marine Claims 'Trans Panic' in Murder of Trans Filipina Jennifer Laude." *The Advocate*. 24 Aug. 2015. Web. <http://www.advocate.com/transgender/2015/08/24/us-marine-claims-trans-panic-murder-trans-filipina-jennifer-laude>.

Butler, Bethonie. "After a shocking death on 'Sleepy Hollow' fans are questioning how the show treats characters of color." *The Washington Post*. 12 Apr. 2016. Web.   <https://www.washingtonpost.com/news/arts-and-entertainment/wp/2016/04/12/after-a-shocking-death-on-sleepy-hollow-fans-are-questioning-how-the-show-treats-characters-of-color/>.

Dalton, Deron. "The 22 trans women murdered in 2015." *The Daily Dot*. 15 Oct. 2015. Web. <http://www.dailydot.com/politics/trans-women-of-color-murdered/>.

Dawes, Dorian. "A Joke in the PowerPuff Girls Reboot is a Sucker Punch to Trans Women." *Bitch Media*. 18 Apr. 2016. Web. <https://bitchmedia.org/article/joke-powerpuff-girls-reboot-suckerpunch-trans-women>.

"Easy Sex Change." *TV Tropes*. TV Tropes, n.d. Web. 25 Apr. 2016. <http://tvtropes.org/pmwiki/pmwiki.php/Main/EasySexChange>.

Erdely, Sabrina Rubin. "The Transgender Crucible." *Rolling Stone*. 30 Jul. 2014. Web.   <http://www.rollingstone.com/culture/news/the-transgender-cruci-

ble-20140730>.

Gaiman, Neil (w), McManus, Shawn, Colleen Doran, Bryan Talbot (p), Giordano, Dick, George Pratt, Stan Woch (i), McKean, Dave, Daniel Vozzo (a). *The Sandman: A Game of You.* Ed. Karen Berger, Alisa Kwitney. New York: DC Comics. 1993. Trade.

"Gender Bender" *TV Tropes.* TV Tropes n.d. Web. 25 Apr. 2016. <http://tvtropes. org/pmwiki/pmwiki.php/Main/GenderBender>.

Hansen, John. "Top 10 books by transgender authors featuring trans characters." *The Guardian.* 1 Feb. 2016. Web. <http://www.theguardian.com/childrens-books-site/2016/feb/01/top-10-books-transgender-authors-trans-characters>.

"Is a person who is intersex a hermaphrodite?" *Intersex Society of North America.* ISNA n.d. Web. 30 Apr. 2016. <http://www.isna.org/faq/hermaphrodite>.

Jitterbug Jive. "April 8th, 2016 at 5:10 PM" Tumblr Post. 8 Apr. 2016. Web. <http://jitterbugjive.tumblr.com/post/142485553459/jitterbugjive-jitterbug-jive-jitterbugjive>.

McKinley Jr., James C. "Manslaughter Charges in Beating Death of Transgender Woman in 2013." *The New York Times.* 3 Mar. 2015. Web. <http://www.nytimes. com/2015/03/04/nyregion/manslaughter-charges-in-beating-death-of-trans-gender-woman-in-2013.html>.

Michaels, Samantha. "More Transgender People Have Been Killed in 2015 Than Any Other Year on Record." *Mother Jones.* 20 Nov. 2015. Web. <http:// www.motherjones.com/mojo/2015/11/more-transgender-people-have-been-murdered-2015-any-other-year-record>.

Roberts, Monica. *Transgriot.* Transgriot n.d. Web. 30 Apr. 2016. http://trans-griot.blogspot.com/

"Seeing Red." *Buffy the Vampire Slayer: The Complete Sixth Season.* Writ. Steven S. DeKnight. Dir. Michael Gershman. 20th Century Fox, 2002. DVD.

"Stop Trans Murders." *National LGBTQ Task Force.* National LGBTQ Task Force n.d. Web. 30 Apr. 2016. <http://www.thetaskforce.org/stop-trans-murders/>.

Takács, Bogi. "now for my BIG thread of cool & mostly FREE speculative fiction by trans/nb/gq/etc non-cis authors for #TDOV! it starts here. :)" 31 Mar. 2016. 10:44 a.m. Tweet thread. <https://twitter.com/bogiperson/status/715595554839875584>.

Takács, Bogi. "Trans SFF by Trans Authors - #ownvoices." Goodreads. Goodreads n.d. Web. 30 Apr. 2016. <http://www.goodreads.com/list/show/93731.Trans_SFF_by_Trans_Authors_ownvoices>.

TransWomen of Color Collective. TransWomen of Color Collective. n.d. Web. 30 Apr. 2016. <http://www.twocc.us/>.

"What is intersex?" Intersex Society of North America. ISNA n.d. Web. 30 Apr. 2016. <http://www.isna.org/faq/what_is_intersex>.

Wise, A. C. "Tag Archives: non-binary authors." A.C. Wise.net. Web. 30 Apr. 2016. <http://www.acwise.net/?tag=non-binary-authors>.

SECTION III:
DEFINING THE TROPES

MONICA VALENTINELLI & JAYM GATES

AFTERWORD: AUTHORS AND THEIR TROPES

trope[1], n.
1a: a word or expression used in a figurative sense
1b: a common or overused theme or device

UPSIDE DOWN: INVERTED TROPES IN STORYTELLING represents a motley collection of fiction in multiple literary forms. Each work was inspired by a specific, unique, and omnipresent trope found in science fiction, fantasy, and horror fiction. Some tropes, such as the Asian Scientist, The Girlfriend in the Refrigerator, or Love at First Sight, reach far beyond the boundaries of genre fiction and are so heavily relied upon they may be found in comics, TV shows, movies as well as others, like The City Planet, remain grounded in genre fiction.

To be considered for publication, authors were first tasked with selecting a unique trope. Then, they were encouraged to creatively explore (e.g. "smash" or "invert") it in their fiction. A few authors selected a prominent trope because they wanted to experiment with it for some tropes (e.g. The Chosen One) are so commonly found, their exact opposite (The Unchosen One) is *also* considered a trope. Other writers, however, picked problematic tropes depicting race, gender, sexuality, etc. (like The Black Man Dies First or the Asian Scientist) because they identified that these stereotypes perpetuate harm and do not accurately reflect their identity or culture. After all, what is the point of fiction but to allow all of us to see ourselves as the believable stars of our own story? Other authors were tired of seeing the same trope used over and over again and opted to tackle tropes including the City Planet, Chainmaille Bikini, and The Super Soldier in both a direct and indirect fashion.

Because these devices were crucial to the author's storytelling process, we felt that identifying the trope would heighten reader satisfaction. Revealing the trope, however, either in the Table of Contents or at the end of an author's story, proved to be problematic. By taking either approach, the trope's identi-

---

1 Merriam-Webster's Collegiate® Dictionary, Eleventh Edition.

fication would devalue the stories by solidifying the reader's expectations before they read the first paragraph. Though some authors, such as Kat Richardson, did choose to reveal their tropes as a clue in their story's title, other writers, like John Hornor Jacobs, took a different, subtler approach. Thus, to separate the author's intent from the reader's experience, we decided to include an afterword to serve a dual purpose: one, to list and define the tropes, and two, to help readers discover more about the authors as well.

Since the essayists have addressed and defined their selected tropes in a direct manner for the purposes of offering their insight, expertise, and nuanced perspectives, we opted to avoid repetition by redressing them in the afterword. Their essays can be found directly before this afterword, and their tropes are defined in the context of their arguments.

By taking the readers' expectations into account, we wish you will enjoy the stories more so than if we matched the tropes to the authors in the Table of Contents. We also hope that the anthology will do what we set out to do: to facilitate deeper conversations about commonly found tropes in response to the creative and analytical efforts of over two dozen unique and talented writers.

Happy reading!

INDEX OF TROPES

AMBIGUOUSLY JEWISH — PAGE 244

Examined in: "Hamsa, Hamsa, Hamsa, Tfu, Tfu, Tfu"

Written by: Alisa Schreibman

Defined as: If you've ever watched a TV show with a doctor whose last name is –berg or a lawyer named –stein, but nothing else about the character seemed Jewish to you, you've been exposed to "Ambiguously Jewish." In most cases, that character's religious and cultural identity will never be resolved, but they exist in a permanent state of limbo, Schrodinger's Jew. The box will only be opened if the showrunners or network are feeling the sting of being too-white for their own good. That's when they pull out Sara Greenberg or Adam Rosenstein and introduce their very Jewish parents, like white rabbits from a hat. Jews are, by their nature, invisible. Anyone could be a Jew, which is what makes them the perfect diversity bait. Too-white? It's cool. Sue's real name is Shoshana Avigayl and she's a Jew. The trope Matzo Fever was also examined here, which is like the Frenchification of sexual attraction, but with Jews.

Author Quote: Jews aren't just invisible in entertainment media. We're invisible in the real world, perceived as white or black or Middle Eastern, depending on the color of our skin. Except when we're not. Like when the anti-Semitic stereotypes start flying and we say "hey, I'm a Jew," and if there's not awkward silence, there's the even more awkward, "well, you're not like that." Gee, thanks. Jews are kind of the ultimate in "the aliens are among us," which is why we make convenient scapegoats and targets in countries in turmoil and token diversity characters on TV. We are always, already passing — whether as white or South American or Middle Eastern or black, or ... As much of a problem as this can be in a representational sense, it's even more a problem for me. I'm a passing-white Jew with minimal religious attachment to Judaism or Israel and massive cultural attachment to being a Jew; on the one hand, I'm benefitting from white privilege, but on the other, I'm always on the lookout for falling shoes (maybe I should say Jews?). I chose this trope as a jumping-off point to explore what it looks like to be Jewish unambiguously.

Author Bio: Alisa Schreibman sometimes wears as many as five different hats in a single day. More than anything, she'd like to reduce her hat collection so she can wear her author hat more often. Published previously in very grown-up romance, her recent writing focuses on adaptations of Jewish folklore, Jewish adaptations of classic fairy tales, and contemporary Jewish urban fantasy. She has a Master's degree from the University of Chicago for which she wrote a thesis on medieval Jewish manuscripts, a law degree from the University of Colorado, and is currently pondering a PhD on representations of Jews and Judaism in 20th century art. She currently lives in Boulder, CO, with her best friend and their dog — who might be Jewish, depending on whether the puppy of two women in a non-lesbian domestic situation is Jewish if one of her mothers is Jewish — the Rabbis are still out on that one.

AND NOW YOU MUST MARRY ME — PAGE 183

Examined in: "Swan Song"

Written by: Michelle Lyons-McFarland

Defined as: Marriage is often presented as the reward or incentive for heroic deeds and accomplishments. This trope is often integrated with many others related to the protagonist's gender, as the hero tends to eye a fair maiden, who is often subverted into a supporting role, and is delighted when she is presented as a winning prize.

Author Quote: We always deal with the hero saving the maiden and then declaring she must marry him, and then we're basically halfway into the story of Bluebeard's Bride. I wanted to flip the script and talk about what happens when the hero has to marry the maiden, who perhaps is more than he bargained for.

Author Bio: Michelle Lyons-McFarland is a writer, editor, and game designer, in addition to being a grad student closing in on her doctorate in English Literature and Composition. Her areas of study include eighteenth-century literature, material culture, gothic literature, film, and game-based pedagogy. She lives in

Cleveland, OH with her husband and fellow game designer, Matthew McFarland, along with two elder Labradors and a highly opinionated corgi mix. Her sons, Alisdair and William, have largely come to grips with the fact that their mother is odd, assisted by the regular stream of non-bespelled hand-knitted items she gives to them.

ASIAN SCIENTIST — PAGE 190

Examined in: "Those Who Leave"

Written by: Michael Choi

Defined as: This trope is centered upon the fact that when an Asian protagonist or antagonist is included in a story, typically they are assigned to the role of the scientist. This role may be both overt and subtle, as the scientist is often coupled with several other tropes in popular media as well to further underline the point that the character is relying on their intellect and little else.

Author Quote: Asian. Math. Science. The cliché is easy to see. What troubles me is the feeling that emanates from the word Asian — cold, robotic, calculating. All intellect. No heart. No passion. Even when applied to beauty and art — Asian Violinist — it carries the same effect. "Those Who Leave" doesn't hide from the trope, but rather adopts it fully; it pushes to where science is love, directly linked to the core of the main character's humanity — the ocean, her mother, and her home.

Author Bio: Michael Choi is a filmmaker based in New York City. An Odyssey Workshop 2014 graduate, he also attended the MFA Film program at Columbia University. He lives in Brooklyn with his lovely wife and their naughty Cavalier Spaniel, and he is currently working on his first novel. Find him online at www.cranevalleyfilms.com.

BLIND PEOPLE ARE MAGIC — PAGE 35

Examined in: "Seeking Truth"

Written by: Elsa Sjunneson-Henry

Defined as: This trope reduces blind characters to rare, special protagonists or, in some cases, antagonists who have extraordinary gifts, either because they are blind or to "fix" the fact that they have no sight. In some stories, the blind character might bestow magical powers on the protagonist, while in others that character is a sage or mystic that is then killed for their abilities. To further underline this trope, The Blind Seer was also examined. This secondary trope often presents the idea that blind people are psychic because they can't "see" anything in reality and goes hand-in-hand with Blind People are Magic.

Author Quote: As a blind writer, I've always been frustrated with the magical fixes for blindness in SFF/H literature. I wanted to address that with a character who was not a psychic, but a person who was highly skilled.

Author Bio: Elsa Sjunneson-Henry is a half-blind, half-deaf SFF/H writer who can be found somewhere near New York City. She's been in *Ghost in the Cogs* from Broken Eye Books and numerous tabletop roleplaying game books including her own, *Dead Scare*, and is currently an assistant editor for *Fireside Magazine*. She is passionate about disability inclusion in both fiction and game products, and works as an advocate for disabled gamers. In her spare time she walks her hound dog on Revolutionary War battlefields. She can be found at feministsonar.com.

CHAINMAILLE BIKINI — PAGE 176

Examined in: "Drafty as a Chainmaille Bikini"

Written by: Kat Richardson

Defined as: The stereotype of female warriors in fantasy (and sometimes other genre) stories wading into battle in nothing more than a couple of triangles of chain mail. Part of the trope is the implication that the woman is so tough she doesn't NEED any other covering, but it's not only impractical, impossible, dangerous, and uncomfortable, it's clearly sexist and used for its titillation factor more than anything else.

Author Quote: I've always found the idea of chain mail bikinis — ridiculous — and not only because they look silly and leave vital areas uncovered. I thought it would be fun to take the real problems of wearing such a useless item and run with them.

Author Bio: Kat Richardson is the bestselling author of the *Greywalker* novels, as well as a small tantrum of short fantasy, science fiction, and mystery stories. She is an accomplished feeder of crows. Find her at katrichardson.com and greywalker.com.

CITY PLANET — PAGE 204

Examined in: "Excess Light"

Written by: Rahul Kanakia

Defined as: Omnipresent in science fiction, the City Planet is a setting-based trope about a world that is covered with futuristic cities that have been built on top of one another, connected by transit systems, or separated by wastelands. The secondary trope examined in this story is the Cycle of Empires — the trope where society is trapped in an eternal rise and fall of imperial powers (in a manner that often bears a more than superficial resemblance to the Roman Empire).

Author Quote: I'm generally bad at writing stories according to prompt, and in this case I needed to give the editors a commitment about my trope before beginning to write the story, so I didn't want to box myself in. I decided to select an evocative image, something that was ripe to be satirized, but which could also support a good many stories.

Author Bio: Rahul Kanakia's first book, *Enter Title Here* (Disney-Hyperion), is a contemporary young adult novel. Additionally, his stories have appeared or are forthcoming in *Clarkesworld*, *Apex Magazine*, *Lightspeed*, *The Indiana Review*, and *Nature*. He holds an MFA in Creative Writing from Johns Hopkins. Originally from Washington, D.C., Rahul now lives in San Francisco. If you want to know more about him, then please visit his blog at www.blotter-paper.com or follow him on Twitter at @rahkan.

DAMSEL IN DISTRESS — PAGE 81

Examined in: "Her Curse, How Gently It Comes Undone"

Written by: Haralambi Markov

Defined as: The Damsel in Distress is a strong, cultural narrative that is concerned with gender-based attitudes towards women. Often, the Damsel in Distress is an incapable female character who cannot take care of herself and needs to be rescued. Alternatively, she is also a character who fails if she attempts to help the protagonist, either by offering advice or by lending a hand, and it is the male hero who must instruct her on how to save herself.

Author Quote: I'm a feminist and want to do revisionist takes on gender politics ingrained in fairy tales.

Author Bio: Haralambi Markov is a Bulgarian critic, editor, and writer of things weird and fantastic. A Clarion 2014 graduate, Markov enjoys fairy tales, obscure folkloric monsters, and inventing death rituals (for his stories, not his neighbors … usually). He blogs at *The Alternative Typewriter* and tweets at @HaralambiMarkov. His stories have appeared in *Geek Love*, *Electric Velocipede*, TOR.com, *Stories for Chip*, *The Apex Book of World SF*, and he is slated to appear in *Genius Loci*. He's currently working on a novel.

EPIC FANTASY — PAGE 201

Examined in: "Noun of Nouns: A Mini Epic"

Written by: Alex Shvartsman

Defined as: Epic fantasy genre is known for its extra-thick volumes filled with Important People doing World-Altering things and engaging in heroic quests. Combined, these tropes form a structure for Epic Fantasy, and the DNA for several of these tropes are examined in this story (hence, a mini Epic).

Author Quote: As a humor writer, I often seek to parody popular tropes and elements of pop culture in my writing. I needed to take a break from writing my fantasy novel, so I amused myself (and, hopefully, the readers) by making fun of the very tropes I had to consider for my not-so-funny book.

Author Bio: Alex Shvartsman is a writer, translator, and game designer from Brooklyn, NY. Over 90 of his short stories have appeared in *Nature*, *Galaxy's*

Edge, *InterGalactic Medicine Show*, and many other magazines and anthologies. He won the 2014 WSFA Small Press Award for Short Fiction and was a finalist for the 2015 Canopus Award for Excellence in Interstellar Fiction. He is the editor of the *Unidentified Funny Objects* annual anthology series of humorous SF/F. His collection *Explaining Cthulhu to Grandma and Other Stories* and his steampunk humor novella *H. G. Wells, Secret Agent* were both published in 2015. His website is www.alexshvartsman.com.

FIRST PERIOD PANIC — PAGE 141

Examined in: "First Blood"

Written by: Delilah S. Dawson

Defined as: First Period Panic is a trope that deals with an uninformed preteen, who gets very worried about the blood appearing in their underwear.

Author Quote: My first period caused a horrible bleed-through in middle school, and I truly wished for Carrie-like powers to blow up everyone who saw the mess I made of my acid-washed jean shorts during English class. I wanted to write a character who not only knew exactly what menstruation was, but who was also able to use her "monthly shame" for public good. Throw in some nice Southern Gothic and Greek mythology, and you've got "First Blood."

Author Bio: Delilah S. Dawson is the award-winning author of *Hit*, *Strike*, *Servants of the Storm*, the *Blud* series, *Star Wars: The Perfect Weapon*, a variety of short stories and comics, and *Wake of Vultures*, written as Lila Bowen. She teaches writing classes online with LitReactor and lives in the north Georgia mountains with her family. Find her online at www.whimsydark.com.

GENDERCIDE — PAGE 257

Examined in: "Real Women Are Dangerous"

Written by: Rati Mehrotra

Defined as: In this trope, half of the population is killed off — men or women —

often with the intent to explore either a female 'utopia' or a male dystopia. The Sexbot trope, whereby a robot is designed as a sexual toy for human beings, is also addressed in this story to a lesser degree.

Author Quote: My story is inspired by the 100 million 'missing women' of Asia. In India for instance, despite the laws, the abhorrent and continuing practices of female infanticide and sex selective abortion means that the gender ratio continues to skew in 'favor' of men until there are some places where there are only 7-8 women to 10 men. One would think that this would make girls and women more precious, but no, quite the opposite. Violent crime against women continues to rise. The average family continues to wish for sons. In some states, 'procuring' women for marriage from other states has become a local election issue. I wanted to explore this by taking it to a literal, unlikely extreme. What happens if all/most of the women are gone? How do men react/cope? Do stereotypes and expectations of women (especially in the Asian context) still persist in men's attitudes? The Gendericide trope seemed well suited to exploring these issues. My story also refers to the presence of sexbots, but also features a subversion of this in the form of the character Devyani. One (Hindu) meaning of the name Devyani is "like a Goddess" and I leave it to the reader to decide who or what she really is.

Author Bio: Rati Mehrotra is a Toronto-based speculative fiction writer whose short stories have appeared in *AE - The Canadian Science Fiction Review*, *Apex Magazine*, *Urban Fantasy Magazine*, and many more. Her debut novel *Markswoman* will be published in early 2018 by Harper Voyager. Find out more about her at http://ratiwrites.com or follow her @Rati_Mehrotra.

GUYS SMASH, GIRLS SHOOT — PAGE 90

Examined in: "Burning Bright"

Written by: Shanna Germain

Defined as: In stories involving combative scenes, many protagonists take action according to their gender. Typically, male characters will be at the heart of a brawl using their fists or throwing chairs against their opponents. Female characters, on the other hand, tend to be off-screen, on a horse, or just out of sight. Often, they are represented as short-to-long range fighters who shoot from a distance to ensure their safety and soften their characters, as the women are perceived as incapable of doling out physical attacks.

Author Quote: I wanted to choose a trope that had layers. This one let me subvert not just the main trope, but also lots of other ones: that women aren't dangerous, that women are always the caregivers and healers, that all mothers and daughters act a certain way, that you can't be both smart/sane and violent ...

Author Bio: Shanna Germain claims the titles of writer, editor, leximaven, and Schrodinger's brat. She is the co-owner and creative director of Monte Cook Games, the author of myriad books and short stories, and the lead designer of the family RPG, No Thank You, Evil! Her most recent works include *Bound by Lust*, *The Lure of Dangerous Women*, and *As Kinky As You Wanna Be*. Find her online at www.shannagermain.com.

HOOKER WITH A HEART OF GOLD — PAGE 148

Examined in: "Red Light"

Written by: Sara M. Harvey

Defined as: This trope is similar to the Thief with a Heart of Gold. The reader is expected to think of the prostitute as an undesirable character, but they wind up feeling something for the prostitute because, on the inside, she's "good" and "honorable." To further play with the reader's expectations, the secondary trope Femme Fatale was also used for this story.

Author Quote: I have long been fascinated by the role of sex work in the overall role of sexuality and relationships.

Author Bio: Sara M. Harvey lives and writes fantasy and horror in (and sometimes about) Nashville, TN. She is also a costume historian, theatrical costume designer, and art history teacher. She has three spoiled rotten dogs and one awesome daughter; her husband falls somewhere in-between. She tweets at @saraphina_marie, wastes too much time on facebook.com/saramharvey, and needs to update her website at saramharvey.com.

LOVE AT FIRST SIGHT — PAGE 235

Examined in: "The Tangled Web"

Written by: Ferrett Steinmetz

Defined as: Love at First Sight is a trope concerned with two characters falling in love instantly after their first meeting without cause or justification for it. Instant romance is present in almost every genre as both the center of a plot, as the couple gets ripped apart and must find their way back together, or as a subplot to quickly push two characters toward a relationship.

Author Quote: Love is something we all too often confuse for chemistry. And chemistry is a necessary starting condition of love, but ... that biological imperative can lead you astray. I wanted to explore something where people had a wildly different imperative and outcome from sex, and it turned out that the emotions were pretty much the same in the end.

Author Bio: Ferrett Steinmetz's debut urban fantasy *Flex* (and its sequels, *The Flux* and *The Fix*) features a bureaucracy-obsessed magician who is in love with the DMV, a goth videogamemancer who tries not to go all *Grand Theft Auto* on people, and one of the weirder magic systems yet devised. He was nominated for the Nebula in 2012, for which he remains moderately stoked, and lives in Cleveland with his very clever wife, a small black dog of indeterminate origin, and a friendly ghost. He tweets at @ferretthimself, and blogs entirely too much about puns, politics, and polyamory at www.theferrett.com. (Or, if your work has blocked his site, try it mirrored at theferrett.livejournal.com.)

MAGICAL NEGRO — PAGE 166

Examined in: "Super Duper Fly"

Written by: Maurice Broaddus

Defined as: The Magical Negro has several hallmarks. They have no history. They exist outside of any community of their own. Much like, if not fulfilling the role of, a fairy godmother, they arrive from somewhere that's vague and otherworldly and return in some manner. At their introduction, The Magical Negro has either a threatening or benign aspect: 1) appearing with an initial sense of danger, such as a Big Black Man, drug dealer, thief, or prisoner, in which case they must be quickly identified as helpful and compassionate; or 2) showing up in some powerless capacity, like a janitor, homeless, or a musician, so that the hero can be approached or approach them without risk (or even demonstrate compassion by interacting with them). It doesn't matter how great their wisdom or the extent of their magical powers, The Magical Negro's sole purpose is to selflessly use their powers to help the white hero in their journey. Depicted as an agent of change/the one who makes amazing things happen, their role is meant to be an exalted position, though their role boils down to fitting a black person into a white person's narrative.

Author Quote: It's easy to believe that this trope came from a good place or at least rose out of benign neglect. After all, a white writer is "writing what they know" or appealing to their target demographic, which is typically people like them, but they want a more diverse world. So the easy solution is to put an "other" at a critical place in their hero's journey to help them along. The Magical Negro is one such other (see also: Magical Native American, Magical Asian, etc). Sometimes I'm grateful just to see a reflection of me included in the story. Other times I don't think that my story is being respected and I get all stabby.

Author Bio: Maurice Broaddus's fiction has been published in numerous venues, including *Asimov's Science Fiction*, *Cemetery Dance*, *Apex Magazine*, and *Weird Tales Magazine*. He co-edited *Streets of Shadows* (Alliteration Ink) and the Dark Faith anthology series (Apex Books). He authored the urban fantasy trilogy, *Knights of Breton Court* (Angry Robot Books). Learn more about him at www. MauriceBroaddus.com.

MANIC PIXIE DREAM GIRL — PAGE 115

Examined in: "Requiem for a Manic Pixie Dream"

Written by: Katy Harrad and Greg Stolze

Defined as: The Manic Pixie Dream Girl is a type of supporting female character that appears so often in a story, she has become her own trope. Bubbly to a fault, her presence is to prod the brooding protagonist, who is typically male, to discover the true meaning of life and lighten up. Though The Manic Pixie

Dream Girl is supportive and nurturing, she doesn't have any agency in her own right, and her happiness takes a back seat as she encourages the hero to discover his — with or without her.

Author Quote: Its ridiculousness begged for satire. BEGGED, I SAY.

Author Bios: Greg Stolze has written novels about vampires (*A Hunger Like Fire*), supervillainy (*Sinner*), demons (*Ashes* and *Angel Wings*), and an amnesiac kung-fu detective (*The Forgotten Monk*). He is equally well known, however, for giving fiction away online at www.gregstolze.com/fiction_library after getting paid for it. He's aware that this seems paradoxical, but it's actually one of those 21st Century business arrangements that we're all still getting used to.

Kate Harrad is a London-based writer. Her first novel *All Lies and Jest*, a gently speculative thriller almost featuring vampires, was published by Ghostwoods Books in 2011 and was reprinted in June 2016. Some of her published short stories are collected in *Fausterella and Other Stories*, and she has also published *Prejudice and Pride*, a gender-switched version of *Pride and Prejudice*, which she wrote about in the *Guardian*. She is the editor of the non-fiction book *Purple Prose: Bisexuality in Britain* (Thorntree Press, 2016). See fausterella.co.uk for her blog and details of her work.

THE BLACK MAN DIES FIRST — PAGE 22

Examined in: "Lazzrus"

Written by: Nisi Shawl

Defined as: This trope is rooted in stories with diverse characters. Often, whenever the protagonists encounter trouble — especially within the horror genre — the black protagonist is the first one to be killed off.

Author Quote: I examined this trope because I'm so tired of it.

Author Bio: Nisi Shawl's story collection *Filter House* co-won the James Tiptree, Jr. Award. She was a Guest of Honor for WisCon 35 in 2011 and for SFRA in 2014. Shawl co-authored *Writing the Other: A Practical Approach*; edits reviews for the literary quarterly *Cascadia Subduction Zone*; and co-edited *Strange Matings: Sci-*

ence Fiction, Feminism, African American Voices, and *Octavia E. Butler.* And *Stories for Chip: A Tribute to Samuel R. Delany* also appeared in 2015. Shawl's Belgian Congo steampunk novel *Everfair* is forthcoming from Tor. She serves on the boards of Clarion West and The Carl Brandon Society. She's fairly active on Twitter and Facebook, and promises to update her homepage soon.

THE CHOSEN ONE — PAGE 56

Examined in: "Chosen"

Written by: Anton Strout

Defined as: The Chosen One is a trope about the protagonist's central role in a story. Typically, the hero is selected by Fate, a divinity, their mentor, etc. to fight an epic battle in order to save the world — and the catch is the hero is the only protagonist destined for this task. The Chosen One is so omnipresent there are many flavors of this trope and its appearance in genre fiction is expected.

Author Quote: I've made a career in writing trying to rip the back out of your standard Chosen One types of tales ... and to have a chance to distill it down to one short story that captures the essence of so many of them was a challenge I got excited about. "Chosen" was as much fun to write as I hope it is to read. Also, it will drive readers mad, which is always a plus!

Author Bio: Anton Strout was born in the Berkshire Hills mere miles from writing heavyweights Nathaniel Hawthorne and Herman Melville and currently lives in the haunted corn maze that is New Jersey (where nothing paranormal ever really happens, he assures you). He is the author of the *Simon Canderous* urban fantasy detective series and *The Spellmason Chronicles* for Ace Books, a division of Penguin Random House. Anton is also the scribbler of short, mad tales published in a variety of anthologies. *The Once & Future Podcast* is his latest project, where he endeavors as Curator of Content to bring authors to listener's ear holes one damned episode at a time. In his scant spare time, he is a writer, a sometimes actor, sometimes musician, occasional RPGer, and the world's most casual and controller smashing video gamer. He currently works in the exciting world of publishing and yes, it is as glamorous as it sounds.

THE GIRLFRIEND IN THE REFRIGERATOR — PAGE 126

Examined in: "The Refrigerator in the Girlfriend"

Written by: Adam-Troy Castro

Defined as: Named after its appearance in a Green Lantern story, where the superhero returned home to discover that a bad guy had left him exactly that nasty surprise, this trope stands in for any story in which a female character exists only long enough to be established before her horrible death motivates the hero. See many James Bond movies, for instance. Although readers and critics have loosely attributed the trope to a number of stories in which female characters with personal agency fail to survive perilous circumstances, it really only applies to those who are introduced only so that they can be killed off.

Author Quote: My story is emphatically not a commentary on the trope, just a vivid demonstration of a certain idea-generation trick of mine, in which I deliberately mangle well-known phrases to see what evocative images come up. The girlfriend in this particular story may be objectified, but that's very much her own playful decision, and she's not about to cough out her last words so that her guy can go on a vengeful rampage.

Author Bio: Adam-Troy Castro's 26 books to date (with more contracted and imminent) include three novels about his profoundly damaged far-future murder investigator Andrea Cort, four novels tie-in novels about Spider-Man, and six novels detail the adventures of that very strange boy raised by shadows, Gustav Gloom. The concluding volume of that series, *Gustav Gloom and the Castle of Fear*, came out in August 2016. Adam's fiction has won the Philip K. Dick and Seiun awards, and has been nominated eight times for the Nebula, three times for the Stoker, and twice for the Hugo. Adam lives in Boynton Beach, Florida, with his wife Judi and a rotating selection of insane cats.

THE HERO/HEROINE LOVES A BAD MAN — PAGE 1

Examined in: "On Loving Bad Boys: A Villainelle"

Written by: Valya Dudycz Lupescu

Defined as: Part of the archetypical attraction to so called "bad boys" is the excitement of being with a partner who lives on the edge. The "bad man" is often the revolutionary or the rebel, the one who challenges authority. In literature, he is the anti-hero, the one who rejects virtue and is the antithesis of heroic ideals. He does not act for the greater good à la Robin Hood, rather he is defiant because he does not wish to be defined, regulated, or tied down. The appeal of such a lover in stories has traditionally been about his inevitable redemption by the "good" lover who will help him to discover his inner hero. We expect that the bad man's inherent heroism must surely be directly proportional to his perceived badness. The greater his bad behavior, the greater the potential of his redemption. According to this trope, all a "bad man" needs is the love of the right partner to show him his mistakes and guide him down the path to heroism (after which he will integrate the best parts of himself to become the ideal partner).

Author Quote: It is the perceived contradiction of the bad man's character that is both the appeal and the danger; and it is this aspect of the trope I was most interested in — the illusory paradox of the "bad boy/man": 1.) there is what we see and 2.) what we envision to lie beneath the surface: brooding (but sensitive), angry (but passionate), fierce (but vulnerable), antisocial (but devoted). The contradiction is at the heart of this bad boy archetype: the hero/heroine wants both excitement and security; they need space for desire and yet also want to feel secure in their relationship, they crave a life both of spontaneity and stability. The bad boy is the embodiment of that paradox. He is the symbol of what our protagonist wants and (eventually) what they need.

In my poem, the narrator does what many people do. They look outward to find in a partner all that they are craving; they project onto their lovers the passion and nonconformity they desire. This obsessive searching, as well as the waffling between wanting space and needing connection lent themselves so perfectly to the villanelle, a poetic form where the first and third lines of the first stanza repeat alternately in the following stanzas.

For the most part, modern poetry has strongly shifted away from formal structure. Many poets reject the constraints of syllable count and stress, rhyme, and repetition, but I love playing with the expectations and limitations of formal poetry, allowing the form to reflect something deeper about the content.

In Dylan Thomas's famous villanelle "Do Not Go Gentle into That Good Night," the repeating lines of "Rage, rage against the dying of the light" and "Do not go gentle into that good night" underscore the narrator's urgency and insistence. My own repetition (although with subtle but important variation) of the lines "The bad is written all over your face" and "Desire grows in the empty space" are meant to emphasize the contradiction and obsession of the narrator's longing.

The narrator of "On Loving Bad Boys: A Villainelle" doesn't need to save the bad man. It's not about the bad boy at all. Rather, the narrator needs to embrace the facets of their authentic self and own the reality that they are actually the one who is bad ... in all the best possible ways.

Author Bio: Valya Dudycz Lupescu is the author of *The Silence of Trees* (Wolfsword Press) and founding editor of *Conclave: A Journal of Character*. Valya earned her MFA in Writing from the School of the Art Institute of Chicago, and her poetry and prose have been published in literary and genre magazines that include *The Kenyon Review, Strange Horizons, Mythic Delirium, Gone Lawn, Scheherezade's Bequest,* and *Abyss & Apex*. Co-written with Stephen H. Segal, her newest book, *Geek Parenting: What Joffrey, Jor-El, Maleficent, and the McFlys Teach Us about Raising a Family* was published by Quirk Books in April 2016. Valya currently teaches at DePaul University in Chicago.

THE POWER OF NAMES — PAGE 41

Examined in: "Thwock"

Written by: Michelle Muenzler

Defined as: The idea of knowing a character's true name is omnipresent, and can be found in many genres ranging from dark fantasy to horror and everything in-between. Often, the trope is concerned with the protagonists either discovering the antagonist's true name in order to command them, or the mystery of the antagonist's true identity is revealed once their real name is found.

Author Quote: The heart of the true name, to me, is as much about recognition as it is power. While in many stories, the name bearer seeks to hide that truth, to safely barricade their inner self against the world, in "Thwock" I wanted to explore a creature of the opposite nature. A man-made creation of myriad possibilities baring herself to her creators in the rawest sense, shouting into an ignorant void that she exists, and hoping for nothing more than recognition in return.

Author Bio: Michelle Muenzler, also known at local conventions as "The Cookie Lady," writes fiction both dark and strange to counterbalance the sweetness of her baking. Her fiction and poetry have been published in magazines such as *Daily Science Fiction*, *Apex Magazine*, and *Crossed Genres*, and she takes immense joy in crinkling words like little foil puppets.

THE RETIRED PRO'S LAST JOB — PAGE 98

Examined in: "No Saint"

Written by: Alethea Kontis

Defined as: Found in police procedurals or high-octane action stories, this trope is concerned with an older hero who wants to hang up their gun. Often, the professional mercenary, cop, bounty hunter, etc. is either pulled out of retirement altogether, or is asked to take on "one last job" before riding off into the sunset. To further underline the point of this trope, the Jolly Old St. Nick trope was also used, as Santa's job never does seem to end.

Author Quote: While writing my latest fairy tale novel, I found myself watching a ton of *NCIS* and *Criminal Minds*. In most of those storylines, like in fairy tales, the intrepid team of investigators (led by their crotchety, jaded old boss) Catch the Bad Guy and Save the World. But how would one truly elevate this type of storytelling into that of a fairy tale? What character in story, myth, or legend would lend himself or herself to this type of tale? What rugged, gruff old coot would try to get out, only to have his devoted team pull him back in for ten more seasons? And then the thought of Santa in the role of Gibbs popped into my mind ... and the story pretty much exploded from there.

Author Bio: Alethea Kontis is a princess, author, fairy godmother, and geek. Her bestselling *Books of Arilland* fairytale series won two Gelett Burgess Children's Book Awards (*Enchanted* and *Tales of Arilland*), and was twice nominated for the Andre Norton Award. Alethea also penned the *AlphaOops* picture books, *The Wonderland Alphabet*, *Diary of a Mad Scientist Garden Gnome*, *Beauty & Dynamite*, *The Dark-Hunter Companion* (with Sherrilyn Kenyon), and a myriad of poems, essays, and short stories. Princess Alethea lives and writes on the Space Coast of Florida with her teddy bear, Charlie. You can find her on her YouTube channel, all the social media, and at www.aletheakontis.com.

THE SINGULARITY — PAGE 2

Examined in: "Single, Singularity"

Written by: John Hornor Jacobs

Defined as: The Singularity has occurred, a machine awareness rises, and after evaluating mankind (or just looking at the Internet), it determines that mankind must be destroyed.

Author Quote: I have never written a "hard" science fiction story (and it's debatable I have here) but I read quite a bit of science fiction and wanted to try my hand at it.

Author Bio: John Hornor Jacobs is the award-winning author of *Southern Gods*, *This Dark Earth*, the young adult *Incarcerado* series, and the critically acclaimed fantasy series, *The Incorruptibles* and *Foreign Devils*. Jacobs resides in the American South and spends his free time when not working on his next book thinking about working on his next book. Learn more about him at johnhornorjacobs. com or follow him on Twitter at @johnhornor.

THE SUPER SOLDIER — PAGE 43

Examined in: "Can You Tell Me How to Get to Paprika Place?"

Written by: Michael R. Underwood

Defined as: The Super Soldier trope is concerned with a character or a series of characters who have been genetically or cybernetically enhanced in some fashion in order to do more violence and win large-scale conflicts. To subvert this type of character, the Talking Animals trope was also examined. That trope is concerned with addressing animals as humans, and if they were to talk, they would freely communicate with humans — and those characters automatically understand them, too.

Author Quote: I really like getting to familiar tropes in a different way — rolling back to first assumptions and starting from a different place.

Author Bio: Michael R. Underwood is the author of several novels and novellas, including the Ree Reyes comedic urban fantasies (*Geekomancy*, *Celebromancy*) and *Genrenauts*, a science fiction series in novellas. By day, he's the North American Sales & Marketing Manager for Angry Robot Books. Mike lives in Baltimore with his wife and their ever-growing library. He is a co-host on the Hugo-nominated *Skiffy and Fanty Show* as well as *Speculate!* the podcast for writers, readers, and fans.

THE VILLAIN HAD A CRAPPY CHILDHOOD — PAGE 215

Examined in: "The Origin of Terror"

Written by: Sunil Patel

Defined as: Often, the justification for an antagonist's harmful and violent acts is their past. Whether the villain was beaten as a child or ostracized and bullied, this trope is rooted in the idea that a child victim will grow up to be the worst kind of bully.

Author Quote: While it's true that childhood trauma may cause aberrant behavior, this tired trope often appears to excuse the villain's actions in a ploy to make them more sympathetic. Oh, something terrible happened to him when he was a kid, of *course* he grew up to be a cannibal, that makes perfect sense, poor guy. Well, guess what, both Harry Potter and Voldemort had crappy childhoods, and only one of them decided to kill everyone. I wanted to explore the idea of a villain who had a *great* childhood and still did terrible things, perhaps *because* of their great childhood. What would it be like if a supervillain's parents were the Ma and Pa Kent of superheroes?

Author Bio: Sunil Patel is a Bay Area fiction writer and playwright who has written about everything from ghostly cows to talking beer. His plays have been performed at San Francisco Theater Pub and San Francisco Olympians Festival, and his fiction has appeared or is forthcoming in *Fireside Magazine*, *Flash Fiction Online*, *The Book Smugglers*, *Fantastic Stories of the Imagination*, *Asimov's Science Fiction*, and *Lightspeed*, among others. Plus he reviews books and TV for *Lightspeed* and he is Assistant Editor of *Mothership Zeta*. His favorite things to consume include nachos, milkshakes, and narrative. Find out more at ghostwritingcow.com, where you can watch his plays, or follow him at @

ghostwritingcow. His Twitter has been described as "engaging," "exclamatory," and "crispy, crunchy, peanut buttery."

WORLD ENDS/RESETS/REBOOTS — PAGE 156

Examined in: "Until There Is Only Hunger"

Written by: Michael Matheson

Defined as: The idea of the world ending and beginning again is pertinent to multiple cultural myth-cycles and saga-myths, among them various Mesoamerican cultures, Scandinavian cultures, etc. The cyclical rebooting is often due to divine influence in those mythologies. However, the function of a world rebooting is also a staple of post-apocalyptic fiction, with survivors facing whatever challenge or fallout the plot centres around. Where it becomes a trope is the way in which the latter is often frequently poorly handled in Western mainstream popular culture: the new world left mostly full of straight white guys — with a little, or a lot, of Hero Complex and The Chosen One thrown into the mix — and the whole thing lacking in cultural, gender, and queer representation.

Author Quote: An ongoing worldbuilding experiment, across multiple stories, set (mostly) after the world ends — and then carries on. Begun because I wanted to, among other things, do pre- and post-apocalyptic worldbuilding in context of queer people of colour. In a world filled with ghosts and mountains that walk in the shape of colossal women, among other things more pertinent to further stories set in that world. The whole thing partly due to two more specific influences: A longstanding love of Hayao Miyazaki's *Kaze no Tani no Naushika* (*Nausicaä of the Valley of the Wind*), and the tone and atmosphere of Junji Ito's work — more specifically Ito's estrangement or distortion of the familiar to terrify and awe.

Author Bio: Michael Matheson is a genderfluid writer and editor. A graduate of Clarion West (2014), their work has appeared or is forthcoming in *Nightmare* (Queers Destroy Horror!), *Grendelsong*, *Ideomancer*, and a growing handful of eclectic anthologies. Their first anthology as editor, *The Humanity of Monsters*, was released by ChiZine Publications in 2015. They can be found online at michaelmatheson.wordpress.com, or on Twitter at @sekisetsu.

YELLOW PERIL — PAGE 70

Examined in: "The White Dragon"

Written by: Alyssa Wong

Defined as: Yellow Peril is the fear that Asia poses a dire threat to Western civilization. "Yellow" refers to the ostensible skin color of East Asian peoples, and while the term did not originate in the United States, the threat of the Yellow Peril was leveraged against Chinese immigrants to the U.S. in the late 1800s when many Chinese men came to the country to help build the Transcontinental Railroad. This resulted in the Chinese Exclusion Act, the first piece of racially specific anti-immigration legislation. Similarly, during WWII, the internment of Japanese/Japanese-Americans citizens was also fueled by Yellow Peril. The fear of a Yellow Takeover — either military or cultural — can also be seen in racist wartime propaganda caricatures, comic books, pulp novels from the early 20th century (eg. Fu Manchu), and even current-day media (eg. the *Sherlock* episode "The Blind Banker" and the 2012 remake of the movie *Red Dawn*). The trope The Villainous Asian Crime Syndicate as antagonists in detective stories, specifically in early 20th century pulp/hardboiled P.I. novels, was also examined for this story. The Villainous Asian Crime Syndicate is a subtrope of Yellow Peril, and it's one we see often in media today (two notable examples, but not nearly the only ones, are Nobu and Gao in Netflix's *Daredevil*).

Author Quote: Yellow Peril is a trope, but it's also a racist perception that has and continues to affect people like me. I think it's definitely important enough to write about, and it's a perception that needs to be brought up and challenged. For this story, I took the trope back to the time period and setting of old-school hardboiled pulp: San Francisco Chinatown in the 1920s.

Author Bio: Alyssa Wong studies fiction in Raleigh, NC. Her story, "Hungry Daughters of Starving Mothers," won the 2015 Nebula Award for Best Short Story, and her fiction has been shortlisted for the Pushcart Prize, the Bram Stoker Award, the Locus Award, and the Shirley Jackson Award. Her work has been published in *The Magazine of Fantasy & Science Fiction*, *Strange Horizons*, *Nightmare Magazine*, *Black Static*, and Tor.com, among others. She can be found online at http://www.crashwong.net and on Twitter as @crashwong.

SECTION IV:
ACKNOWLEDGMENTS AND
ADDITIONAL BIOS

ESSAYISTS' BIOS

Jerry Gordon is the Bram Stoker Award-nominated co-editor of the *Dark Faith, Last Rites, Invocations,* and *Streets of Shadows* anthologies. His short fiction has appeared in *Apex Magazine, Shroud,* and *The Midnight Diner*. He teaches college classes, runs a software development company, and dreams of a good night's sleep.

Patrick Hester is an author, blogger, 2013 & 2014 Hugo Award Winner, podcast and audiobook producer, and all around Functional Nerd. He writes science fiction and fantasy available in several anthologies and ebooks, and his latest novel, *Samantha Kane: Into the Fire,* is coming in 2016 from WordFire Press. He is @atfmb on Twitter and Facebook, where he talks about all things writing, gaming, music and nerd-life that amuse and distract him. He produces and co-hosts the multi-Parsec Nominated *Functional Nerds* podcast, produced and hosted the Hugo Award Winning SFSignal.com podcast for nearly 7 years, and also produced *I Should Be Writing,* the podcast for wannabe fiction writers, created and hosted by 2013 Campbell Award Winner, Mur Lafferty, for several years. He maintains a twice-monthly column for the *Kirkus Reviews* blog on comics and graphic novels, writes for his own sites atfmb.com and functionalnerds.com, for the Pikes Peak Writers blog, and various other sites. He is a Scrivener Guru and teaches several classes to writers throughout the year.

Lucy A. Snyder is a five-time Bram Stoker Award-winning writer and the author of the novels *Spellbent, Shotgun Sorceress,* and *Switchblade Goddess*. She also authored the nonfiction book *Shooting Yourself in the Head For Fun and Profit: A Writer's Survival Guide* and the story collections *While the Black Stars Burn, Soft Apocalypses, Orchid Carousals, Sparks and Shadows,* and *Installing Linux on a Dead Badger*. She lives in Columbus, Ohio and is a faculty member in Seton Hill University's MFA program in Writing Popular Fiction. You can learn more about her at www.lucysnyder.com and you can follow her on Twitter at @LucyASnyder.

ESSAYISTS' BIOS, CONT.

A.C. Wise's fiction has appeared in publications such as *Clarkesworld*, *Apex*, *Shimmer*, and *The Year's Best Dark Fantasy and Horror 2015*, among other places. Her debut collection *The Ultra Fabulous Glitter Squadron Saves the World Again* was published by Lethe Press in October 2015. In addition to her fiction, she co-edits *Unlikely Story*, and contributes a monthly review column, *Words for Thought* to *Apex Magazine*. Find her online at www.acwise.net and on Twitter as @ac_wise.

Victor J. Raymond, PhD, is an activist, a sociologist, a writer, and longtime gamer. A member of the Rosebud Sioux Tribe and also having English and Scottish heritage, Victor's multiracial background has shaped his activism in a variety of areas. A founding committee member of the BECAUSE conference, he has been a National Co-coordinator for BiNet USA, an invited speaker at Creating Change, and the co-chair of the People of Color Caucus of It's Time, Minnesota. Currently an adjunct instructor at Madison College in the Department of Sociology, he's the founding member and Secretary of the Board of Directors of the Carl Brandon Society, which works to increase racial and ethnic diversity in the production of and audience for speculative fiction. He is also the chair of the Tekumel Foundation.

Keffy R. M. Kehrli is a science fiction and fantasy writer, editor, and podcaster currently located in Long Island, NY, where he is working toward a PhD in genetics. His short fiction has appeared in magazines such as *Lightspeed*, *Apex*, and *Uncanny*, as well as in anthologies such as *Clockwork Phoenix 5*. In 2015, he launched *GlitterShip*, (http://www.glittership.com) which is a podcast that has audio versions of LGBTQ science fiction and fantasy short stories. You can find more about him at http://www.keffy.com or @Keffy on Twitter.

ACKNOWLEDGMENTS

Upside Down: Inverted Tropes in Storytelling would not have been possible if it weren't for 1,399 fine individuals who pledged to bring this collection to life. Thanks to our backers, this anthology was successfully funded by a crowd-funding platform called Kickstarter in March 2016. The crowd-funding video, photos, and author/editor updates may be viewed via this link: www.kickstarter.com/projects/apex-publications/upside-down-inverted-tropes-in-storytelling-anthol.

Additionally, the anthology would never have been funded without the additional artistic contributions of John Hornor Jacobs, Dan O'Shea, Meredith Gerber, and our fine authors. Lastly, we would like to thank Lesley Conner, Steve Drew, Andrew Girdwood, Matt M. McElroy, Melanie Meadors, Matt Staggs, John DeNardo, and many others for their enthusiasm, support, and coverage of this unique collection of fiction and essays.

ABOUT THE EDITORS

Monica Valentinelli is an editor, writer, and game developer who lurks in the dark. Her work includes stories, games, and comics for her original settings as well as media/tie-in properties such as the *Firefly* TV show, Brandon Sanderson's *Mistborn*, and *Vampire: The Masquerade*. Her nonfiction includes reference materials such as *Firefly: The Gorramn Shiniest Language Guide and Dictionary in the 'Verse*, and essays in books like *For Exposure: The Life and Times of a Small Press Publisher*. For more about Monica, visit www.booksofm.com.

Jaym Gates is an editor, author, and communications manager. She's the editor of the *Rigor Amortis*, *War Stories*, *Exalted*, and *Genius Loci* anthologies, as well as a published author in fiction, academic nonfiction, and RPGs.

ABOUT THE ARTIST

Galen Dara likes monsters, mystics, and dead things. She has created art for *Uncanny Magazine*, 47North publishing, Skyscape Publishing, Fantasy Flight Games, Tyche Books, *Fireside Magazine*, *Lightspeed*, *Lackington's*, and Resurrection House. She has been nominated for the Hugo, the World Fantasy Award, and the Chesley Award. When Galen is not working on a project you can find her on the edge of the Sonoran Desert, climbing mountains and hanging out with a friendly conglomeration of human and animal companions. Her website is www.galendara.com plus you can find her on Facebook and Twitter at @galendara.